D1596154

The Administration of Sponsored Programs

*Handbook for Developing
and Managing Research Activities
and Other Projects*

Kenneth L. Beasley
Michael R. Dingerson
Oliver D. Hensley
Larry G. Hess
John A. Rodman

The Administration of Sponsored Programs

Jossey-Bass Publishers

San Francisco • Washington • London • 1982

THE ADMINISTRATION OF SPONSORED PROGRAMS
Handbook for Developing and Managing Research Activities and Other Projects
by Kenneth L. Beasley, Michael R. Dingerson, Oliver D. Hensley,
Larry G. Hess, and John A. Rodman

Copyright © 1982 by: Jossey-Bass Inc., Publishers
433 California Street
San Francisco, California 94104
&
Jossey-Bass Limited
28 Banner Street
London EC1Y 8QE

Library of Congress Cataloging in Publication Data

Main entry under title:

The Administration of sponsored programs.

Bibliography: p. 410
Includes index.
1. Research—Management. I. Beasley, Kenneth L.
Q180.55.M3A35 1982   658.4'04   82-48074
ISBN 0-87589-542-5

Manufactured in the United States of America

The paper in this book meets the guidelines for
permanence and durability of the Committee on
Production Guidelines for Book Longevity of the
Council on Library Resources.

JACKET DESIGN BY WILLI BAUM

FIRST EDITION

Code 8228

A joint publication in
The Jossey-Bass
Higher Education and
Social and Behavioral Science Series

Preface

The rise of sponsored programs in the years since World War II has created a new set of administrative functions involved with developing, supporting, and managing sponsored activities. These new administrative functions are collectively referred to as sponsored program administration—defined as the management of activities associated with development, policies, organization, communications, and reporting necessary to obtain support, conduct projects, and meet sponsors' requirements. Sponsored program administration has become an integral part of higher education, medical research organizations, profit and nonprofit institutions, and agencies of local, state, and national government. Because many of these organizations receive funding from sponsors, the importance of sponsored program administration to the organizations' overall goals is gaining greater recognition. In a little over thirty years, sponsored program administration has grown into a major field whose practitioners influence the acquisition and management of a significant portion of institutional programs and resources.

The growth of these new administrative functions has brought forth a new group of practitioners called research or sponsored projects administrators who perform tasks involved in sponsored program administration. The sponsored project administrator also plays a key role as liaison between the recipient organization and its sponsors. Most sponsored projects administrators acquire the requisite skills and knowledge through job experience rather than through a planned training program. Individuals are appointed or selected to manage sponsored activities on the basis of related skills developed in other positions. Although most sponsored projects administrators have either a science background or business management experience, others have diverse backgrounds, in such fields as journalism or philosophy. Experience in government funding agencies or procurement responsibilities in the military services have also led to positions as sponsored projects administrators. Currently there are no comprehensive professional training programs or recognized qualifications for positions in sponsored program administration.

The literature on sponsored program administration is still in the formative stage. Most books on the subject concentrate on specific functional areas; for example, two recent publications concern the sources of support and methods for obtaining funds: *Complete Grants Sourcebook for Higher Education* (American Council on Education, 1980) and *Getting Grants* (Smith and Skjei, 1980). Another recent book, *Grant Budgeting and Finance* (Sladek and Stein, 1981), presents information that primarily pertains to the fiscal management of sponsored projects. Two previous books present a descriptive look at the administration of research but do not offer a detailed approach to developing and managing sponsored programs: *Sponsored Research in American Universities and Colleges* (Strickland, 1967), and *Management for Research in U.S. Universities* (Woodrow, 1978); the latter is directed primarily toward large research universities. *The Journal of the Society of Research Administrators,* the major periodical in the field, publishes articles related to various issues and practices in sponsored program administration.

The present volume is the first to provide a comprehensive discussion of the functions performed by sponsored projects administrators and a detailed explanation of how to manage the various aspects of sponsored projects. The authors believe that sponsored program administration is an emerging professional field whose practitioners need a

comprehensive text that formally identifies and describes the responsibilities and specific tasks performed by sponsored projects administrators. Specifically, this book seeks to (1) establish sponsored program
administration as a discrete management field by defining and detailing
the services performed by sponsored projects administrators and (2)
improve sponsored program administration by providing a practical
guide—a how-to-do-it book—that assists the reader in learning how to
plan, organize, and manage sponsored projects. This practical approach
to sponsored program administration is thus intended to help both experienced and novice administrators understand sponsored projects as
an integrated and specialized activity within any organizational framework.

Although the experiences of the authors and many of the examples in this text are in higher education institutions, the management
functions described apply equally to medical research organizations,
profit and nonprofit research institutions, and agencies of government
at all levels. The principles and procedures discussed in this book will
thus be of interest to sponsored projects administrators, research directors, laboratory business managers, departmental business managers,
research accountants, research managers, and administrators whose
broad responsibilities include the supervision of research and other
types of sponsored projects. In addition, this book will be useful to academic vice-presidents, provosts, deans, department chairs, and center
directors in higher education. Individuals responsible for securing sponsored support for public schools, local governments, and community
agencies will also benefit.

In Part One we examine the evolution and current status of sponsored program administration within organizational settings and as an
emerging profession. Chapter One reviews the role of sponsored projects in society and traces the development of sponsored program
administration. Chapter Two examines the role and current status of
sponsored program administration and describes the professional
associations in the field. Institutional goals, policies, and organizations
to manage sponsored projects are discussed in Chapter Three.

Part Two concerns the major management activities of the sponsored projects administrator. Each chapter describes the functions of a
management activity and the practices required to successfully administer it. Chapter Four explains how to create a successful sponsored proj-

ects operation: the establishment of attitudes, capabilities, priorities, and organized efforts to enhance sponsored projects activity. The organization and staffing of the sponsored projects office, including sample organization charts and job descriptions, are presented in Chapter Five. Chapter Six discusses management information systems and various automated systems for sponsored program administration. Communications and sources of information, including sources of funding, are presented in Chapter Seven. Chapter Eight treats the preparation and processing of proposals within the organization; types of assistance, monitoring, and regulatory responsibilities are examined. Indirect costs and cost sharing are the topics of Chapter Nine. The types of awards and practical advice on how to negotiate and accept an award are described in Chapter Ten. Chapter Eleven includes the financial management of sponsored awards with special emphasis on allowability of costs, prior approval systems, and expenditure control systems. The management of facilities and equipment is the subject of Chapter Twelve, and Chapter Thirteen describes the reporting requirements for sponsored projects.

Part Three contains four chapters that pertain to special topics in sponsored program administration. Chapter Fourteen examines the compliance areas associated with the management of many sponsored projects: laboratory animal care, patent policy, protection of human subjects, and safety in the experimental use of recombinant DNA. Chapters Fifteen, Sixteen, and Seventeen then address specific aspects of sponsored program administration in small organizations and developing institutions, in nonprofit organizations and university-connected research foundations, and in medical research organizations.

In Part Four, Chapter Eighteen considers emerging trends and the future of sponsored program administration.

Acknowledgments

The authors would like to acknowledge those who have been helpful in contributing to the completion of this book. Special appreciation is due to Nancy Arnold, Byron Backlar, Robert E. Krebs, Lorraine Lasker, Jay M. Lewallen, and Charles R. MacKay for contributing materials and assistance in preparing sections of the text. Several other colleagues in sponsored program administration assisted by reviewing the manuscript and providing valuable suggestions. The authors acknowledge the important contributions of the following colleagues: Jack L. Balderston, Truman Cook, Roger D. Hartman, Charles R. McCarthy, Victor Medina, Anthony Merritt, Julie T. Norris, and Charles E. Smith, Jr.

Special recognition is extended to Christine A. Murphy, University of Illinois, Urbana, whose editorial and production skills were essential in producing several drafts and the final manuscript. The appreciation of the authors for the important contributions of their respective associates and office staff members is especially noted. Equally important is the recognition due to the authors' families whose support, understanding, and patience during many absent hours spent preparing the book were an inspiration.

Acknowledgment is due to the Research Management Improvement Program of the National Science Foundation for stimulating studies in the field of sponsored program administration. The idea for this book originated with John A. Rodman, University of Texas, Dallas.

August 1982

Kenneth L. Beasley
DeKalb, Illinois

Michael R. Dingerson
Carbondale, Illinois

Oliver D. Hensley
Carbondale, Illinois

Larry G. Hess
Urbana, Illinois

John A. Rodman
Dallas, Texas

Contents

▭▭▭▭▭▭▭▭▭▭▭▭▭▭▭▭▭▭▭▭▭

Preface   ix

The Authors   xxi

Part One: Introduction

1. Development and Scope of Sponsored Program
    Administration   1
    Sponsored Programs and Society
    Roles of Sponsored Projects
    History of Sponsored Programs

2. Role of Sponsored Projects Administrators   12
    An Emerging Profession
    Voluntary Associations

3.   Goals, Policies, and Organizational Structures   23
      Goals
      Policy Considerations
      Commitment to Sponsored Projects Administration
      Administrative Structures

Part Two: Administrative Functions and Practices

4.   Developing the Capacity for Project Support   37
      Building Attitudes Toward Sponsored Projects
      Capabilities
      Establishing Priorities for Sponsored Projects
        Support
      Programs to Enhance Sponsored Projects Activity

5.   Organizing the Sponsored Projects Office   52
      Organizational Structures
      Scope and Functions
      Staffing
      Organizational Models
      Division of Responsibilities and Duties
      Evaluation

6.   Establishing Management Information Systems   69
      General Types of MIS
      Trends in Management Information Systems

7.   Developing Communication Systems and Information   96
   Sources
      External Communications
      Sources of Information
      Internal Communications

8.   Managing Proposal Preparation and Processing   111
      Proposal Preparation Services
      Proposal Processing and Coordination
      Regulatory Responsibilities

9.   Determining Indirect Costs and Cost Sharing   127
     Indirect Costs
     Cost Sharing

10. Negotiating and Accepting Awards   141
     Types of Awards
     Negotiations
     Acceptance of Awards

11. Financial Management of Projects   163
     Allowability of Costs
     Prior Approval System
     Budget and Expenditure Control

12. Administering Facilities and Equipment   187
     Facilities
     Facilities Automated Inventory and Billing
       System
     Equipment
     Equipment Automated Inventory System

13. Preparing Reports for Sponsors   219
     Activity Reports
     Project Results
     Financial Reports
     Other Reports

Part Three: Management Issues in Special Areas

14. Compliance with Legal and Ethical Requirements   236
     Care of Laboratory Animals
     Patent Policy
     Copyright
     Protection of Human Research Subjects
     Research Involving Recombinant DNA

15.   Administration in Small Organizations   285
        Goals, Capabilities, and Motivation
        Organizing and Staffing
        Assessing Capabilities
        Communication Systems
        Stimulating Project Development
        Postaward Administration

16.   Administration in Nonprofit and University-
        Connected Organizations   293
        Nonprofit Research Organizations
        University-Connected Research Foundations

17.   Administration in Health Science Organizations   311
        The Nature of Health Science Organizations
        Special Considerations

          Part Four: New Developments

18.   Emerging Trends and the Future of Sponsored
        Program Administration   324
        Industry-University Cooperation in Sponsored
          Projects
        Consortiums for Sponsored Projects Administration
        Three-Sector Partnerships to Promote Industrial
          Research and Development
        Sponsored Projects and Program Development
        Decentralization and Block Grants
        The Future of Sponsored Program Administration

Resource A: Special Research Program   346

Resource B: Office of Sponsored Projects
               Faculty Evaluation Form   352

Resource C: Excerpts from NSF Guidelines for
               Preparation of Proposals   355

Resource D: Checklist for Proposal Budget   368

Resource E: Sample Human Subjects Review Forms   374

Resource F: Acronyms *Used in Sponsored Projects
               Administration*   388

Resource G: Federal Regulations Pertaining
               to Sponsored Projects   396

Resource H: Select Bibliography of Information
               Sources   400

References   410

Index   419

The Authors

==

KENNETH L. BEASLEY is currently assistant to the president, Northern Illinois University, and has held this position since 1972. He has also concurrently been executive director, The Central States Universities, Incorporated (a science consortium of twelve universities). He received the Ph.D. degree in history and philosophy of education from Northwestern University (1962), the A.M.T. in history from Harvard University (1953), and the A.B. degree in history from Wabash College (1952).

His research administration experience has included terms as president, Society of Research Administrators; chairman, Board of Advisors, Society of Research Administrators; founder and president, Mid-America Region, National Council of University Research Administrators; director, National Science Foundation (NSF) Research Management Improvement Program; member, NSF Advisory Panel on Research Management Improvement; and consultant, speaker, and workshop director of "Topics in Sponsored Program Administration." He has also been the recipient of the "Excellence Award in Research Administration" from the Society of Research Administrators.

He has authored many publications related to his doctoral field as well as in the field of research administration, the latter being published primarily in the *Journal of the Society of Research Administrators*. He has been editor of the respective research newsletters of The Central States Universities, Incorporated, and Northern Illinois University. He is on the editorial board of the *Journal of the Society of Research Administrators* and also of *Federal Notes*.

Of particular interest and concern to Beasley is the development of sponsored program administration with particular emphasis on the role and improvement of performance of sponsored program administration.

MICHAEL R. DINGERSON is currently the associate dean of the Graduate School; director of the Research Development and Administration office; and assistant professor, Department of Higher Education, Southern Illinois University at Carbondale. He has held this position for the past eight years. He received the Ph.D. degree in academic administration (1974), the M.S. degree in education (consumer problems) (1971), and the B.S. degree in business administration with a major in marketing (1963)—all from Southern Illinois University at Carbondale.

He is a member of and has held office in several national research administration organizations, and is currently president of the midwest section of the Society of Research Administrators. He has been involved in research administration for the past thirteen years and has published several articles on research administration in the *Journal of Higher Education* and in the *Journal of the Society of Research Administrators*. He has also published on other topics of interest to higher education in the *Journal of Higher Education* and *Research in Higher Education*.

OLIVER D. HENSLEY is presently the program development officer for the Research Development and Administration office at Southern Illinois University at Carbondale. He received the Ph.D. and M.S. degrees in education from Southern Illinois University at Carbondale in 1968 and 1963, respectively, and the B.S. degree in education from Harris Teachers College in 1958.

Hensley has taught in public schools and universities, worked in and supervised an industrial laboratory, and served as director of research and projects at Northeast Louisiana University. In 1980 he was the recipient of the Society of Research Administrators' "Excellence Award in Research Administration."

He is director of the Clearinghouse for Research Administration and editor for the *Register of Publications for Research Administrators*. He is the author of several articles on research administration and has been the editor of the *SRA Annual Meeting Proceedings* for three years. He is currently involved in organizing government, industry, labor, and university partnerships for regional development.

LARRY G. HESS is the business manager of the School of Chemical Sciences, University of Illinois, Urbana. He has twenty-three years of experience in sponsored projects administration. Hess received the B.S. degree in accounting from the University of Illinois at Urbana in 1960 and has continued his professional development through participating in graduate courses, seminars, and workshops. As an extension of his professional development, he recently participated in a one-year IPA management systems assignment at NASA Ames Research Center, Procurement Division, Moffett Field, California.

Hess is active in professional research administration organizations, particularly the Society of Research Administrators, having served as president of the society as well as in various section offices, committee chairmanships, and membership on the board of advisers. He has co-authored several articles in the *Journal of the Society of Research Administrators*. He is currently investigating the development and refinement of automated management information systems for use in sponsored projects administration decentralized to the unit level. He is also an instructor for the University of Texas at Dallas Continuing Education Office's workshops on computerized management information systems.

JOHN A. RODMAN is the director of the Office of Sponsored Projects, University of Texas, Dallas. He received the M.B.A. degree (1969) and the B.S. degree in marketing (1965) from Southern Illinois University at Carbondale.

Rodman has twelve years of experience in university research administration, having served as director of the Office of Research and Projects at Southern Illinois University at Edwardsville prior to his present position. He has been active in both the Society of Research Administrators and the National Council of University Research Administrators for many years and is currently chairman of Region V of the latter.

He has presented papers and published in the area of computerized faculty information systems and the professionalization of research administrators through national research administration organizations' publications, conferences, seminars, and workshops and is the principal investigator of a National Science Foundation–National Endowment for the Humanities grant entitled "Experimental Projects: The Development and Implementation of a Keyword Thesaurus."

Rodman is currently active in presenting nationwide training sessions on pre- and postaward computerized management information systems.

The Administration of Sponsored Programs

―――――――――――――――――――――

*Handbook for Developing
and Managing Research Activities
and Other Projects*

1

Development and Scope of Sponsored Program Administration

The growth of sponsored support in the years since World War II has created a new set of administrative functions involved with developing, supporting, and managing sponsored activities. *Sponsored program administration* describes the various responsibilities associated with the development, support, and management required to secure awards, conduct projects, and maintain compliance with sponsors. Sponsored program administration is practiced by such organizations as colleges and universities, hospitals, businesses, profit and nonprofit institutions, and governmental agencies at the local, state and federal levels. This book will be useful to all these organizations, although most of our examples illustrate applications in higher education.

The terms *sponsored program administration* and *sponsored projects administration* require clarification as to usage in practice and in this book. Sponsored program administration refers to a broad field of activity or a major function within an organization, while sponsored projects administration refers more directly to the individual management activities necessary to achieve the purposes of sponsored projects. The sponsored projects administrator or officer manages these activities, and the organizational unit within an institution from which the administration of sponsored projects is conducted is commonly referred to as the office of sponsored projects (OSP). Thus, sponsored program administration is used primarily to describe a field of management and development functions, and sponsored projects administration is used to describe the office and the specific activities performed to achieve institutional goals in receiving and managing sponsored awards. There is some obvious overlap in the usage of the terms in practice and also in this book.

The primary purposes of sponsored program administration are: (1) To serve as the organizational unit of the institution to develop, manage, and report sponsored activities; (2) to provide services to project directors to enable them to secure support and conduct sponsored projects; and (3) to represent the institution in transactions with sponsors. The evolution of the field of sponsored program administration reflects the increase in sponsored activities supported by government and private foundations. In general, such support is intended to improve knowledge and human well-being through basic research, applied research, and education programs.

In this chapter we present an overview of the types of organizations that conduct sponsored programs, the types of programs they conduct, and the growth of sponsored programs since the 1940s.

Sponsored Programs and Society

The agencies, associations, foundations, and businesses that provide financial support to conduct sponsored programs do so in order to promote research and other activities that will add to current knowledge and problem-solving techniques, thus improving the human condition. Sponsors' objectives can be as broad as a mandate to develop science in the nation or as specific as a project to improve legal services to the unemployed in a large city. The ultimate goal of all sponsored projects is to meet a need, as expressed in the priorities of sponsors, by financing projects directed by specialists in various institutions in society. Institutions that conduct sponsored programs both reflect the history of society and represent the cutting edge of discovery for the future.

Colleges and universities have three general goals: teaching, research, and public service. The achievement of these goals is important to the continued development of human understanding and improved living conditions. Higher learning and professional training in our culture are primarily the province of our colleges and universities, although the transmission of knowledge is not limited to these institutions. Often faculty members and practitioners in the field work together, and this extension of faculty expertise is one element of educational institutions' public service. Indeed, applied research is the primary form of extending institutional services to the public, and the public service contributions of colleges and universities have played a significant role in the application of knowledge. One of the most successful examples of such contributions is the revolutionary advances in agriculture provided to American farmers by the agricultural extension services of colleges of agriculture at land-grant universities.

Since 1945, the public service role of American colleges and universities has increased significantly. Faculty members have applied their knowledge to the solution of problems through advisory services, education and training programs, and demonstration projects. The beneficial services of faculty have been recognized and funded by government agencies and private foundations wishing to use this knowledge and experience to achieve their goals.

Basic research discoveries and the application of expertise to the general public are not limited to colleges and universities. In the area of medicine, extensive programs in basic research and public education are conducted by many medical schools, hospitals, and medical organizations. These organizations have been an integral part of the national research program that has made the great discoveries in medical science. Research or training institutes, both profit-making and nonprofit, also conduct research in special laboratories and direct education programs to achieve specific goals. Most of these institutes were established after 1945, and usually their goals limit their activities to a certain area. Examples of limited areas of concentration are electronics technology for the Air Force, training programs for inner city preschool children, marine studies, prediction of future economic and social changes, and research and education to improve the production and distribution of the world's food supply. A few institutes have a broad base of expertise and conduct a wide variety of projects. The growth in research and training institutes indicates their success in attracting funds and completing projects. An important aspect of an institute is its ability to quickly assemble interdisciplinary teams and focus the collective wisdom of many different experts on a problem. Such concentration of expertise on a single problem is not always feasible in a university.

In addition to medical facilities and profit and nonprofit institutes, many other organizations contribute to the creation and dissemination of knowledge. Government laboratories, local and state government programs, and community organizations are all part of this network. All these organizations, some to a greater extent than others, rely on sponsored support to conduct their activities. Like colleges and universities, these organizations contribute to the needs of society in many ways. Since the mid 1940s, sponsored support by government agencies and private foundations has become a dominant means to meet societal needs for the discovery of knowledge and the solutions to problems. The infinite variety of programs supported—running the gamut from basic research to direct applications of skills to a specific problem—reflects the heterogeneous interests of the sponsors. Higher education, government, hospitals, businesses and nonprofit organizations have prospered and grown as a result of the increase in projects. The increase in fiscal support to meet society needs has also produced a new administrative position—that of sponsored projects administrator.

Roles of Sponsored Projects

Although each sponsored project is designed to meet a specific societal need, a given project will fall under one of the following categories: research, instruction, training, demonstration or pilot program, and evaluation.

Research. Colleges, universities, medical research facilities, research institutes, and governmental agencies are vital to the growth of scientific research in the United States. Research is an important part of faculty responsibilities and is an integral part of the education of graduate students, and academe is the major producer of basic research discoveries in the United States. This integration of basic research and graduate education contrasts with the pattern in many European countries and the U.S.S.R. where basic research is primarily performed in specialized institutes. The advantage of the American system is that conducting research in tandem with advanced study emphasizes the necessary relationship between the two as a joint process of learning and discovery. Another stated advantage for performing research as part of the advanced education program is that the diversification of the system, both on a single campus and between campuses, assures a better atmosphere for the interplay of ideas from other areas than that in a single-focus institute. Many observers of scientific progress feel that the American system of diversified research in educational institutions has proved to be the best system as measured by the number of research discoveries and Nobel prize winners from the United States in the post-World War II era.

A review of the three main purposes of research in higher education explains the rationale for sponsored research and the importance of the sponsored projects administrator to the achievement of institutional goals.

The Extension of the Boundaries of Human Knowledge. The search for new principles or new truths is the unique role of the university in society. The search for knowledge is recognized as *basic* or *pure research*, defined thus by Bush (1960, pp. 18–19): "Basic research is performed without thought of practical ends. It results in general knowledge and in understanding of nature and its laws. . . . Basic research leads to new knowledge. It provides scientific capital. It creates the fund from which the practical applications of knowledge must be drawn. New products and new processes are founded on new principles and new conceptions, which in turn are painstakingly developed by research in the purest realm of science." The unfettered search for new knowledge in the physical and biological realm described by Bush is equally necessary in the social sciences, the humanities, and the arts as the individual researcher seeks to find new truths.

The university is the one institution in our society that allows clever and innovative researchers to pursue knowledge in their own field, following their intuitive insights and without regard to utilitarian results. To the person unfamiliar with basic research this freedom may appear to be an unwarranted blank check, but the historical record clearly illustrates the value of basic research; advances in knowledge and technology rely on the insights and information supplied by basic research.

Research and Instruction. The discovery of new knowledge

through basic research is diffused through teaching and applied research projects. As Machlup (1962, p. 200) notes, "basic research and advanced teaching and learning are complementary rather than competitive activities." Education at its best includes not only a study of the past but a study of the potential developments of a changing future. Only through involvement in the production of new knowledge through participation in current research projects do the professor and student fully achieve their instructional and educational goals.

The Training of Qualified Researchers. The third purpose of research in colleges and universities is the training of competent researchers in all fields. Higher education is the principal supplier of researchers in this country, furnishing undergraduate students with a general base of knowledge and graduate and professional students with specialized research training.

Nonresearch Sponsored Activities. Nonresearch sponsored activities involve the application of individual faculty expertise and the utilization of the institution's resources. Such activities range from a single consultant advising a small town on its traffic system to a multidisciplinary team planning and managing a major segment of the economy in a developing country. The three major types of nonresearch sponsored programs are described below.

Education and Training Programs. Higher education and special institutes are often called upon to set up programs to educate or train individuals for special purposes. Programs may be the same as courses offered on campus, such as foreign language training, or they may be entirely new materials devised for a specific purpose. Many of the social programs of the 1960s utilized universities as education and training agents—for example, the Peace Corps Training Centers, the Job Corps Centers, Project Head Start, Upward Bound, and programs associated with Community Action Agencies. Now many training grants and contracts are awarded to profit and nonprofit institutes.

Demonstration, Model, and Pilot Programs. The conceptualization of a program is often not sufficient to demonstrate or prove its usefulness in a given situation. An actual working program or a model of a program is required to gain public understanding and acceptance. For example, hybrid-seed corn dealers found that merely talking about their new product did not convince farmers of its utility; they had to show the value of the product by planting demonstration plots and proving that the yield was greater.

College and university professors are frequently engaged in sponsored public service programs to build a simulation model and test a new product. Likewise, new ideas are tested in pilot programs to ascertain their reliability and applicability to a selected situation. Indeed, many new ideas, products, and programs require a real-life test to determine their usefulness, and sponsors seek talented faculty with the expertise to develop the appropriate model or pilot program. Higher education plays an important role in demonstrating the applicability and proving the reliability of products and programs.

Evaluation Services. Another principal public service function that faculty, medical staff, and institute personnel fulfill is to evaluate programs and products. Evaluation requires the determination of quantifiable criteria to measure goals, the development of measuring instruments, the application of the measurement, and the analysis of results. Such evaluation is needed for programs as diverse as lunar landings and new infant formulas.

The skills required to conduct evaluation activities are skills developed by researchers in their graduate training and in their professional experience. Sponsoring agencies and foundations realize the importance of evaluating programs they sponsor and regularly secure the services of trained researchers and evaluators.

History of Sponsored Programs

Federal support of research and education activities in higher education was initiated by the passage of the Morrill Act (1862) and the Hatch Act (1887), which provided funding for research, training, and demonstration activities in agriculture and vocational education. These activities were conducted in the land-grant colleges and schools of agriculture and mechanical arts. Through the 1930s there was little extramural research support in other fields in colleges and universities.

During World War II many scientists were enlisted or employed in special projects related to the discovery and development of better weapons, materials, and medicines for the armed forces. The Office of Scientific Research and Development stimulated and coordinated these scientific efforts. The success of the wartime science programs is witnessed by the advanced development in weaponry, aviation, radar, sonar, and the atomic bomb. This success highlighted the potential contributions of research to postwar American society and the important role that university researchers could play in all aspects of societal progress.

While no particular event marks the birth of sponsored program administration, the transmittal on July 5, 1945, of the report *Science: The Endless Frontier* from M. Vannevar Bush, director of the Office of Scientific Research and Development, to President Truman signaled the beginning of greater federal support for academic science and the resulting need for institutions to establish an administrative office to manage the sponsored programs (see Bush, 1960). Bush was responding to a request made in November 1944 by President Roosevelt to make recommendations for a program for postwar scientific research. His report was the seminal document in justifying the need and prescribing the conditions for the federal government to begin to support science projects conducted outside government laboratories.

The report stressed the need for the federal government to institute new programs to stimulate research and develop a greater pool of scientists. Bush felt that colleges and universities should be the centers for conducting basic research and developing new scientific talent with support from the government. In the final part of the report, Bush recommended that a new federal agency be founded to assist and encourage research and distribute public funds for that purpose. Most of the recommendations in *Science: The Endless Frontier* were adopted and implemented in the legislation authorizing the creation of the National Science Foundation (NSF) in May 1950.

Although federal interest in medical science research preceded the Bush report, the Medical Advisory Committee to Bush recommended that a new organization, the National Foundation for Medical Research, be established to direct and encourage basic medical research in the care and cure of diseases. The National Institutes of Health (NIH), founded in 1944 as a result of this recommendation, initiated support for medical research both within its divisions and at colleges, universities, hospitals, and independent research organizations.

The creation of NIH and NSF represented the start of a new era in the relationship between research institutions and the federal government. These agencies were charged with the responsibility of stimulating research and developing the pool of talented researchers in their respective fields. Colleges and universities were to be important partners in the achievement of these goals. The basic rationale for the cooperative partnership between government and academe is:

- Academic research is important to the common welfare, and thus public funds should be used to encourage and support research.
- Basic research is fundamental to all research and development; since colleges and universities are institutions devoted to knowledge and freedom of inquiry, they should be supported as centers for basic research.
- A national program of research requires a large pool of trained scientists; since higher education is charged with the responsibility of training young scientists, the government should encourage and support the training programs at colleges and universities.

These principles of federal support for basic science and medical science, established at the end of World War II, are still held today.

A new type of support for research and other programs began in the 1950s. The sponsors were the so-called mission agencies, and their intention was to enlist higher education faculty in solving problems. Among the agencies that utilized university faculty in applied research in the early years were the research offices of the various armed services, such as the Office of Naval Research, the Army Research Office in Durham, and special mission agencies like the Atomic Energy Commission and the National Aeronautics and Space Administration. As new mission agencies were established to address specific societal problems, they also inaugurated support programs for institutional research, education, and training. Examples of some of these later agencies are the Law Enforcement Assistance Administration, the Department of Energy, and the Environmental Protection Agency.

In the 1950s and 1960s some mission agencies sponsored programs that were to directly address the solution of a problem, while others funded basic research projects in areas that promised to be of value to their goals. The practice of funding for basic research in the Department of Defense was curtailed by the Mansfield amendment in 1970, which prohibited funding of basic research unless the relevance of the project to Department of Defense needs could be demonstrated. This legislation affected the funding sources and research patterns of several institutions.

The distribution of federal grants and contracts and the procurement of services required a system of management and accountability between the government and the institutions. Each sponsoring agency developed its own procurement and grants management regulations to govern the relationship to recipients. In addition, the Office of Management and Budget (OMB), formerly Bureau of the Budget, established regulations for the management of projects. The regulations of the sponsoring agencies and OMB describe the contractual responsibilities of recipients and define their working relationship with the sponsor. As the amount of government sponsorship increased and the attendant regulations became more complex, recipient institutions established offices to administer sponsored programs. Sponsored projects administrators are in the best position to interact with the sponsors and their program and regulatory officers since they do work with them on a regular basis. Such ongoing contact is important because it assures continuous experienced representation for the institution and frees the project director to devote more time to the management of the research or other project.

At the same time that the federal government was expanding support for colleges and universities, the private foundations were also increasing their activities in support of research and education programs in higher education. The older, better-known foundations like Ford, Carnegie, and Rockefeller became interested in higher education itself and sponsored many projects to investigate and improve various facets of academe. The foundations also sponsored projects to explore societal concerns relevant to their particular goals. The number of foundations providing support for education increased in the 1970s when a change in the Internal Revenue Act required foundations to divest a percentage of their assets each year or lose their tax-exempt status. This legislation compelled many foundations to increase their annual expenditures for sponsored projects.

State governments also began funding projects during this era of growth, although at a much lower level than the federal government. A major portion of state funds was directed, usually in the form of contracts, to education and training programs in specific areas such as vocational education, special education, and programs for the disabled. State sponsorship of higher education projects has varied widely among the states.

In general, the total amount of expenditures increased dramatically during the 1950s and 1960s. Increases in support continued through the 1970s and into the 1980s, but the rate of increase leveled off.

The distribution of sponsored funds from all sources has followed a consistent but uneven pattern during this period. The primary recipients of research dollars have been the large comprehensive research universities, medical research organizations, and institutes of technology. These institutions, both public and private, are centers for most of the basic research in our society. In the late 1960s and 1970s many of the developing universities and aspiring private institutes argued for more parity in funding and were successful in increasing their sponsored support.

The future of federal support for projects in higher education, medicine, profit and nonprofit institutes, and other areas is dependent upon the vagaries of Congress and the president. Although growth in federal sponsorship of programs in many areas has been steady, it has not been even nor constant. The legislative and executive branches of government are sensitive to public opinion, and as that opinion changes so does the funding.

As this text goes to press, the federal government is attempting to decentralize sponsored support by delegating more decision-making power to local and state governments. Many federal programs are being reduced or eliminated with the expectation that they will be replaced by locally funded programs. Other programs will no longer receive direct federal funding; rather federal funds will be distributed to the states as block grants, and the states will assume responsibility for distributing the funds. This effort to eliminate some federally funded programs and delegate others to state and local governments reverses a trend of the last thirty years.

As we have seen, sponsored program administration plays a vital part in the creation and transmission of knowledge to improve the human condition. Support for sponsored projects has grown steadily in areas regarded as important to our national interest, and the future of sponsored programs depends on the priorities of government agencies, foundations, associations, businesses, and industry.

2

Role of
Sponsored Projects
Administrators

A sponsored projects administrator is an organizational official with responsibility for developing, supporting, and managing all or part of the administrative functions required to represent the institution's interest, to serve the project director, and to provide liaison with sponsors in order to support the institution's programs. Sponsored projects administrators serve in many types of organizations and at different levels of responsibility within organizations. The laboratory business manager in a physics department in a university and the president of a nonprofit research institute can be sponsored projects administrators. Thus the administrative duties performed, rather than the location of employment or level in the hierarchy, identify sponsored projects administrators.

The sponsored projects administrator serves as a liaison among different parties that seek to achieve a common goal. Such parties include the institution, project directors, and sponsors. Their common goal is the achievement of research, education, or public service, agreed upon by the parties as important to each of their interests as expressed in a proposal application. But this description is deceptively simple, since reaching agreement on the achievement of the goal and the obligations of the three parties requires considerable communication and broker- ing. The sponsored projects administrator is the primary catalyst, bring- ing the parties together to achieve their goals. Beasley (1970) describes this role of the sponsored projects administrator as that of a "mediator- expeditor" between groups with different viewpoints and aims.

The successful sponsored projects administrator must be able to communicate effectively and to negotiate compromises between conflict- ing points of view. Although managerial ability, an understanding of the role of research and public service, and a knowledge of accounting and proposal writing are essential skills, unless the sponsored projects ad- ministrator can communicate and work with others, he or she will be ineffective as the liaison and broker.

In addition to bringing together the institution, project director, and sponsor, the sponsored projects administrator also directly attends to specific arrangements between any two of the three parties involved. Thus, if a question arises regarding release time or space approved in a proposal, the sponsored projects administrator works with the appropri- ate organizational administrator and the project director to arrange a solution. Similarly, a question regarding allowable cost expenditures re- quires negotiations between the institution and the sponsor. A significant change in the procedures for an awarded project or an extension of the project may require the sponsored projects administrator to help the project director facilitate the change with the sponsor. Thus the charac- terization of the sponsored projects administrator as being in the eye of a hurricane is incorrect; the sponsored projects administrator works from deadline to deadline with no calm lull in between.

Eurich (1967, p. 2) offers a most challenging and foreboding de- scription of the administrator of sponsored projects: "The administra- tion of sponsored research in the university is one of the crucial areas in this whole field. For here the university and the surrounding society work out the terms of their symbiotic relationship. The university needs the wherewithal to pursue its knowledge-producing activities; the society needs the collective brainpower which the university represents. How the needs of each can be met without violating the rights of any is an increasingly delicate and complex problem. The man who administers research is at the interface between the university and society. And interfaces mean friction, constant change, wear and tear."

Note that Eurich emphasizes the ethical responsibilities of the sponsored projects administrator in meeting the needs of the involved parties. The dimensions of such ethical considerations are described by Cebik (1980), who explains that the problems of the sponsored projects administrator fall into two categories: (1) operational problems, which concern developing effective systems, rules, and regulations; and (2) ethical problems, which concern choices among conflicting values where there are no guiding standards or principles. Cebik notes that ethical problems for sponsored projects administrators may arise in determining an institution's capabilities for accepting certain grants and contracts; regulating oversight in research involving human subjects, laboratory animals, biohazards, and recombinant DNA; recordkeeping, fiscal responsibility, and the interpretation of federal regulations; matching institutional goals and the direction of sponsored projects; determining responsibilities of investigators in completing projects; and devising a code of professional conduct for sponsored projects administrators. By their nature, ethical dilemmas do not have standard solutions. As the person responsible for the interface between investigator, institution, and sponsor, the sponsored projects administrator frequently must resolve conflicting value-based claims.

In sum, sponsored projects administrators play an important role in the successful completion of research and public service projects. Sponsored projects administrators serve three masters, and they must facilitate communications, negotiate any differences, and manage the interests of all three parties. This challenging position requires dedication and patience; the reward for success is the attainment of the research and public service goals of the institution, the professional development and project accomplishment for project directors, and the achievement of specific goals by the sponsor. The ultimate beneficiary of the research discoveries and public service programs is our society as a whole.

An Emerging Profession

Sponsored program administration is a new career field that is still evolving. The essential functions of the position have been identified but are continually being refined. The number and importance of sponsored projects administrators have grown significantly in a relatively short period of time.

For example, in higher education, the importance of the sponsored projects administrator to the institution's research and public service goals is gaining greater recognition as the role of the administrator emerges. At present, a major part of the research activities at colleges and universities is guided by policies administered by the sponsored projects administrator. Activities such as training, demonstration, community service, and experimental programs are also assisted and directed by the procedures administered by the sponsored projects office. Sponsored program administration is now an integral part of American higher education, and the sponsored projects administrator is an essential partner of the project directors in achieving the institution's goals.

With this increasing importance, the number of sponsored projects administrators has grown from only a few in 1946 to several thousand today. The two largest organizations for sponsored projects administrators, the National Council of University Research Administrators (NCURA) and the Society of Research Administrators (SRA), have approximately 1500 members each. Although the membership in these two organizations overlaps, many other sponsored projects administrators only belong to smaller specialized organizations or do not belong to any group.

As the number of practitioners has grown, sponsored projects administrators have also increased their sophistication in carrying out tasks and developing a division of labor to efficiently segment the required functions into specialized positions. The growth in size and sophistication in sponsored projects administration has resulted in a change from the one-person shop to an office populated by many people performing specialized duties. The centralized office is usually staffed by a director and several employees who are specialists with titles such as budget analyst, proposal development officer, information specialist, preaward grants specialist, and postaward services officer. The proliferation of specialists in sponsored program administration is an indication of the maturation of this field. The emergence of organizations devoted to the interchange of ideas and improvement of performance in specialized areas, like patents or licensing, complements this growth.

Another measure of the evolving status of sponsored projects administrators is the increased number of educational opportunities for improvement of knowledge and skills. Conferences and workshops are offered on a regular basis by NCURA, SRA, many universities, and several private organizations and individuals. These programs instruct participants in the improvement of a wide variety of tasks related to the work of the sponsored projects office. Offered on a regular basis are workshops such as "How to Stimulate Faculty to Write Proposals," "How to Organize Your Office," "How to Computerize a Grants Accounting System," "How to Comply with Federal Regulations," and "How to Identify Sponsors for Your Programs." The popularity of these programs indicates the desire and the need for individual improvement. Eventually, an educational syllabus will be derived from such topics, and it will become the basis for an advanced education program required to establish standards for certification.

The successful development of sponsored program administration as a career field may lead one to ask whether sponsored program administration is a profession. Indeed, sponsored projects administrators often call themselves professionals, and their voluntary organizations strive to define professional standards, provide professional advancement programs, and increase professional recognition. However, professions such as medicine, law, or architecture are defined by six criteria: (1) an advanced body of knowledge and skills specific to the field of work; (2) a long period of advanced training to acquire the knowledge and skills; (3) rigid standards of entrance usually measured by an intensive examination (for example, state bar or medical examination); (4) licensing or certification of members; (5) a code of ethics; and (6) disciplinary procedures determined and regulated by the members of the profession to expel anyone who violates the ethical code or does not perform at competency levels.

Sponsored projects administration does not now meet these six requirements for a profession. There have been a few efforts by individuals and organizations to define the duties of sponsored projects administrators and establish a formal educational program leading to a baccalaureate or master's degree. The Society of Research Administrators has established internship programs with institutions and with federal agencies to improve the preparation of newcomers to the field. However, no advanced body of knowledge applies to all sponsored projects administrators, and there are currently no standards of entrance, certification requirements, or disciplinary procedures for self-regulation of sponsored projects administrators. Thus sponsored program administration is emerging as a profession, but it is still a relatively new field and needs time to develop the requirements for acceptance as a profession.

Sponsored projects administrators face two particularly vexing problems in establishing a profession. First, most sponsored projects administrators are not self-employed and thus have a difficult time establishing conditions of employment, licensing requirements, and the right to expel incompetent members. Second, various subfields of sponsored projects administration require different training, experience, and professional standards—an administrator at one level differs from a manager at another level. This differentiation in responsibilities and levels of competence may lead to levels of professionals, such as the lawyer and the clerk or the doctor and the medical technician.

In summary, such important determinants of a profession as the definition of duties, the development of methodologies, and the identification of required knowledge and skills have emerged during the last three decades. Still to emerge are other professional requirements such as an advanced specialized preservice training program, licensing or certification for employment, and the maintenance of quality standards. The continuing professional progress from the founding research administrators of the 1940s to the sponsored projects administrators of today is a measure of the potential for full professional status in the future.

Voluntary Associations

As the number of people engaged in sponsored projects administration increased, they began to discuss their responsibilities informally. It was not long until voluntary associations were formed to meet the needs of practitioners. The organizations are divided into two types: (1) comprehensive organizations for a broad spectrum of sponsored projects administrators and (2) specialized organizations for administrators of specific functional areas of sponsored program administration.

There are three major voluntary organizations for sponsored projects administrators. All three are continuing to increase their membership and services, a development indicative of the growing number of sponsored projects administrators and their desire for professional development. A brief review of the goals of each organization provides an overview of the history of sponsored program administration and the current state of the field.

The National Conference on the Advancement of Research (NCAR) had its first meeting at Pennsylvania State University in 1947. NCAR was conceived by a group of research directors who held administrative positions in government research laboratories during the latter years of World War II. After the war they returned to university campuses, government, and industry and applied their experience to administering their organizations' research programs. These pioneer research administrators decided to organize a national conference that offered an opportunity to exchange information regarding policies and procedures in the administration of research programs. The first conference was considered a success, and NCAR has held annual meetings since 1947.

The purpose of NCAR is to provide "an annual active forum in which top-level research leaders in universities, industry, and government can exchange ideas and experiences on the management and administration of research on an informal basis. It focuses upon those facets having to do with the place of research in the organization and the community at every level" (National Conference on the Advancement of Research, n.d.).

The primary activity of NCAR is the annual meeting that provides this "active forum" for the exchange of ideas. The meeting logistics are managed by a host institution, usually a university located near the conference site. The program includes presentations and discussion groups concerning a chosen central theme. The speakers are usually high-ranking government officials and practicing research administrators with considerable knowledge in their respective areas of specialization. Presentations treat both current practices and predictions of future trends in research and development. Attendance is by invitation only and is limited to 200, with representation equally divided between government, industry, and university research administrators. The proceedings of each annual meeting are published and include the presentations as well as many of the discussion sessions. These proceedings are an excellent source of information on various aspects of research administration; as stated in the conference brochure, "these proceedings constitute the foremost body of knowledge on the subject of research administration."

The second oldest organization for research administrators is the National Council of University Research Administrators (NCURA). The first NCURA meeting was held in 1960. The preamble to the NCURA charter states that the organization is "a group of individuals with professional interests in problems and policies relating to the administration of research, education, and training activities at colleges and universities" (National Council of University Research Administrators, 1980, p. 8). The charter defines a member as "any person engaged in the administration of research, training, and educational programs in a college or university, a teaching hospital, or an organization wholly organized and administered by a college or university or a consortium of colleges and universities or an association or society with individual or institutional members predominantly from colleges or universities" (p. 8). Associate membership is offered to individuals engaged in the administration of sponsored programs who are employees of a not-for-profit organization, a public agency, or an industrial research and development organization. Emeritus membership is available for regular or associate members who were active for at least five years before retirement.

NCURA was formed to provide a voluntary association that addressed the specific concerns of sponsored programs in higher education, especially the relationship of grantee organizations to federal sponsors. The NCURA charter lists four objectives for the council's activities: (1) "To promote the development of more effective policies and procedures relative to the administration of education and research programs to assure the achievement of the maximum educational potential in academic research"; (2) "To provide a forum through national and regional meetings for the discussion and exchange of information and experiences related to sponsored educational and research programs, policies, and problems in colleges and universities"; (3) "To provide a nonregular publication for the dissemination of current information and the exchange of views on mutual problems"; and (4) "To foster the development of college and university research administration as a professional field, and to stimulate the personal and professional growth of the members of the council."

The primary activity of NCURA is the annual meeting, usually held in November and since 1965 always held in Washington, D.C. Each annual meeting has a theme, and presentations are centered upon this theme. Because members are interested in federal funding developments, many presentations are conducted by speakers from federal agencies. To encourage professional development, NCURA directs training workshops, develops and evaluates training materials, recommends professional standards, and suggests evaluation procedures to recognize outstanding contributors to the field of university research administration. The workshops, for example, are offered throughout the year at different locations. Some workshops are offered jointly with other appropriate national associations such as the National Association of College and University Business Officers (NACUBO) and the Council for the Advancement and Support of Education (CASE). NCURA's activities in this area have been successful in improving and enhancing sponsored program administration as a professional field.

In the early 1970s NCURA created geographical regions to serve members through regional workshops and activities. The primary regional activities are a spring meeting and selection of representatives to serve on national committees. NCURA also publishes a newsletter and an annual membership directory.

The newest of the comprehensive associations for research administrators is the Society of Research Administrators (SRA). SRA was founded in 1967 at Amherst, Massachusetts, as an organization "to improve the efficiency and effectiveness of the administration of research," as stated in the society's bylaws (Society of Research Administrators, 1980, p. 2). The bylaws list the society's purposes as (1) promoting the exchange of information among research administrators; (2) encouraging research in the area of administration of research; (3) developing and promoting professional standards; and (4) improving the relationship between research and administrative functions.

Members of SRA are research administrators from industries, universities and colleges, government agencies, nonprofit institutions, medical research institutions, and private foundations. SRA is an all-inclusive organization for research administrators and, consequently, has a very heterogeneous membership that includes individuals at various levels of responsibility in sponsored projects administration, from presidents of private research labs to beginning grants accountants.

The founding purposes and membership of SRA reflect the development of sponsored program administration as a field. By 1967 there were thousands of practitioners whose management responsibilities required job differentiation and specialization at various levels; additionally, there were many practitioners in nonuniversity settings such as independent hospitals, government, nonprofit laboratories, and businesses. SRA was formed to serve the needs of sponsored projects administrators in all types of employment and work settings. The two premises for founding a comprehensive organization were: (1) that all sponsored projects administrators perform a common set of functions; and (2) that by exchanging information and conducting research, practitioners could develop the field as a profession and increase the recognition and rewards.

SRA has a regular publications program that is headed by the quarterly *Journal of the Society of Research Administrators*. The *Journal* fulfills an important role in the achievement of SRA's goals of dissemination of information and professional development. Special studies, such as membership profiles, salary surveys, and reports on responsibilities and other employment conditions, are regularly conducted by the SRA research committee and published by SRA. The *SRA Newsletter* informs members of the various activities of SRA.

As part of a program to develop the professional skills of sponsored projects administrators, SRA conducts workshops related to specific job functions and career development. These programs are offered at locations throughout the country and in connection with the annual meeting. SRA also directs an internship program to train sponsored projects administrators through on-the-job experience. Some of these internship experiences are in federal agencies and are arranged for various lengths of time. Finally, SRA offers the Chester M. Sinnett Tuition Award, donated by the magazine *Industrial Research and Development* (formerly known as *R&D*), to support the continuing education of a sponsored projects administrator.

In summary, NCAR, NCURA, and SRA provide both a source and an outlet for practitioners and persons new to the field to learn and exchange information concerning current issues. Through the exchange of information about common experiences, sponsored projects administrators can develop as professionals and achieve a professional identity for the field of sponsored program administration. As a natural consequence of the growing professionalism and specialization of duties in the field, several associations have been formed for individuals with specific interests. A partial list of such specialized organizations illustrates these functional interests and represents the diversity of job specialization in sponsored program administration:

> Council on Governmental Relations (COGR) of the National
>   Association of College and University Business Officers
>   (NACUBO)
> Licensing Executives Society (U.S.A.), Inc. (LES)
> National Assistance Management Association (NAMA)
> National Association of Scientific Materials Managers (NASMM)
> National Contract Management Association (NCMA)
> Society for College and University Planning (SCUP)
> Society for Property Administrators (SPA)
> Society of University Patent Administrators (SUPA)

— 3 —

Goals, Policies,
and Organizational
Structures

The diversity of institutions of higher education is a source of strength in American society. This same heterogeneity also characterizes medical, nonprofit, and government organizations that receive and administer sponsored programs. Such diversity makes it impossible to formulate a uniform system of policies and practices for the management of sponsored projects. Consequently, any discussion of organizational goals, policies, and administrative structure for sponsored program administration must begin with an understanding of the organization's purpose.

23

Goals

The first consideration in determining the goals of an institution's sponsored programs is the institution's overall mission. A brief look at four types of higher education institutions illustrates the relationship between institutional mission and sponsored program goals.

For example, a small liberal arts college has as its primary mission the teaching of undergraduate students in the arts and sciences. While faculty may conduct research projects, research is not within the primary mission of the institution. Similarly, public service activities might engage some faculty members, but public service is not a basic priority for the institution. Such a college does not expect its sponsored projects office to develop, support, and manage large research projects nor to coordinate professional school support on campus or training programs and other sponsored projects off campus. Rather, the goals of the sponsored projects administration are directed toward garnering support for teaching improvement and curricular development. The prime concerns of the sponsored projects administrator are funds to support liberal arts education and general gifts to sustain programs. The scope of the sponsored projects office and the resources available to support it would probably be limited.

In contrast, the primary mission of most community colleges is instruction and service to the local community. Sponsored program goals for community colleges usually focus on support for off-campus activities that enable faculty to provide services to the local community. Agency and foundation support for training activities, development programs, demonstration projects, and other programs to enhance local conditions is essential to the institution's mission. Sponsored project goals and policies of community colleges reflect their community service mission, with the size of the sponsored projects staff depending on the emphasis and number of community service projects.

A different mission characterizes the developing college or university that has a broad academic program through the master's level and perhaps a few doctoral programs and professional schools. For the most part, these institutions are growing state colleges and universities.

The mission of these institutions embraces teaching, research, and public service, and their sponsored program goals reflect this breadth. The research capabilities of these institutions are limited by the size of their doctoral programs and the number of laboratories and graduate assistants. Although faculty members of developing colleges and universities are qualified researchers, only those institutions with an unusually favorable financial situation will have sufficient resources to support faculty research.

In the area of public service, developing institutions play an important role in extending the expertise of the campus to the community. Many of these institutions are strongly identified with a portion of a state or an urban area. This regional identity and the range of faculty capabilities result in excellent public service programs for the area and should be reflected in the goals of the sponsored projects office.

Our fourth type is the large university, public or private, deeply involved in research and public service as part of its institutional mission. Scholarly productivity is an essential part of the academic endeavors of such a research university. Most research universities receive millions of dollars each year to support research and graduate education, and their policies toward research support and sponsored program administration reflect their extensive research activity.

According to the National Science Foundation (1981a, p. 29), the top fifty doctorate-granting universities account for 62 percent of research and development expenditures from all sources—federal, state, and local government; industrial, instructional, and other—and the top 100 account for 86 percent of such funds. Therefore, of the approximately 3,000 institutions of higher education, the great majority of research and development funds are expended by 100 doctorate-granting universities.

These multipurpose universities also conduct extensive public service activities. Indeed, those that were originally land-grant colleges have service to the public included in their original purposes. The large universities serve a broad public constituency that extends worldwide. The breadth and size of their academic programs, including many professional schools, allow them to offer public service activities in many fields.

The preceding descriptions of institutional missions represent four points on a broad spectrum of missions and appropriate sponsored projects. Just as each institution is unique and determines its sponsored program goals according to its mission, so also each institution develops its policies and organization for sponsored program administration according to its goals.

Policy Considerations

Policies are rules that guide the activities of the sponsored projects administrator in achieving the goals of the office of sponsored projects. Policies are, of course, derived from the specific goals. Basic considerations guide the development of policies for sponsored programs in all organizations, but each organization must also consider its special conditions that warrant particular policies. Policies for sponsored program administration should be developed cooperatively by the sponsored projects officer and other appropriate officials and then approved through the organization's regular procedures.

In this section, two sets of general policy considerations are presented to illustrate the basic elements of policies for sponsored program administration. The first set includes general policy topics and a brief discussion of each. The second set is a checklist of policies for sponsored research to be used by chief academic officers in institutions of higher education.

Basic Policy Considerations for Sponsored Programs

Statement of Commitment. The first policy for the sponsored projects administration should be a clear statement of the institution's commitment to instruction, research, and public service. The statement can begin with a rationale for disseminating the information gained through scholarly research and for reaching beyond the boundaries of the campus to serve the public. The policy should state that this type of activity is important to the institution's goals and will be supported.

Acceptance of Outside Support. The institution should indicate that it recognizes the importance of support from government agencies, private foundations, and industry and accepts outside support to help achieve its commitment. Although this policy states the obvious, it is needed to indicate the willingness of the institution to work with sponsors to achieve mutual goals.

Conformance to Institutional Programs. Even though the institution is committed to accept outside support to achieve its mission, it cannot blindly accept every award it might be offered. The institutional mission is accomplished through programs conducted in colleges, departments, institutes, and centers. If an award is not related to existing capabilities and interests or if it interferes with ongoing activities, then the institution should reserve the right to refuse it.

Reward Systems. The institution's commitment to support sponsored activities can be reinforced by reward systems. The most effective reward systems in colleges and universities are the annual salary increment, the granting of tenure, and the promotion to a higher rank. The criteria related to successful attainment in these areas should include a measure of success in the appropriate activity (teaching, research, or public service) within the institution's mission. The policy must, of course, recognize that achievement in such activities can be attained without outside support. Also, determinations of salary, tenure, and promotion are decisions made through the academic governance structure and not by the sponsored projects office. Nevertheless, many faculty members achieve success and meet the advancement criteria through work supported by an outside sponsor. The importance of sponsored projects in achieving institutional goals and professional development should be recognized in the reward system, even though the reward system is not administered by the sponsored projects office.

Other rewards, such as reduced teaching load and summer research or project support, should also be considered for inclusion in the policy.

Central Control of Sponsored Projects Administration. The office of sponsored projects should be designated as the central office for the administration of sponsored projects activities. Centralization is essential to ensure that organizational policies are observed and to provide coordinated control of the sponsored activities. Many large organizations decentralize most of the sponsored projects administration to the department level. This system is satisfactory, in fact in many cases more efficient, as long as all proposals and awards are monitored by a central office to ensure compliance with organizational policies and commitments.

Required Approvals for Proposal Submission. A corollary to the policy for centralized control is a policy regarding approval of the submission of a proposal. The two primary review areas are the substantive aspects of the program and the budget. The substance of the proposed program should be consistent with the institution's goals and programs and approved by the unit administrator. The budget should be approved by a fiscal administrator to assure that all items are correct according to agency and institutional rules and that any resources committed— funds, space, or equipment—are approved and available.

The official who is responsible for the final approval for the institution should be identified as the last signer in the approval process.

Auxiliary Policies. Auxiliary activities related to a sponsored projects program may require specific institutional policies. Auxiliary areas of concern include patents, copyrights, human subjects experimentation, care of laboratory animals, and biohazards. For more discussion on these topics, refer to Chapter Fourteen.

Sponsored Research Policies

The American Council on Education recommends that in determining the basic institutional policies for sponsored research, the chief academic officer should address the following (Stauffer, 1977, p. 1):

1. Relation of sponsored research to the general institutional mission.
2. Relation of sponsored research to the continuity of instructional, public service, and research policies of the institution.
3. Rationale for sponsored research being undertaken by the institution in the context of other priorities.
4. Rationale for involvement of faculty members in research activity.
5. Criteria which sponsored research projects must satisfy before they are undertaken at the institution.
6. Outline of existing policies where such policies exist, on such matters as overhead, consultation practices of faculty members, patents, and copyrights.
7. Outline of basic issue areas where policies on sponsored research have yet to be determined and a timetable for resolution of the outstanding issues.

8. Outline of governance procedures for determining sponsored research policies, especially as they affect institutional autonomy.
9. Degree of centralization of policy determination on sponsored research and support services.
10. Relation of financial rationale for sponsored research programs to the academic mission of the institution.

Commitment to Sponsored Projects Administration

An institution's commitment to its sponsored projects program is essential to the achievement of the goals of the program and should be a part of its policy. This commitment has to be more than a public statement filled with platitudes about the values of research and other projects. Good intentions without appropriate supporting actions do not achieve the necessary objectives. Thus in addition to policies, the institution's commitment should be reflected in the attitude and encouragement given to project directors for their good work. As with goals, the degree and form of commitment depend on the institution. Such forms of institutional commitment include: (1) reward systems to reinforce the policies; (2) allocation of institutional resources to supplement sponsored projects activities; (3) establishment and support of a sponsored projects office, including adequate funding for staff and office operations and location in the administrative hierarchy that enables the chief sponsored projects administrator to participate in policy decisions related to sponsored projects; (4) public recognition of the importance of sponsored projects activities through speeches to outside groups, presentations on campus, and institutional publications; and (5) recognition of faculty conducting sponsored activities by awards, letters of commendation, and visits to laboratories or project sites.

Administrative Structures

The location of the office of sponsored projects within the administrative hierarchy of the institution is extremely important because it reflects the expectations of the institution's administration toward the functions of the office. It also determines the level of decision-making authority and the working philosophy of the office. The goals of the office and the attitudes of the staff are influenced by the administrative location. Reporting relationships are essential to the success of any program and the administrative structure is the primary means of setting communication linkages.

Administrative Structures in Nonacademic Organizations

The administrative structure for sponsored projects offices in profit and nonprofit organizations is typically a hierarchy of working teams reporting upward to a group manager and ultimately to a vice-president for research and development (or vice-president for program administration or director of operations). The activities conducted by the profit and nonprofit organizations are almost always called research management and not sponsored projects administration. The teams are usually organized on the basis of either a specific project or an area of scientific investigation. For example, a research team might be assigned to develop an automated radar response system to avoid midair collisions by airplanes. Such a team would require an interdisciplinary group of individuals applying their knowledge to the solution of a specific problem. Many of the not-for-profit "think tanks" that receive contracts from the federal government organize teams to achieve the objectives stated in the contractual agreement. Institutions concerned with basic research often organize teams by areas of scientific investigation, for example, low-temperature physics team, human engineering team, or surface chemistry team.

Each team or group of teams, depending on their size, will have a project manager or team leader. The manager at this level is located in the laboratory area and works directly with the investigators in conducting activities. The manager or group leader provides direction, support, and control of the sponsored projects activities.

A senior research director is responsible for the next level in the structure. In a small organization this position may be the senior officer responsible for research activities and his or her title is vice-president for research. In a large organization the leader at this level would have the title of group leader, research section manager, or division research director; the vice-president for research and development would be at the next level upward. The responsibilities of the officials at the upper levels of research management are to determine policy, establish research priorities, secure funds and plan budgets, and provide overall direction and evaluation.

Figure 1. Sample Organizational Structure in Profit and Nonprofit Organizations.

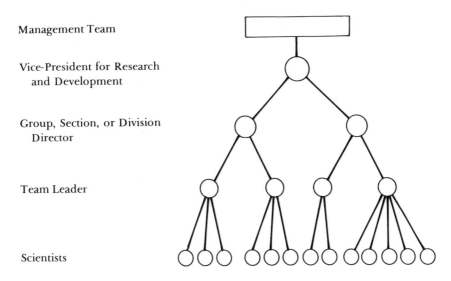

Management Team

Vice-President for Research
and Development

Group, Section, or Division
Director

Team Leader

Scientists

An example of an administrative structure for a profit or nonprofit research organization is presented in Figure 1.

Administrative Location in Higher Education

The approach and role of the sponsored projects administrator in higher education are affected by the division in which the office is located. The academic and business divisions serve the faculty in different ways. If the sponsored projects office is conceived as part of the institution's research and public service functions and develops programs to stimulate and assist faculty in securing sponsored support, then it belongs in the academic affairs division of the institution. Such an office is viewed as a service unit to support the academic mission of the school. The title of the director of the office, who would report to the vice-president of academic affairs, is usually research administrator or sponsored projects administrator.

If the primary purpose of the sponsored projects office is to manage and account for the sponsored funds received and assist faculty with the fiscal requirements associated with a grant or contract, then it should be located in the business affairs division. Office directors who report to the vice-president of business affairs are usually called grants administrators or grants and contracts administrators.

In actual practice in higher education, some institutions have sponsored projects offices in both the academic and business divisions. They operate parallel offices to support the sponsored projects activities and provide the appropriate services for each. Employees of the business affairs division may be called accountants or business managers, but they are providing support for sponsored projects and function as sponsored projects administrators.

The relationship between the parallel sponsored projects offices usually follows one of two patterns. The first pattern is determined by the preaward and postaward phases of sponsored projects (see Figure 2). The office of sponsored projects in the academic division performs the preaward services of planning, communicating, assisting in preparing the proposal for submission to the sponsor, and negotiation and award acceptance. Once the project is funded, the grants and contracts office in the business division manages the expenditure of funds, procurement of equipment and supplies, hiring of staff, and monitoring of compliance policies. This pattern was common in the 1950s and 1960s, and it is used by institutions that are just establishing offices to administer sponsored projects.

The second pattern of coordination assigns complete and parallel responsibility to both divisions throughout the project, with communication and cooperation at specific points as needed (see Figure 3). This tandem arrangement reflects the increased sophistication of sponsored projects administrators in expanding their services to assist project directors during all phases of a project. This pattern is used by institutions with an established program of sponsored projects administration in both the academic and business affairs division.

The effectiveness of sponsored program administration requires that the person responsible for all sponsored activities be a high-ranking officer who is directly involved in policy determination, decision making, and resource allocations. In this way, the administration is kept informed of the plans, accomplishments, needs, and policies associated with sponsored activities, and such plans and needs can be integrated into the overall goals of the institution. The title of the top-level administrator in the academic division responsible for sponsored projects is usually vice-president for research, associate vice-president for research, dean for research, or dean of graduate studies.

Figure 2. Pattern of Segregated Responsibilities for Pre- and Postaward Services.

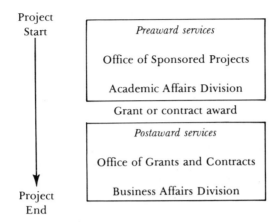

Figure 3. Pattern of Cooperative Management for Pre- and Postaward Services.

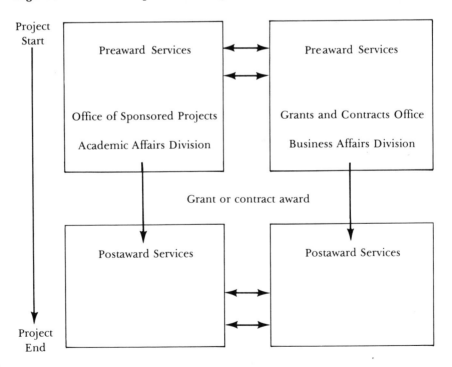

Directly below this vice-president or dean is the administrator who manages the actual operation of the sponsored projects office. The operations officer implements the goals, policies, and procedures determined by the administration. The title of the chief administrator at this level of the hierarchy is assistant vice-president for research, director of research, director of sponsored projects, or assistant or associate dean for research.

Sponsored projects administrators located in the business division of a college or university are usually in a middle-management position. The reporting pattern for a grants and contracts administrator is to the business manager, director of accounting, or controller. These latter positions report to the vice-president of business affairs.

The sponsored projects office at the operations level can be a one-person operation or a large office with many employees performing duties at various levels. The functions of sponsored projects administration are managed by the personnel at this level.

Some typical organizational charts indicating the location of sponsored projects administration in the hierarchy are presented in Figures 4 through 8. Organizational charts for sponsored projects offices are presented in Chapter Five.

Figure 4. Vice-President Level.

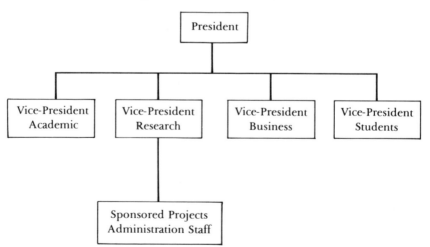

Figure 5. Associate Vice-President Level.

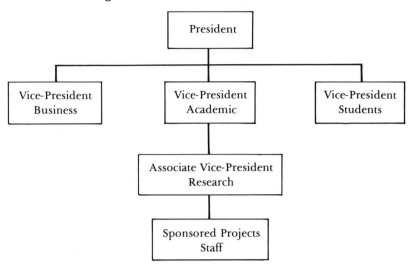

Figure 6. Dean's Level in a College.

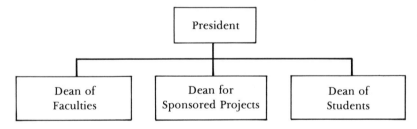

Figure 7. Dean's Level in a University.

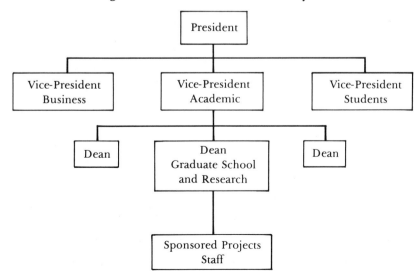

Figure 8. Business Affairs Organization.

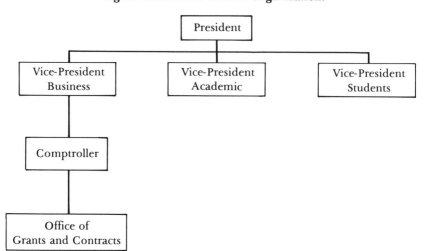

4

Developing the
Capacity for
Project Support

Institutions both large and small, research oriented or not, have the responsibility to develop and maintain the potential for sponsored projects activity. This concern may also relate to individual units at all levels within an institution. Obviously, specific approaches to this problem are dictated by local conditions in addition to the institution's and unit's philosophy and intentions. The focus of this chapter is primarily on enhancing sponsored projects potential at the institutional level, but most of the suggestions can be implemented at the unit level with little or no modification. Although the university setting is used for purposes of illustration, the concepts presented are applicable to other organizations engaged in sponsored projects administration.

No one set of activities will foster the development of attitudes and capabilities for sponsored projects activities in all organizations. For instance, sponsored projects administrators in large universities frequently feel that their institution's ongoing efforts are sufficient and that any change deemed necessary will be recognized and addressed at the departmental level. In this type of setting, an institution-wide effort may, in fact, be counterproductive or inappropriate. Most institutions, however, would benefit from a comprehensive effort to enhance their potential for sponsored projects.

The sponsored projects office is the natural setting for devising policies and procedural recommendations to establish positive institutional attitudes toward sponsored projects activities. The sponsored projects administrator should play a key role in advising other administrators about effecting appropriate changes in attitudes. Once these efforts are underway, the sponsored projects office should actively assist potential proposers in planning, coordinating, and stimulating sponsored projects activity. This office should be a valuable information source and catalyst for these purposes.

Building Attitudes Toward Sponsored Projects

Efforts to create positive attitudes toward sponsored projects activities must begin with the president of the institution and must be supported throughout the administration, especially by the academic vice-president and the deans. Once the institution's philosophy and policies are established, the active cooperation of departmental chairpersons is mandatory for the effective implementation of those policies. Of course, faculty support for enhancing the role of sponsored projects is crucial. Statements by faculty governing bodies within an institution can provide the impetus for a change in philosophy and practice, allowing key administrators to begin concerted efforts to improve the institution's sponsored activities.

There must be timely, consistent, and definite communications from the president and academic vice-president concerning the future of the institution and the role of sponsored projects in that future. To inform faculty members and secure their participation, the president and academic vice-president should use every available forum, from the annual address to faculty to the local Rotary club, to discuss and emphasize the changing mission of the institution and the importance of research and other sponsored projects to that mission. Projections of the annual funding that the institution is capable of attracting should be made and addressed as goals. The activities sponsored by those funds should be discussed in terms of their ability to enhance personal, professional, and institutional achievements. Indeed, the emphasis must fall on the intrinsic value of such activities and not on generation of institutional revenue. If faculty members perceive that revenue—and not achievement—is the chief goal of sponsored projects, they will form attitudes that restrict rather than support institutional progress. The perception that administrators are only interested in the overhead generated by a project must be consciously faced and dispelled.

Assessing the Climate. It is well known that successful organizational and attitudinal change in institutions comes only with careful planning and implementation. The receptivity of an organization to an effort to increase the amount of sponsored projects activities is site-specific, and programs designed to effect such a change must be custom-tailored to that setting.

The impetus to enhance sponsored projects activity may result from one of several situations: an institution's desire to upgrade its programs, particularly at the graduate level, or to mitigate decreases in support funds that threaten to cause decreasing graduate enrollments; an institution's financial inability to pursue project research at an appropriate level; its financial inability to participate in professionally rewarding and important activities or to expand programs; or a mandate from an external governing authority. Clearly, the main impetus for change relates to shrinking resources and the decreasing ability of an institution to support activities of value to its programs and research staff. Few research institutions today do not face some or all of these constraints, and indeed research staff often are among the first to recognize them. When such constraints become apparent, the institution must initiate organized efforts to enhance the sponsored projects activity.

Although researchers may already be receptive, support for enhanced sponsored projects activity may vary on the part of sponsored project directors. Some project directors may resist such activity because they are reluctant to take on new responsibility, fear being incapable of completing projects, and believe that teaching and other efforts may suffer. The degree of their resistance should dictate the approach to changing attitudes in a particular institution. As attitudes begin to change favorably, the institution will develop a self-sustaining acceptance of increased sponsored projects activity. The institution and its members will view sponsored projects activity as a routine way of life.

An effort to enhance attitudes must also effect and maintain a level of institutional self-esteem appropriate to anticipated sponsored projects activity. The effort may resemble a chicken-and-egg proposition in that this type of esteem grows with success and usually advances in geometric proportions once underway. Enhancement of institutional esteem is important in fostering an environment in which organized efforts at increasing sponsored projects activity will have a reasonable chance for success.

Although there are no established and tested measures of institutional attitude or environment for sponsored projects activity, the perceptive administrator can usually judge progress in this regard. The most obvious indicator is the willingness of research staff to write and submit proposal applications. Changes in the number of proposals submitted annually, albeit a gross measure, is a guide in assessing attitude.

Attitudes of concern include individuals' needs, self-esteem, and recognition of the professional advantages of sponsored projects activity. Administrators such as chairpersons and deans should understand and promote the value of sponsored projects activity to their faculty. They can also play a vital role in helping individuals develop a level of self-esteem that will support initial efforts to apply for external funding. Many individuals have little or no experience in seeking sponsored project support and may, in fact, have the impression that only the "heavyweights" in a particular area are capable of gaining such recognition. It is incumbent on unit and department needs to help individuals understand the value of sponsored projects and the realities of the grant process. Suggestions to address these sorts of concerns are presented later in this chapter.

Incentives. The first incentive to support the development of a sponsored projects program is to align the institution's existing reward structure with those activities of importance to sponsored projects. In higher education the most important rewards are promotion, tenure, and merit salary increases.

Promotion and tenure are awarded for academic achievement in the areas of teaching, research, and service. Policies must emphasize that achievement—and not the means through which the accomplishment is pursued—is the standard; that is, promotion and tenure are not rewards for the receipt of grants and contracts but for the accomplishments that such sponsored projects activity supports. However, the quality and quantity of such achievement can be enhanced by the support of sponsored projects. Thus, sponsored projects activity is not an end in itself but rather an important means to an end that benefits all parties.

Merit salary increases are usually decided at the departmental level and take into account the entire range of expected activities of a unit member. The criteria for such increases can provide a strong incentive for the development of sponsored projects activities. Proposal submissions and awards should be among the variables considered in reaching these decisions, and this criterion can carry substantial weight in a unit that stresses sponsored projects activity. Another method to reward researchers for sponsored projects activity is to set aside a fixed percentage of the available merit salary funds and distribute them solely on the basis of achievement related to sponsored projects.

Nonfinancial types of recognition for achievement with sponsored projects can also be very important. Some are as simple as a word of congratulations from a colleague, a sponsored projects administrator, an academic vice-president, or the president. A formal letter of congratulations from the vice-president or president can reinforce favorable attitudes toward sponsored projects.

Efforts to publicize sponsored projects activities can be rewarding to project directors. Such outlets as newspapers, local radio and television, institutional newsletters and publications intended for broad distribution are useful and supportive of the sponsored projects effort.

The granting of awards and honors by the institution for sponsored projects achievement is valuable in recognizing outstanding contributions as well as in motivating younger colleagues to pursue their work in quest of such recognition. Although these awards are usually few in number in a single institution, their effect is often felt quite broadly.

Capabilities

The building or enhancing of an institution's capabilities for sponsored project activities requires the participation of many individuals and offices. The efforts of an organization that has no experience with sponsored projects and seeks to initiate such projects will be much different from one in which expansion is the primary concern. But the mandatory first step in both processes is recognition that sponsored projects activity is vital to the institution and that it is a high institutional priority. Only then will attitudinal changes, through efforts elaborated in the previous section, be effected.

The institution must also assign an individual the responsibility for enhancing the institution's capabilities for sponsored projects. Although an individual may already have this responsibility, a formal assignment or reaffirmation is helpful. This individual must assess the institution's capability in terms of its capacity to compete for funds for different types of efforts and from different agencies. During this assessment, the institution should begin to offer support services for individuals ready to make applications while developing and implementing programs to assist others in reaching the level of capability needed to compete for sponsorship. The service aspect of this role is addressed in Chapter Eight. Suggestions for developing capabilities follow.

Long-Term Planning. Institutions that are creating a sponsored projects function usually have to build on their existing capabilities. However, plans for new programs and program expansion should be incorporated in the institution's long-term planning. Such planning is crucial to the institution's long-term development of capabilities and future competitiveness. The more advanced an institution, the more likely there will be concern for new and expanded programs. The long-term planning should address both program expansion and program deletion. Administrators, such as deans in colleges and universities, should project the likely growth or decline of their units. Realistic planning is imperative for an institution to achieve its desired program level and mix.

An institution with an established sponsored projects program should include in its formulation of the program's goals the development and growth of capabilities for sponsored projects. Such growth may include adding new sponsored projects staff to an existing program to provide more breadth or depth, or adding an essential piece of equipment that will be useful to present researchers. The addition of appropriate techniques and equipment is crucial to progress in most natural and biological sciences. The realistic development of capabilities requires an awareness of institutional needs and a clear assessment of the probability that they will be fulfilled.

Another type of program expansion or enhancement is the creation of a new organizational unit that will utilize the institution's existing capability. This new organizational entity, usually a center or institute, serves as a coordination and support unit for a discipline or area of interest, and it may function like a specialized sponsored projects office by identifying and enhancing institutional capabilities in an area of interest while actively seeking external support and assisting staff in producing competitive proposals. Where a "critical mass" of expertise or capability exists, such a unit can be the proper stimulus for a very successful program.

Enhancement of Existing Units. In institutions that have an established program base and some sponsored projects activity, the sponsored projects administrator should play a key role in planning and supporting the expansion of capabilities. This person should have the attention of the appropriate institutional authority and should actively participate in institutional planning, particularly with regard to developing and strengthening capabilities that will lead to increased sponsored projects activities in existing units. The sponsored projects administrator can address such matters as the addition of new positions, enhancement of existing units, and the establishment of new research units in terms of the institution's overall priorities, a perspective that unit administrators may be unable to bring to a given issue.

Establishing Priorities for Sponsored Projects Support

Priorities for sponsored projects activities will and should develop at both the institutional and unit level. For instance, departments should assess research capabilities and agree on sponsored projects directions and the possible role of each participant's expertise in the department's sponsored projects program. This same consideration and acknowledgment of direction is appropriate at the institutional level. In addition, multiple-unit programs will evolve over time and change as institutional capabilities and outside interests change.

Why should a department attempt to determine program priorities and target groups of project directors rather than only support the desires of individual project directors to pursue their individual interests? The answer is clear—there are seldom adequate resources to allow each project director to pursue his or her own interests. Clustering of like interests can produce a coordinated and effective program of research. The unit need not prohibit a project director from pursuing a career in a certain area, but rather the unit should identify a broad area of interest to which the talents of each researcher can be applied. Such a departmental agreement can be accomplished on an individual and voluntary basis coordinated by the chairperson. Individual support for these kinds of efforts can be important to the evolution of a project director's career and may also elicit added support that allows individuals to pursue those interests they do not share with their colleagues. Departmental identity on a national or international scale can result from such program priorities, to the benefit of the department and institution as well as the individuals involved.

In universities, each college should develop sponsored projects priorities. These priorities will, of course, be more broad and more generally described than those of a department. However, they are equally important to the institution's effort to develop an identity and effectively allocate resources.

Programs to Enhance Sponsored Projects Activity

In addition to setting departmental and college goals and establishing organized research units in response to faculty capability, the institution should initiate central programs, directed by sponsored projects administrators, to enhance sponsored projects activity.

Proposal Writing Workshops

Critical to a project director's development is the acquisition of proposal preparation skills. Because few graduate schools provide such training, it is incumbent upon institutions to assist faculty in this area. Many institutions offer their research staff structured workshops or courses for the specific purpose of developing proposals. Such efforts range from one-day programs on a specific topic to a semester-long series of meetings that address a spectrum of issues.

Experience suggests to the authors that an integrated series of workshops offered over an extended period of time (three to five months), if structured properly, may be the best investment of faculty time. A program of this sort works best with small groups (preferably limited to twenty participants); those involved need not be from the same discipline, but groups whose members have similar backgrounds are usually more effective.

At the initial meeting of the group, the leader should emphasize that the purpose of the program is to assist participants in becoming more proficient at proposal writing and communicating with outside sponsors and thus enable participants to better realize their career goals. During the program each participant will develop a proposal, ready for submission, relying on the group's response and criticism in refining and shaping the proposal. Thus the active participation of all members of the group is important. Often as many as one half of those who attend the first meeting decide not to complete the workshop. Those who withdraw may not be ready for the process or may have another method of acquiring the requisite skills for preparing a competitive proposal.

It is suggested that members of the group undertake the following activities in the order of presentation:

One-paragraph description: To inform members of the group about each other's ideas and the types of proposals likely to be developed, each member should present a one-paragraph description.

Write letter of inquiry: Each member should develop a letter of inquiry that may be directed to several potential sponsors for the purpose of determining if there is interest in learning more about a particular project. For a description of the purpose and content of a letter of inquiry, see Exhibit 1 (page 49).

Review letter of inquiry: The group review should begin by assigning one member to present his or her letter, and each member should have a copy of the letter. This process helps the member refine the letter and serves as a rehearsal for presentation to an outside sponsor. The review should address each of the five parts of the letter of inquiry described in Exhibit 1.

Write prospectus: A prospectus is a brief, preliminary statement of the problem, objectives, procedures, and budget in order to determine the interest of a potential sponsor. Using Exhibit 2 (pages 50–51) as a guide, each member of the group should write a preliminary submission for presentation to the group.

Review prospectus: The prospectus review should be undertaken with Exhibit 2 in hand. Ideas can be further refined at this stage according to the group's suggestions.

Seek funding agency: At this point, each member's ideas should be definite enough to pursue a useful search for potential funding sources. Members should consult with the sponsored projects office's resource librarian. Each should select one sponsor and use its guidelines to prepare the final proposal.

Write the proposal: The parts of a proposal and their development and format are discussed in Chapter Eight. In preparation for this exercise members should be referred to one of the several good books published on this subject.

Review the proposal: This review is similar to those for the letter and the prospectus. Subsequent to this review any work that needs to be done should be undertaken on an individual basis.

Internal Research Programs

Internal research programs are funded by the institution to support research and development for short-term, project-oriented proposals (Dingerson, 1977). One type of internal research program is designed to provide seed grants to researchers who are aspiring to better their ability to attract external sponsorship. The seed grant enables researchers to generate preliminary data or publications that enhance their reputation and increase their chances of gaining external sponsorship. A second type of internal research program is designed to support all or most of the costs for projects that are considered unlikely to receive external sponsorship or short-term projects of high merit that require only a modest expenditure of funds.

Most internal research programs are administered by a committee. The committee ranks proposals based on the merit of the proposed work and either recommends or makes decisions on awards and their amounts. More often than not internal research programs are handled through the graduate school with applications solicited on a campuswide basis. Some programs are small, but many administer more than $500,000 annually.

Resource A provides a sample description and application form for an internal research program. This sample program is administered by three committees that make recommendations to a research director. The committees also suggest to the proposer how to improve the proposal and recommend potential external sponsors. This review process is quite valuable to the aspiring project director seeking to improve a proposal.

Mini-Sabbaticals

A mini-sabbatical program is an organized institutional effort to provide faculty the financial support and time to gain a skill that will benefit a planned or organized research effort. Mini-sabbaticals are usually one week in length and with support between $700 and $1,000. With this support, a project director may visit a collaborator's laboratory to gain new techniques, attend an intensive seminar on an appropriate subject, or learn to operate a new item of equipment. A program of this sort is relatively inexpensive and can provide a productive return. By publicizing the program, the institution offers its members tangible evidence of its support for research and sponsored projects.

Visits by Agency Personnel

By developing and supporting a steady flow of visits from sponsoring agencies' program personnel, an institution can nurture a creative, stimulating, intellectual atmosphere conducive to sponsored projects. Program personnel are frequently at the leading edge of a field or discipline; they can both present seminars that treat research at the forefront of a field and acquaint researchers with opportunities available from the sponsor. Such visits also allow program personnel to learn about campus capabilities and to form overall opinions about the institution.

The sponsored projects office can arrange an extended series of visits without great expenditures. Many federal program officers may not accept travel reimbursement from an institution; such costs are frequently assumed by the sponsor. However, institutions may choose to pay for the visitor's other expenses, particularly for lunches or evening meals. Such expenses are relatively minimal, and meals and social events provide the institution's staff with vital personal contact with potential sponsors.

Other Development Programs

Research Scholar Award. Many universities seek to encourage proposal submissions and improve the quality of the applications by sponsoring a competition for a significant award, $15,000 to $25,000, depending on the researcher's need. For this type of program proposals are prepared on the appropriate sponsor application form and are submitted to the sponsor for consideration. The university review is conducted by experienced external peer reviewers who evaluate the proposals and offer comments to improve them. These reviewers are paid a reasonable fee for their services. The office of sponsored projects staff then uses these evaluations to work with project directors to improve their proposals before final submission to the appropriate sponsors. A faculty research committee assists in the overall review.

Such programs encourage investigators to prepare external applications for their research ideas and to develop more competitive proposals, and they stimulate younger researchers to apply for external funding. Each college or school can have its own competition, or the competition can be campuswide for junior and senior awards. A program of competitive university summer research fellowships can achieve similar objectives.

Matching Award Funds. The sponsored projects office can set aside matching funds for equipment and travel grants for which project directors may apply when submitting applications that require matching cost-sharing funds. A research committee consisting of project directors would evaluate and assign priorities to these requests.

Faculty Visits to Sponsors. Many offices of sponsored projects provide project directors with travel grants to visit sponsors. Project directors request funds from this program to enable them to present their prospectus and make personal contacts with program officers. Often the researcher agrees to submit a formal proposal upon return.

School or College Research Coordinator. An institution can also improve competitive proposal submission and foster research by having the office of sponsored projects appoint a faculty researcher to assist both the office of sponsored projects and research colleagues in disseminating information, developing ideas, writing proposals, and generally improving the sponsored projects environment in that college or school. The position must be a recognized administrative appointment. The individual in that post must be a respected researcher who enjoys working with faculty and is rewarded for this important service.

Exhibit 1. Contents of the Letter of Inquiry.

The purpose of the letter of inquiry is to identify possible funding sources for a meritorious idea. In writing, one seeks to determine that the prospective proposal falls within the scope of the sponsor's current interests and priorities, and that the sponsor has funds available during the planned project period. If the sponsor deems the prospective proposal appropriate it will assign a program officer to offer the project director technical assistance in developing the proposal to meet the sponsor's specific requirements. The letter of inquiry also serves to introduce the project director to a person in the sponsoring agency and is usually the first point of personal contact.

The letter of inquiry generally has five parts:

1. An introductory paragraph containing the title of the proposed project
2. A persuasive statement of the need and a clear statement of the objectives of the project
3. A description of the unique qualifications of the researchers' abilities and facilities and their institution's commitment to the area of work
4. A list of the benefits that will accrue to society or the discipline at the completion of the work
5. An offer to talk personally with the sponsor officers and to submit a prospectus or fully developed proposal if the work is judged meritorious.

Source: Adapted from Hensley, 1977.

Exhibit 2. Guidelines for the Prospectus.

The prospectus is written to secure from an agency an invitation to write a proposal for high-priority work related to the mission of the agency. It has two functions. First, it serves to convince the agency that the research question, training activity, or service is of sufficient importance to the agency and of significance to a particular field of knowledge or client group. Second, it must convince the agency that the project director and his or her team are the best qualified to carry the research or service to a successful conclusion.

The prospectus is, in essence, an outline of the final proposal. Thus in writing the prospectus, one must have thought through all the operational features of the proposed project and be able to headline those features concerned with the need, significance, impact, and evaluation of the project. The prospectus is a technical document addressed to experts in a particular field, and the style and language should be appropriate to this intended audience. Further, these experts are knowledgeable about operating conditions in their field. They will quickly spot vague or poorly stated ideas, unrealistic planning, and ill-conceived methodology.

A prospectus is usually three to five single-spaced pages in length and has seven basic parts: (1) abstract, (2) purpose statement, (3) statement of the problem, (4) procedures, (5) evaluation, (6) dissemination, and (7) budget.

The abstract should not exceed 150 words. Its title should clearly describe the work to be performed. The first sentence should state explicitly what one proposes to do. Then the problem one wishes to alleviate by the planned action should be identified precisely. Next the proposed solution to the problem is explained briefly. Finally, the benefits of the project are enumerated and the unique qualifications of the project director and the institution to solve the problem are stated in a modest and cogent manner.

The purpose statement should be detailed enough to clearly convey the intent of the project and yet general enough to serve as an effective overall guide in planning the project operations:

> *Specific objective:* At the conclusion of the project, 95 percent of the fifth-grade pupils in Wyman School will gain 1.2 years in reading comprehension, as measured on the Iowa Test of Reading Skills, Form Y, a pretest score administered in September 1980 and a posttest score on Form X in June 1981.

> *Vague objective:* All students in the school will improve in reading comprehension.

Proposal objectives must state in measurable terms exactly what will be achieved during the project. One's objectives will, of course, develop from one's assessment of the problem and proposed solution. Objectives should also reflect

Exhibit 2 (continued)

current knowledge and practice in the appropriate discipline or field, and their relationship to the mission of the parent institution and the sponsoring agency should be articulated.

The statement of the problem should identify precisely the problem as it relates to social needs, disciplinary imperatives, and institutional mission.

The procedures section is devoted to the methods to be employed in investigating the problem, the activities to be used in delivering a service, or the instructional strategies planned for training. When possible classical methodology and research designs should be used. If the protocol represents a significant departure from or improvement on existing practice, explain the advantages of the new procedures. If the project will explore a new approach or take one side of a controversial issue in preference to others, the existence of other protocols and the justification for the selection of methodology should be discussed briefly. This section should also supply information on the following items:

- the personnel and resources that will be used and how they will be used and organized
- the population that will serve as subjects or clients
- the research protocol
- the plan for selecting, gathering, and analyzing data

The evaluation statement should briefly explain the design of the evaluation protocol. The evaluation protocol must contain measures that will assess the effectiveness of the project in meeting its objectives. Sponsors are reluctant to fund projects whose objectives or evaluation protocol lack explicitly defined measures; such measures enable the sponsor to assess the value of the proposed project and later to assess whether the project was successful and the funds well spent. The achievement of evaluation goals ultimately establishes the reputation of the project director and the "track record" of the institution.

Source: Adapted from Hensley, 1977.

⊟⊟ 5 ⊟⊟

Organizing
the Sponsored
Projects Office

⊟⊟⊟⊟⊟⊟⊟⊟⊟⊟⊟⊟⊟⊟⊟⊟⊟⊟⊟⊟⊟⊟

As discussed in Chapter Three, the location of the office of sponsored projects in the administration is important to the role and functions of the office within the institution. Any institution that receives extramural support for research, educational, or service projects must have a centralized office of sponsored projects. This centralized office is a service office established to facilitate searches for external funding, to assure that sponsored support is compatible with institutional objectives, to avoid unnecessary duplication of programs, and to ensure that all funds are expended in accordance with recipient and sponsor regulations. *All* sponsor applications should be reviewed and approved by the office of sponsored projects before being forwarded to the authorized institutional official for final approval and signature.

Organizational Structures

The location of the office of sponsored projects within the institution and the official to whom the office reports depend on the institu-

Table 1. Organizational Control of Research Administration.

Research Administrator Reports to	Number of Institutions
Academic vice-president	35
President	27
Graduate dean	22
Vice-President, Research	15
Provost	12
Vice-President, Finance	11
Executive vice-president	7
Vice-President, Development	5
Comptroller	5
Other	13
TOTAL	152

Source: Steinberg, 1973.

tion's tradition, the volume of sponsored projects, the type of institution, and its system of management.

From a study of 152 representative universities, Steinberg (1973) reports the figures shown in Table 1 regarding organizational placement of the office of sponsored projects; although location varies, depending on the institution, the majority of offices report to the academic side of the house.

A more recent study conducted by Murray and Biles (1980) yielded the information shown in Table 2. The survey included 93 of the top 100 universities receiving government awards in 1977 and 37 additional institutions that offered doctorates in several disciplines and had enrollments over 10,000.

To provide the full complement of both pre- and postaward services to its project directors, and to enhance the relationship between the office and the recipient community, it is preferable for the office of sponsored projects to report to the vice-president for academic affairs, provost, vice-president for research, or graduate dean, depending on the size and complexity of the institution. In many large institutions the office reports to the vice-president for research. In a university, the graduate dean often has the overall responsibility for sponsored projects administration, depending on the role of research in graduate education and the type of external awards received. Another top candidate for this

Table 2. Characteristics of Office for Sponsored Programs.

Organizational Structure	N	Percentage
Office reports to:		
Dean or assistant vice-president	35	37.6
Vice-President or provost	51	54.8
President	7	7.6
Total Annual Office Expenditures		
Under $80,000	12	12.9
$80,000–149,000	31	33.3
$150,000–219,000	16	17.2
$220,000–289,000	8	8.6
Over $290,000	16	17.2
No response	10	10.8
Source of Sponsored Funds		
Federal government:		
Under 70 percent	16	17.2
70–79 percent	20	21.5
80–89 percent	32	34.4
Over 90 percent	17	18.3
No response	8	8.6
Private foundations:		
0–9 percent	51	54.8
10–19 percent	19	20.4
20 percent or more	7	7.6
No response	16	17.2
Fund Searching		
Visit private foundations	24	25.8
Person-days in Washington, D.C., per year:		
Under 10	14	15.1
10–19	33	35.3
20–49	28	30.2
Over 50	10	10.8
No response	8	8.6

Source: Murray and Biles, 1980, p. 2.

responsibility in large universities is the vice-president for academic affairs or the provost. This placement allows the director of the office of sponsored projects better accessibility to top management and overall institutional planning, provides better communications, and enhances the status of the office.

In some large institutions much of the management (both proposal processing and administration of awards) is decentralized to individual units; the central office may only disseminate information to potential proposers and review and approve applications for external funds. Of course, the functions of each office of sponsored projects depend on the requirements and needs of the individual institution. There is no one right way to establish an office, for each institution is unique.

Scope and Functions

The institutional philosophy and location of the office of sponsored projects within the organization determine the scope and functions of the office. Offices of sponsored projects have a considerable range of responsibilities, from the large operation organized to provide complete proposal development and processing, with a full complement of pre- and postaward services, to the one-person office where proposals are simply reviewed and signed. Table 3 reflects the diversity of services provided by the offices of sponsored projects within universities.

A comprehensive office of sponsored projects may provide the following services:

1. Maintain current material and information regarding sources of funding (federal, state, and private), proposal development, and reference documents:
   a. Program announcements, regulations, guidelines, application forms, and the like
   b. Reference books on potential sources of funding
   c. Proposal writing resource books
   d. Newsletters, *Commerce Business Daily, Federal Register, Federal Telephone Directory,* and other pertinent publications
   e. Names, addresses, and phone numbers of appropriate agency personnel
2. Disseminate pertinent materials regarding sponsored projects:
   a. Semimonthly newsletters on research highlights
   b. News bulletins
   c. Project director meetings, office visits, and telephone calls
3. Maintain a computerized profile system to provide timely and accurate information regarding potential sources of funding.

Table 3. Services Provided by Offices for Sponsored Programs.

Proactive Emphasis[a]	N	Percentage
Less than 10 percent of time	12	12.9
10–19 percent	19	20.4
20–29 percent	18	19.4
30–39 percent	10	10.8
40–49 percent	12	12.9
Over 50 percent	17	18.2
No reply	5	5.4
Number of Proposals Written by Office		
None	25	26.9
1–2	8	8.6
3–5	18	19.4
6–8	7	7.5
9 or more	19	20.4
No reply	16	17.2
Specific Services Provided		
Prepare budgets	71	76.3
Provide typing assistance	38	40.9
Mail proposals: routinely	58	62.4
on request	17	18.3
Routinely notify faculty of		
opportunities in *Federal Register*	57	61.3
Communications with Faculty		
Use letters to describe *Commerce*		
Business Daily opportunities	12	13.6
Use phone to describe *Federal*		
Register opportunities	44	47.3

[a]*Proactive* is defined on the questionnaire as "contacting agencies to determine interests and funding sources and then encouraging an appropriate faculty response; stimulating proposals by actively contacting faculty members; helping to write proposals."

Source: Murray and Biles, 1980, p. 3.

4.   Maintain a computerized program information system.

5.   Develop and administer a program to provide seed grants.

6.   Provide seminars on effective proposal writing and grants-manship.

7.   Provide contacts and sources of funds for visits to sponsors.

8.   Establish and help administer human subjects compliance, animal welfare compliance, biohazards compliance, and patents and copyrights.

9. Provide proposal typing and duplication.
10. Provide boilerplate information for proposal writing.
11. Assist the researcher by providing budgeting and editing services.
12. Provide information and assistance concerning institutional guidelines and practices as they relate to sponsored projects.
13. Assist the researcher by evaluating proposals in terms of program guidelines, content and style, budget matters, and institutional and sponsor systems and regulations.
14. Process the proposal for review and signature by appropriate administrative officers.
15. Submit or mail the proposal.
16. Handle proposal negotiation—all external negotiations are the responsibility of the director of sponsored projects who works in conjunction with the project director.
17. Provide postaward administration and support services, including:
    a. Institutional acceptance of award
    b. Briefing of award document
    c. Estimating and revising budgets
    d. Signature authorization
    e. Time and effort reporting
    f. Budget and expenditure control
    g. Closeout, reporting, and termination assistance

It is necessary for the office of sponsored projects to assist the project director in administering the award and to serve as the facilitator or expeditor with the business office regarding proper financial execution of the award. The project director and the office of sponsored projects both have invested valuable time and resources to obtain the award, and the expertise of the office in administering the grant can preclude any problems that might discourage the project director. If the institution's accounting office provides postaward services, the sponsored projects administrator must help the business office in dealing directly with project directors. The sponsored projects administration is responsible for providing current information to the accounting office and working with that office to accomplish not only the financial control objectives, but also the technical requirements. The accounting office must be sympathetic to the project directors and have an appreciation of the scientific process. The sponsored projects office should promote cooperation between business staff and project directors. By involving the business office staff with professional associations, the sponsored projects office enhances the overall institutional effort.

A grants and contracts handbook that informs faculty of the services of the sponsored projects office, sponsor regulations, and institutional policies and procedures is an essential document. The offices of sponsored projects at many universities have excellent manuals that are available upon request (for example, University of California–San Diego, University of Texas at Dallas, University of Illinois–Medical Center). The content of the handbooks varies, but most include the following elements:

1. Introduction
2. Proposal development procedures and proposal writing techniques
3. Budget preparation procedures
4. Proposal processing procedures
5. Proposal submission procedures
6. Sources of support
7. Institutional regulations
8. Proposal negotiation procedures
9. Procedures for acceptance of award
10. Institutional compliances
11. Procedures for highlighting important award provisions
12. Procedures for setting up an account and budget
13. Procedures for budget and expenditure control
14. Termination and reporting procedures

Staffing

Staffing depends on institutional philosophy and the type of services the institution wants to provide. Sponsored projects administrators must have the respect of their clientele, and that is usually earned through experience and measured by perfe   nance and quality of services offered. For the head of the office, many institutions no longer hire an experienced researcher; they prefer an individual who has experience in administering grants and contracts, has good contacts with sponsors, has worked with proposers in developing proposals, is an efficient administrator and good communicator, has an appreciation for re-search, and truly enjoys working with people. Recent trends indicate that these qualifications are weighted more heavily than such factors as a doctoral degree, length of service to the institution, or research history. Rodman and Dingerson (1979, p. 6) report the educational attainment statistics shown in Table 4 for the academic nonmedical members of the Society of Research Administrators in 1979–1980:

Table 4. Education Attainment of Sponsored Projects Personnel.

Degree	N	Percentage
No degree	73	14.15
Associate's	11	2.13
Bachelor's	177	34.30
Master's	109	21.13
Doctorate	135	26.16
Law	11	2.13
TOTAL	516	100.00

Source: Rodman and Dingerson, 1979, p. 6.

This survey, which included the entire university membership of the Society of Research Administrators—not just the heads of the offices of sponsored projects—reports that approximately 50 percent hold an ad-vanced degree, and the average educational attainment is one year of postbaccalaureate work.

No universities currently offer a specific degree in sponsored projects administration. Thus search committees must look at candi-dates' prior experience, educational background, knowledge of gov-ernment agencies and regulations, ability to work well with people and to work under severe time pressures, and understanding of the scien-tific process. The specific skills needed depend on the position to be staffed; however, coursework in organizational management, marketing, psychology, English, evaluation techniques, cost accounting, proposal writing, and education administration provides a strong background for a position in university research administration (Rodman and Dingerson, 1979).

The number of individuals required to staff an office of spon-sored projects varies directly with the institutional philosophy and the services provided by the office. Some of the important variables that determine office size include services provided (pre- and postaward), number of proposals processed, and dollar amount of extramural funds. Some large institutions with $60–75 million of external research funding a year have a small office staff: director, assistant, one professional, and four clerical positions. Many of the pre- and postaward services are decentralized and handled in the unit, or perhaps the accounting office handles postaward activities. Other institutions with less than $5 million in federal research and development have a large staff consisting of seven or eight professionals and six or more clerical positions. An old rule of thumb—one staff position for every $1 million in sponsored research—seems of doubtful value today; rather, the size of the staff depends on the organizational structure of the office of sponsored projects.

Organizational Models

The organizational models presented in this section illustrate the ways in which the philosophy of the institution and its size and the total dollar amount of sponsored research influence the structure of the office of sponsored programs. For example, Figure 9 depicts the organizational model of an office that does little postaward administration but offers full, complete preaward services with approximately 200–500 annual proposal submissions, 100–250 awards, and $5–$15 million in research and development. The office has a director, two administrators, and two secretary-clerks. One administrator works with proposal processing and budgeting, while the other is an information specialist and editor. A similar operation with postaward responsibilities would probably require two additional administrators and one more clerk. Working closely with the project director, the postaward services officer would establish accounts, monitor reporting requirements, control expenditures and perform other related duties.

In a small institution with minimal sponsored projects activity, the individual responsible for the office of sponsored projects usually reports to the president or chief administrative officer and has other institutional responsibilities such as development and news and information services. This arrangement is depicted in Figure 10. (Further information on small institutions is provided in Chapter Fifteen.)

Figure 9. Organizational Chart for Medium-Sized Centralized Office of Sponsored Projects.

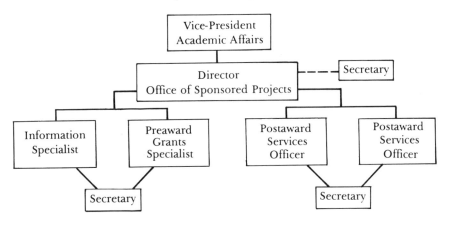

Figure 10. Organizational Chart for Small Centralized Office of Sponsored Projects.

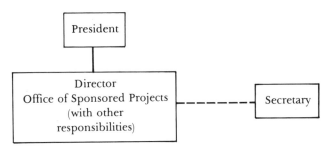

A university that has $15–20 million annually in sponsored projects with all functions highly centralized might follow the model depicted in Figure 11. In this model the office of sponsored projects has the responsibility to promote, develop, and administer all activities involving sponsored projects, including centralized research supporting services, such as animal caretakers, glass blowers, and electronics and mechanical technicians. The director is also associate dean of the graduate school and has a role in research policy development.

Figure 11. Organizational Chart for Large Centralized Office of Sponsored Projects.

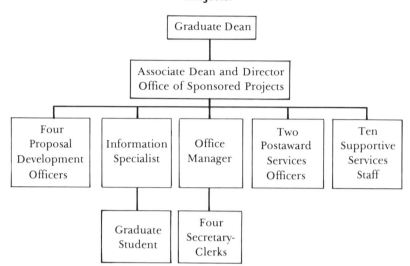

A fourth model is a decentralized organization for the support and administration of sponsored projects, shown in Figure 12. This model is used by many large institutions that receive over $50 million of external research support. The office of sponsored projects provides only the major services of processing proposals, negotiations, and acceptance of awards. The accounting office is responsible for postaward administration of sponsored projects, and other preaward services are provided at various unit levels.

Another model involves the establishment of a research foundation, which provides all services including personnel, purchasing, accounting, and development for all sponsored programs. This type of organization is discussed in Chapter Sixteen.

Division of Responsibilities and Duties

Unless the office of sponsored projects is a one-person shop, each employee will have distinct responsibilities and duties. Following are typical job descriptions for six specialists within the office.

Figure 12. Organizational Chart for Large Decentralized Office of Sponsored Projects.

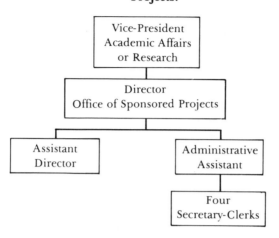

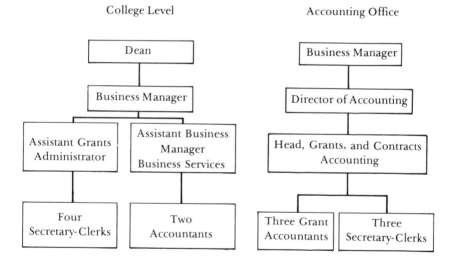

Director

The principal responsibility of the director of sponsored projects is to promote research and other sponsored activity at the institution by assisting individuals in the acquisition of project support and to protect the interests of the institution by supervising the administration of sponsored programs. More specifically, the director:

1. Is responsible for general management of the office.
2. Maintains a centralized information file on grant and contract opportunities and solicitations (requests for proposals) by government and other funding agencies; this function may include matching project directors' research interests with specific requests for proposals.
3. Is responsible for proposal submission:
   a. Reviews project budgets to ensure that, for example, campus space provisions, indirect cost, and cost-sharing requirements are met.
   b. Reviews proposals to ensure compliance with institution policies, systems policies, and any requirements of sponsoring agencies, particularly with regard to sensitive issues (for example, the use of human subjects).
   c. Initiates postsubmission inquiries concerning the status of proposals in sponsor offices and any anticipated problems suggested by those offices; such inquiries may require visits to sponsor offices.
4. Administers grants and contracts in accordance with the rules and regulations of various sponsors:
   a. Negotiates contracts with appropriate sponsors when necessary.
   b. Maintains a file of government regulations applicable to grants and contracts.
   c. Supervises staff who have a direct liaison with project directors and who are responsible for budgetary and other contractual arrangements in designated areas.
   d. Monitors expenditures for compliance with institutional accounting procedures and agency requirements.
   e. Enforces reporting requirements.
   f. Supervises final reports and termination procedures, including

arrangements by the property office for transfer of title of equipment to the institution or other specified entity.

5. Reviews institution's research administration policies and advises the institution's officers of needed changes in policy.
6. Represents the institution in sponsor offices in Washington, D.C.; determines the status of pending proposals in sponsor offices and secures the cooperation of personnel in sponsor offices to keep the paperwork moving. Such duties usually require bimonthly visits to Washington.
7. Develops and implements seminars on proposal writing, sources of funding, grantsmanship, and institutional business procedures.
8. Serves on appropriate organizational committees, often as executive secretary and ex officio member of the research committee, and member of human subjects, biohazards, and animal welfare committees.

Budget Specialist

1. Assists faculty and researchers in developing project budget.
2. Prepares final budget to be inserted in the proposal.
3. Maintains current knowledge of institution, system, and state requirements.
4. Maintains current knowledge of all sponsor regulations, including indirect cost rates.
5. Answers questions on such topics as indirect cost or fringe benefit rates.
6. Understands indirect cost calculations.
7. Prepares the sponsored projects office's operational budget.

Proposal Development Officer

1. Assists project directors in proposal writing.
2. Works with investigators in developing ideas and identifying potential sources of support.
3. Develops interdisciplinary research teams.
4. Assists college deans and chairpersons with program development.
5. Presents effective proposal writing and grantsmanship seminars.

6. Visits sponsors to determine new programs, priorities, and future trends.
7. Provides potentially fundable ideas to project directors.
8. Assists in award negotiations.

Information Specialist

1. Reads various materials regarding external grant and contract opportunities, including the *Federal Register, Commerce Business Daily, Federal Notes, College and University Reports,* and the like.
2. Maintains a library of information for all federal and state agencies and private foundations.
3. Assists in writing a semimonthly sponsored projects newsletter.
4. Disseminates materials on external grants to researchers by writing letters, phoning, and supplying copies of bulletins and requests for proposals.
5. Answers inquiries regarding sources of funding for individual research interests.
6. Assists researchers in writing extramural grant proposals.
7. Stimulates project directors to develop proposals.
8. Provides editorial assistance in the development of proposals.
9. Is responsible for a manual or computerized profile system and program information system.

Preaward Grants Specialist

1. Completes standard application forms, assurances, cover page, and the like.
2. Completes the certification form, making sure all conditions are met.
3. Prepares additional special forms as necessary.
4. Assures that all the necessary signatures are affixed to the certification form.
5. Submits the proposal to the agency.
6. Maintains an automated or manual management information and reporting system for the office of sponsored projects.
7. Maintains current knowledge of sponsor guidelines, application forms, and the like.
8. Assists in the negotiation of grants and contracts.

Postaward Services Officer

1. Establishes accounts.
2. Highlights project conditions.
3. Monitors expenditures and assists project directors in the timely expenditure of funds.
4. Approves all requisitions and vouchers for values greater than a set amount; approves transfer of charges, travel, time sheets, and termination.
5. Assists project directors with paperwork.
6. Monitors fiscal and program reporting requirements.
7. Works with sponsors' grants and contracts personnel in grants management.
8. Establishes project budgets and budget revisions.
9. Maintains the postaward and management information and reporting system.
10. Maintains an automated or manual accounting system.

Evaluation

The effectiveness of the office of sponsored projects is critical to the institution's success in meeting its research objectives. Measuring effectiveness may be achieved through such techniques as a formal evaluation and informal feedback. A formal evaluation questionnaire may be addressed to users of the office services, such as project directors, asking them to rank the effectiveness of the services provided by the office. Another evaluation effort would be to hire an outside consultant with expertise in sponsored projects program administration to visit and evaluate the office of sponsored projects on the basis of objectives, responsibilities, duties, services, and accomplishments. Existing faculty councils or research committees could also perform a periodic evaluation of services. And finally, a supervisor of the office of sponsored projects, probably a vice-president or an assistant vice-president, may measure the effectiveness of the office based on plans and objectives approved earlier by that office.

Of course, informal evaluation should exist as an ongoing effort by soliciting administrators' and project investigators' feedback, usually by phone or letter contacts with users of services. Directors of sponsored projects offices should also be alert for comments from sponsors' personnel regarding the administration of proposals and awards. A checklist at the office of sponsored projects for project directors' opinions is a useful internal mechanism. These evaluation efforts, both formal and informal, will enable a projects office's director to monitor and upgrade the office's services.

All participants in the evaluation should be informed of the standards by which it is to be conducted and should realize that subjective evaluations of the system are important. Although it is easy to evaluate the office of sponsored projects using such quantifiable measures as dollar volume, percentage of increase in dollars funded, success ratio, number of audit disallowances, and the like, subjective measures must also be considered. Such measures include an improvement in faculty and administrators' attitudes toward sponsored projects, the success of young investigators in competing for awards, rapport with project directors, improved relationships with sponsors, and the institution's ability to attract staff. In assessing the evaluation, institution officials must remember that the factor most critical to the success of any office of sponsored projects is the capability of the institution's staff, an area in which that office has little, if any, responsibility.

An example of a faculty evaluation instrument used by the Office of Sponsored Projects at Texas Tech University is shown in Resource B at the end of the book.

6

Establishing Management Information Systems

One major element that distinguishes sponsored projects administrators of the 1980s from their predecessors is the accessibility of both internal and external information, which allows better management decisions in administering sponsored projects. The instant accessibility of data is universally available to sponsored projects administrators through the implementation of management information systems.

Management information systems can best be understood by examining separately the three components of the term: management, information, and system. *Management,* simply put, consists of activities performed by managers: the planning, organizing, staffing, directing, and controlling of the enterprise. *Information* is classified and interpreted data that are used for decision making. A *system* is a set of two or more people, things, or concepts that are joined to attain a common objective.

A *management information system* (MIS), therefore, is the means by which the management operating system exchanges information. Its specific objective is to provide information for decision making essential to planning, organizing, staffing, directing, and controlling the major management activities of the organization (Murdick and Ross, 1975).

The acronym MIS may be considered an example of computer jargon, and the term produces an uneasiness and apprehension in individuals who are not computer oriented. However, MIS need not directly involve computers, and many small offices of sponsored projects have manual MIS that aid in their decision-making processes.

The office of sponsored projects at a college or university handles tens of thousands of pieces of information regarding sources of funding, faculty research interests and expertise, government regulations, guidelines and application forms, award notices and proposals. Offices of sponsored projects are managers of information and provide the facilitating and expediting functions necessary for effective service to the faculty and administration. In pursuing the primary objective of providing excellent services for the institution, most offices rely on an automated MIS. For example, the office of sponsored projects must supply accurate and timely information to project directors and faculty; the institution's research office, systems office, board of trustees, and officers, deans, and department chairpersons; the state board of higher education and state legislators; and the federal government. The office is accountable to all these users, and a well-developed automated system is essential to its success (Rodman and Peters, 1980).

General Types of MIS

There are three general types of MIS about which the sponsored projects administrator should be knowledgeable.

The first system is basically a faculty profile system. Each faculty member completes a form with such items as name, rank, position, school, and phone number as well as a list of keywords describing expertise and current interests. A staff member in the office of sponsored projects underlines keywords from *Commerce Business Daily*, program announcements, and other publications that describe research opportunities with the federal government, private foundations, and other external sponsors. He or she then searches all profiles in the system by keyword, either manually or by computer, and notifies the faculty members having the keyword in their profiles of the new announcements. This system is termed an *active* system in that the office uses its MIS to notify individuals.

In contrast, a program information system is a *passive* system in that the faculty must request that information be pulled for them. The office reviews all program opportunities, edits them by keywords, and then inputs them into the computer. Basic information regarding program descriptions and titles, eligibility, deadlines, contact person, and agency is stored in the data base. Faculty members who are looking for funding sources visit the office of sponsored projects and select keywords based on their needs. The computer then searches the program data base and lists the basic information for all appropriate programs.

A third system is a management information and reporting system (MIRS) that enables the office of sponsored projects to access detailed information needed for effective managerial decision making. In this system, detailed information on all applications submitted to external agencies is input into the system: project director, school and department, project title, sponsor, budget, abstract, amount of award, reporting requirements, and program and grants and contracts officers. Such a system has considerable specific as well as general reporting capability. Reports by activity of project director, school, center, department, deadline, type of agency, and comparisons by month or quarter are available instantly to assist in the management of sponsored projects.

Let us now examine in detail each of these three information systems.

Faculty Profile Systems

One major objective of many offices of sponsored projects is to match faculty members' expertise with research and project opportunities in a timely manner. As external research and development funding to higher education continues to increase, better methods must be developed to make the current system of program announcements and proposal responses more accurate and effective. Also, as faculty members' areas of interest and research become more diversified, and the institution's quest for external funds for research and educational projects becomes more diligent, it becomes increasingly important for an office of sponsored projects to evaluate its current system of collecting and disseminating information. Few offices can continue to rely on staff memory or a limited card inventory and hand sorting system. The increased opportunities for faculty research, the short lead times on many program announcements, and the recent emphasis on applied research (which often requires interdisciplinary teamwork) require that information be transmitted to the faculty as quickly as possible. Finally, effective communications with the faculty depend on their receiving accurate, timely information only in their areas of interest. The office of sponsored projects must carefully screen the amount and type of information transmitted to individuals; two or three mailings of irrelevant materials to a faculty member can hinder the office's credibility and can damage its reputation.

To accomplish the objectives of good information collection and dissemination, offices of sponsored projects in many universities (including the University of Michigan, New York University, the University of Pennsylvania, the University of Pittsburgh, Stanford University, SUNY Research Foundation, and the University of Texas at Dallas) are taking advantage of computerized information systems to identify matches between extramural program opportunities and faculty expertise.

There are two basic faculty profile systems. One is based on a keyword thesaurus: Faculty members, when completing their profile forms, are asked to choose up to ten words that best describe their expertise from a keyword dictionary of 300 to 3,000 words. When staff members read about a funding opportunity, they select appropriate codes from the dictionary, and the computer then searches those codes. The second system is a text search system that does not use a dictionary of keywords, but searches the complete text of research interests; if the input word is in the text, the match is made.

Some universities have systems that use both keyword dictionaries and text searching to match their faculty with research opportunities. Because there are advantages and disadvantages to each type of system, the integrated system provides the most comprehensive search. For example, the keyword dictionary limits the faculty members in describing their specific research capabilities. The keywords are often too general to target only the appropriate announcements. Too, the operator must be proficient in selecting the appropriate keywords for each program announcement. The text search overcomes most of these objections, but if the specific word the operator inputs is not located in the faculty members' descriptions of their interests, they will be overlooked completely; for example, an input of *elderly* would not elicit a match with *old, gerontology,* or *aged.* Integrated systems with both keyword searching and text searching are currently available at the University of Pittsburgh, Stanford University, SUNY Research Foundation, and the University of Texas at Dallas.

To implement a faculty profile system on campus, the administration and the research committee should determine the need for such a system. Several universities have found, however, that an effective computerized faculty information systems increases the number of proposal submissions and the volume of funded projects and improves the research environment on campus. Some institutions feel this type of preaward research development service is not appropriate or necessary for their faculty. If this type of preaward activity is deemed desirable, then the software must be developed or purchased to meet the specific needs of the college or university.

The next step in developing a faculty profile system is to have the faculty members complete a faculty profile form, such as that shown in Exhibit 3 (page 87). It is recommended that the form be as brief as possible and request only the information needed. Also, a letter from the vice-president for research or an equivalent officer should accompany the form, succinctly explaining the service and potential benefits of the program. Exhibit 4 (page 88) shows a sample output for a faculty profile system using a keyword search with and/or logic.

Automated Program Information Systems

The development and access to program information using the computer is a more recent trend in automated research management. The *Catalog of Federal Domestic Assistance* is currently computerized. The Federal Assistance Programs Retrieval System (FAPRS) is a computerized retrieval system that can quickly identify and provide information on available federal programs. Through the use of a simplified query format to search the data base, FAPRS eliminates the extensive manual effort required to identify applicable federal programs in the *Catalog of Federal Domestic Assistance.* A request for information includes such things as the researcher's name, city, county, state, type of organization, functional area of interest, and types of assistance desired. The output provided by FAPRS is a list of the titles and identifying numbers of the applicable federal programs from the *Catalog of Federal Domestic Assistance*. FAPRS is available in every state through one of three time-sharing companies, and currently every state has a designated access point where FAPRS printouts may be obtained.

The Foundation Center's COMSEARCH is a computer-produced subject guide to foundation giving. COMSEARCH printouts present information from the *Foundation Grants Index* in easy-to-use subject listings. The COMSEARCH program allows information on 109 subjects, ranging from the broad headings of communications to welfare as well as regional and special interest topics. If one needs information about which foundations have been active in the past year in broad categorical areas, COMSEARCH printouts are one resource in beginning the research. Reports can be received on hard paper or microfiche, with the latter being considerably less expensive.

Another automated service matching faculty with potential sources of support for specific projects is the Association for Affiliated College and University Offices' (AACUO) Grant Information and Search System. In this system, the faculty member completes an interest information card, selects keywords, and the program searches the entire AACUO grants file for potential sources of support and prints out information as shown in Exhibit 5 (page 89).

Another program search system is the Illinois Researcher Information System (IRIS) which makes available, in capsule form, current information on funding opportunities for higher education.

Overall, automated program search systems provide an efficient way to make information on sponsor programs accessible to investigators. These systems are designed to provide: (1) timely, usable, accurate, and accessible information; (2) personalized searches; (3) low-cost searches; and (4) ease of use for persons with no data processing experience. To illustrate these design goals, we examine the Illinois Researcher Information System (IRIS).

The computer program for IRIS is capable of scanning a large volume of data in seconds, and the design of the system enables users to obtain individually tailored searches in minutes. The uniform coding of program information in IRIS facilitates personalized searches and allows office staff to monitor those agencies whose published guidelines are incomplete and require clarification. Sponsor agencies are contacted once each year to review and update the coded information extracted from the IRIS data base. This method of updating is far more effective than sending mailing-list announcements. It also allows sponsors to clarify specific details, and it provides advance information on program trends and new developments within the agencies (Lowry, Bradshaw, and Sansone, 1979).

The sponsored projects office trains editorial staff to incorporate into the system information from current agency publications and letter and telephone contacts with sponsor representatives. These editors daily analyze and update the program entries, adding new programs to the data base as details become available. This data base has two logical components: (1) *Agency programs* — a directory that includes names, addresses, requirements, and short program descriptions; and (2) *subject keywords* — a dictionary of terms that are cross-referenced with the agency programs as an index to the data base. The editorial staff routinely enter data and cross-references, enabling searchers to use the subject keywords (the IRIS index) to retrieve program information. The index, which consists of subject keywords, is the reference from which the editorial staff codes the funding opportunities, and from which users of the system identify terms that most accurately describe their areas of interest. An example of the output from a search is shown in Exhibit 6 (pages 89–90).

The Research Foundation of the State University of New York (SUNY) has established a Sponsored Program Information Network (SPIN) that gathers and disseminates sponsor opportunity information to SUNY faculty through a computerized network. The specific objective is to assist faculty in identifying the most appropriate sponsors to support their specific research interests. Over 1,400 programs from both federal and private sponsoring agencies are on file. The SPIN system is currently marketed nationally. All sponsors are contacted annually to verify that the programmatic material on file is still accurate. At that time, sponsors forward a copy of their most recent publication detailing programs offered, amount of money available, award policies, and any eligibility restrictions on the submission of proposals. Whenever new sponsors are added to the file, staff contact them by letter to obtain the most timely and accurate information.

o

The current SPIN staff consists of a program coordinator, two staff editors, and a computer operator. As incoming information is received, the staff review and edit all pertinent information. Staff prepare and input a brief synopsis of each program, including sponsor name, award type code, keyword code(s), deadline date, program title, program objectives, eligibility restrictions, and contact address and telephone number.

To help staff and faculty quickly identify sponsored programs within specific research areas, the SPIN staff developed a keyword index. The index is an alphabetical list of subject areas extracted exclusively from sponsored program announcements. Each program announcement on the SPIN data base is assigned up to ten keywords. This cataloguing technique enables users to quickly extract from the data base all programs for a given keyword. To maintain the integrity of the keyword index, only those keywords identified by the sponsors are used. Thus each keyword listed in the index will elicit at least one program announcement where the word itself appears. The index is updated regularly. As new keywords are entered and assigned numeric codes, a revised index is forwarded to the campus research office as a reference source.

On occasion, the SPIN staff receives requests from faculty seeking specific types of programs within their area of research interest, such as a travel grant, an equipment grant, or a publication grant. To assist faculty in locating these specific types of programs, the staff also catalogues and codes its programs on the basis of the type of award. An example of the output of the SPIN program is shown in Exhibit 7 (pages 91–92).

If administrators are interested in implementing an automated information system, they should first garner support for such services from the faculty research committee. The sponsored projects administrator must be aware of the systems available, discuss the potential benefits with the faculty, and gain their willingness to participate in the program. Many universities feel that this type of preaward research development activity is not necessary for their institution. Others establish their own system, and still others purchase services from organizations such as the University of Illinois at Urbana, SUNY Research Foundation, or AACUO. Institutions that have a computer terminal and phone coupler can purchase access to these established, comprehensive data bases.

It is the office of sponsored projects' responsibility to evaluate the various systems to see which is the best for its particular operation. The institution's specific needs may be such that it should develop its own automated program information system. This decision, however, is an expensive one and requires long-term funding for maintaining and updating the data base.

Once an automated system or access to an external system is in place, the sponsored projects administrator must make sure the system is functioning properly before advertising its availability to the investigator. A letter from the chairperson of the research committee and vice-president for research announcing the service and benefit to the investigator is an appropriate manner in which to initiate the new available service. An open house in the research office is one way of acquainting faculty members with the system and allowing them to see it at work. An open house can also enhance the visibility of the office of sponsored projects.

Sponsored Projects Information and Reporting System

Decision making is the act of choosing among the various alternatives available. Effective institutional decision making and management require that the office of sponsored projects provide information that is usable, accurate, timely, and accessible. Sponsored projects administrators are managers of information, and the amount of information they must handle makes it virtually essential to utilize automated systems to store, access, and manage such information. Automated management information and reporting systems are no longer a luxury for offices of sponsored projects; rather, they are required for effective and efficient administration. Indeed, experience at colleges and universities shows that failure to provide accurate and timely information for required administration of sponsored projects leads to both sponsor and management dissatisfaction, and, in the long run, to possible loss of opportunities for the investigator to conduct the sponsored projects necessary for continued excellence of the institution.

The office of sponsored projects is the major unit responsible for the management of records relating to pre- and postaward activities (with the exception of accounting) of external grants and contracts. The office must provide information to: (a) aid in maintaining accurate records for all grant and contract actions, current pending proposals, rejected proposals, current awards, and terminated awards; (b) develop monthly, quarterly, and yearly comparison reports by unit, agency, faculty members, and type of agencies to assist the sponsored projects administrator in planning and managing; (c) prepare for budget purposes activity projections that take into account summaries of selected information from each of the appropriate data bases; and (d) communicate selected information from these data bases to project directors, deans, accounting, vice-president for research, other university administrators, government legislators, legislative committees, and state coordinating boards.

In summary, the system must provide accurate and timely identification of the current status of each of the records useful to the efficient management of the overall research program. It must also provide updated information useful in the administration of both institution and sponsor obligations relating to the pre- or postaward aspects of the contract or grant.

Implementation. Information must be available in the office of sponsored projects to assist the sponsored projects administrator in effectively performing the managerial functions of planning, organizing, staffing, directing, and controlling. Timely access to good information requires the office of sponsored projects to consider the implementation of an automated sponsored projects information and reporting system. As an example of such a system, we briefly describe a current system that has over 250 data elements in the data base grants file with 10 standard reports and a general report-writing capability.

Hardware Configuration. The main computer used is an IBM 370/155 with two megabytes of memory. With this computer, the full hardware configuration is:

IBM 370/155 OS/MVT with HASP 2.0 megabytes memory
6 3330 disk spindles
2 3333 disk spindles
3 3420 9-track 1600 tape drives
2 3420 9-track 800/1600 tape drives
1 3420 7-track 556/800 tape drive
1 1403N1 printer, 1100 lines per minute
1 2540 reader/puncher, 1000/300 cards per minute

The University of Texas at Dallas' Computing Center has a data base/ data communication system, DATACOM/DB/DC. The data communication software (DC) supports page IBM 3270 terminals or line-by-line ACSII type terminals. The page terminal was chosen for this sponsored projects system because it allows easier input, easier update, and faster transmission, and it can provide hard copy.

Input Formats. Figure 13 shows the format for the input of general information regarding the application, project director, sponsor, and type of award. Figure 14 shows the input for the first-year and total budget requests, including cost sharing and percentages. Figure 15 shows the input for an abstract of the proposal, completed by the project director. If the application is approved, the account number is assigned, and the status is changed to "funded" on the preaward screen (Figure 13). Four postaward screens then become effective.

The first postaward screen, Figure 16, shows agency name, award number, account number, award dates, award total, cost-sharing account number, funded dates, and a detailed budget breakdown for the funded period, history, and modifications. The program justifies the numerical input and can calculate sums and select percentages. A second postaward screen (not shown) is simply a continuation of four additional budget modifications to the budget project list. The third screen, Figure 17, gives current information on the project and grants officer, as well as reporting information. The project director's name, social security number, and account number are automatically generated on all screens by this program. This information assists the office of sponsored projects in the postaward administration of its grants and contracts. The fourth screen, Figure 18, indicates pertinent information regarding inventory, equipment, conditions of the award, and the renewal proposal deadline—again, all essential information for the effective postaward management of grants and contracts.

If the proposal is rejected, all information is transferred to a rejected file where it will be stored for five years. The data for pre- and postaward information are stored together in the data base. They can be stored together, even though a proposal is never funded, because the data base system can compress elements that are not entered, thus saving space. There are approximately 250 data elements in the pre- and postaward data base. The four postaward screens and three preaward screens are supported by nine on-line program modules.

Figure 13. Preaward Project Information.

DATE: YY/MM/DD   THE UNIVERSITY OF TEXAS AT DALLAS   MSK068
TIME: HH:MM:SS   OFFICE OF SPONSORED PROJECTS

PRINCIPAL INVESTIGATORS: SOCIAL SECURITY NO:
1) FRANK POWELL   405 32 4803
2) _____   ___ ___ ___
3) _____   ___ ___ ___
4) _____

PROPOSAL NO: 005080   SCHOOL/OTHER   PROGRAM/CENTER
PROJECT TITLE:
EXTENDED LIVING PROGRAM FOR DEAF/BLIND STUDENTS 1979/80

AGENCY:
TEXAS EDUCATION AGENCY

TYPE AGENCY: STA
TYPE PROJECT: TR   TYPE AWARD: CON   CLASS: N

PROPOSAL SUBMITTED: 79 12 07   PROJECT BEGINS: 80 01 07   PROJECT ENDS: 82 06 30

HUMAN SUBJECTS REVIEW REQUIRED   (DATE   )

AGENCY ID: 875/12/11/79-0230   STATUS: F   UTD ACCOUNT NO: E1295-01

Figure 14. Preaward Budget Request.

DATE: YY/MM/DD   THE UNIVERSITY OF TEXAS AT DALLAS   MSK069
TIME: HH:MM:SS   OFFICE OF SPONSORED PROJECTS
SOCIAL SECURITY NO: 405 32 4803   NAME: FRANK POWELL
PROJECT TITLE:
EXTENDED LIVING PROGRAM FOR DEAF/BLIND STUDENTS 1979/80

	FIRST YEAR	TOTAL
PERSONNEL COSTS	30,920	30,920
FRINGE BENEFITS	6,988	6,988
EQUIPMENT	7,825	7,825
OTHER DIRECT COSTS	26,462	26,462
SUM DIRECT COSTS	72,195	72,195
INDIRECT COSTS	3,805	3,805
ALL COSTS	76,000	76,000
INDIRECT COST % ALL COSTS		
DIRECT COST SHARING		
INDIRECT COST SHARING		
SUM COST SHARING		

Figure 15. Preaward Project Abstract.

DATE: YY/MM/DD   THE UNIVERSITY OF TEXAS AT DALLAS   MSK037
TIME: HH:MM:SS
SOCIAL SECURITY NO: 405 32 4803   NAME: FRANK POWELL
PROJECT TITLE:
EXTENDED LIVING PROGRAM FOR DEAF/BLIND STUDENTS 1979/80

ABSTRACT:
DESIGN AND IMPLEMENT AN EXTENDED LIVING PROGRAM FOR DEAF/BLIND STUDENTS
AGES 16 TO 21. ESTABLISH PARENT AND FAMILY SERVICES TO INVOLVE PARENTS IN
RELATING TO STUDENTS IN RESIDENTIAL FACILITY. ESTABLISH ENTRANCE AND
EXIT CRITERIA OF COOPERATING AGENCIES, I.E., VOCATIONAL AGENCIES.

Figure 16. Postaward Funding Information.

DATE:　YY/MM/DD
TIME:　HH:MM:SS
SOCIAL SECURITY NO:
ACCOUNT NO:　E1295-01

THE UNIVERSITY OF TEXAS AT DALLAS　　　　MSK036
OFFICE OF SPONSORED PROJECTS
405 32 4803　　　　NAME:　FRANK POWELL
AGENCY:　TEXAS EDUCATION　　AGENCY NO:　1234F

AWARD DATES:　BEGIN:　80 01 07　　END:　82 06 30　　AWARD TOTAL:　76,000
COST SHARING ACCT NO

HISTORY　　MOD

COSTS	FUNDED
DATES	80 01 07　82 06 30
PERSONNEL COSTS	30,920
FRINGE BENEFITS	6,988
EQUIPMENT	7,825
OTHER DIRECT COSTS	26,462
SUM DIRECT COSTS	72,195
INDIRECT COSTS	3,805
ALL COSTS	76,000
INDIRECT COST % ALL COSTS	
DIRECT COST SHARING	
INDIRECT COST SHARING	
SUM COST SHARING	
FRINGE BEN COST %	

Figure 17. Postaward Sponsor and Reporting Information.

```
DATE:    YY/MM/DD        THE UNIVERSITY OF TEXAS AT DALLAS              MSK079R
TIME:    HH:MM:SS        OFFICE OF SPONSORED PROJECTS
SOCIAL SECURITY NO:  405 32 4803        NAME:    FRANK POWELL
ACCOUNT NO:   E1295-01

                                                        GRANT/CONTRACT OFFICER
        PROJECT OFFICER                                 JILL GRAY
     DON L. PARTRIDGE
     ASSOC. COMM. FOR SPEC. ED.
     TEXAS EDUCATION AGENCY              TEXAS EDUCATION AGENCY
     201 E. ELEVENTH ST.                201 E. ELEVENTH ST.
     AUSTIN, TX 78701                   AUSTIN, TX 78701
         TEL:   822-3042                    TEL:    822-3507
```

REPORT		DUE DATE	TYPE	COPIES	SUBMITTED
TECHNICAL	1	80 10 30	F	3	
	2				
	3				
FINANCIAL	1	82 06 30	F	3	
	2				
	3				
	4				

Figure 18. Postaward Equipment and Additional Information.

DATE: YY/MM/DD THE UNIVERSITY OF TEXAS AT DALLAS
TIME: HH:MM:SS OFFICE OF SPONSORED PROJECTS
SOCIAL SECURITY NO: 405 32 4803 NAME: FRANK POWELL

INVENTORY OF EQUIPMENT REPORT   DUE DATE   COPIES   DATE SUBMITTED
        REQUIRED   N   _-_-_   _____   _-_-_

EQUIPMENT TITLE VESTED IN _____UNIVERSITY_____
EQUIPMENT TITLE REQUEST REQUIRED __N__
GOVERNMENT FURNISHED EQUIPMENT ITEMS:
    NONE
    _____
    _____
    _____

CONDITIONS:
    U.S. O.E. Equipment regulations are applicable.
    RENEWAL PROPOSAL DEADLINE: _-_-_

Once the information is stored in the data base, it can be accessed by social security number, account number, or proposal number. Exhibits 8, 9, and 10 (pages 93–95) are a sampling of the types of reports available from the system. Other special reports can be printed on a high-speed printer by using an easy report-generating system called DATACOM/DR (data reporter).

Many universities—such as Cornell University, Massachusetts Institute of Technology, University of Pennsylvania, and Stanford University—have automated management information and reporting systems (MIRS) that provide unique information for their specific requirements. Many other colleges and universities are currently designing or redesigning information systems for their sponsored projects offices. Systems differ, but the preceding examples typify the data and reports that are vital to sponsored projects administrators.

Trends in Management Information Systems

The importance of good information to sponsored projects administrators' decision making will continue to increase during the 1980s. Within a few years, the cost of mini- and microprocessors will be low enough that every sponsored projects office will have its own computer equipment.

The mini- or microcomputer can be used as a stand-alone processor, but the need to access common information makes it probable that all units will be linked to the larger institution data base through some type of central computer; this distributive processing concept is discussed in Chapter Twelve. Distributive systems allow project directors to use their own terminals to access their office's data base as well as that of the institution. The hardware capability is currently available and will improve greatly so that the cost of storage will continue to decrease. A new development, "bubble memory," allows the capability to store large amounts of data at minimal cost. This hardware can also be used for word processing.

Anticipated changes in software will enable users to develop personal applications. Personnel in the office of sponsored projects will be able to develop the screen formats, processing programs, and report-writing output in user terms from the terminal in their office. Thus users will be able to bypass their institutions' central data processing office. Also, applications developed at the central site will be available to any node in the distributive system, as will be generalized inquiry programs to search the entire data base and provide user-developed reports.

Microprocessors, minicomputers, distributive systems, and software versatility will become common terminology of sponsored projects administrators. These aids will provide the good information necessary for decision making by these administrators.

Exhibit 3. Faculty Profile.

Name: <u>I.M. Smart</u> Date: <u>06/15/80</u> SS#: <u>123-45-6789</u> Staff #: <u>0123</u>

Highest Academic Degree, Discipline, and
Date Received: <u>Ph.D., Nursing, 1970</u> Academic Rank: <u>Associate Professor</u>

Title: <u>Program Head</u> Office Phone: <u>2222</u> Bldg. & Rm. #: <u>F03.606</u> Mail Stn: <u>F03.2</u>

Professional identification (for example, applied mathematician, chemist, economist, immunologist, statistician, literary critic)—more than one is acceptable.
<u>Psychiatric Nurse and Nursing Educator</u>

Current Research Interest (please limit to 10 typewritten lines):
<u>To determine the self-concept of undergraduate and graduate</u>

<u>nursing students in relation to clinical performance and</u>

<u>selected biographical variables. Also concerned with the</u>

<u>preparation of competent advanced nursing practitioners</u>

<u>at the master's level and their utilization throughout the</u>

<u>health care system.</u>

Please designate ten specialty areas with which you feel most closely identified:
<u>Higher Education; Nursing Research; Graduate Education in</u>

<u>Nursing; Curriculum Design; Health Education Research;</u>

<u>Health Sciences; Humanistic Psychology; Continuing Education;</u>

<u>Maternal-Child Nursing; Health Care Systems and Issues</u>

Please list your current external review panel memberships and dates.
<u>NIMH — Psychiatric Nursing (7/77–6/78)</u>

<u>Health Service Administration — Community Health (1/78–12/79)</u>

Exhibit 4. Faculty Interest Display.

DATE: YY/MM/DD   THE UNIVERSITY OF TEXAS AT DALLAS   MSK039
TIME: HH:MM:SS   OFFICE OF SPONSORED PROJECTS

LOGIC	SEARCH KEYWORD
1)	ATMOSPHERE
2) AND	MOLECULAR
3) AND	POLAR
4) AND	WIND
5)	

NAME	SSN	MAIL	BLDRM	PHONE	RESEARCH AREA
HOFFMAN	468284167	F022	F02.377	6902840	
CUNNINGHAM	360409504	F023	F02.716	6902884	
HANSON	447125999	F022	F02.304	6902851	
PLENETIS	453230804	F022	F02.708	6902853	

Exhibit 5. Grant Information and Search System Output.

TITLE:
  ROCKEFELLER FOUNDATION—HUMANITIES FELLOWSHIPS

FIELDS:

PURPOSE:
  SUPPORT PRODUCTION OF WORKS OF HUMANISTIC SCHOLARSHIP INTENDED TO ILLUMINATE AND ASSESS VALUES OF CONTEMPORARY CIVILIZATION. APPLICANTS WITH INTERDISCIPLINARY SKILLS AND INTERESTS ARE SPECIALLY WELCOMED.

QUALIFICATIONS:
  SCHOLARS IN TRADITIONAL HUMANISTIC DISCIPLINES WHOSE PROJECTS ARE CONCERNED WITH CONTEMPORARY VALUES.

GRANTS:
  USUALLY ONE YEAR; MAY COVER TRAVEL, SECRETARIAL HELP, RESEARCH SUPPORT; USUALLY MADE THROUGH INSTITUTIONS.

MISCELLANEOUS:
  EACH PROPOSAL SHOULD SEEK TO FULFILL ONE OR MORE OF THESE OBJECTIVES: (1) ILLUMINATE CONTEMPORARY SOCIAL OR CULTURAL PERPLEXITIES, (2) SEARCH FOR COMPARATIVE CULTURAL VALUES IN PLURALISTIC SOCIETY AND WORLD, (3) EXPLORE CONTEMPORARY RELEVANCE OF OUTSTANDING LITERARY, CULTURAL, HISTORICAL PHILOSOPHICAL TRADITIONS, (4) CLARIFY OR EXPAND HISTORIC MEANING AND TASKS OF THE HUMANITIES.

Exhibit 6. Illinois Researcher Information System Output.

250* WORK AND EMPLOYMENT **250

2895 UPJOHN (W E) INSTITUTE FOR EMPLOYMENT RESEARCH
1376*   GRANT PROGRAM

300 South Westnedge Avenue
Kalamazoo, MI 49007

AGENCY TYPE:
  Non-federal
TEMPORARY RELOCATION:
  Not Required
CITIZENSHIP REQUIRED:
  U.S. Citizen; Permanent U.S. Resident; Other
ACADEMIC BACKGROUND REQUIRED:
  Doctorate/Professional
SUPPORT:
  Research (may include Dissertation).
DEADLINE(S) ANNOUNCED:
  None.

Exhibit 6 (continued)

The Institute emphasizes research in the following categories: job creation, job stabilization, the matching of jobs and people, alleviation of unemployment hazards, the political science of manpower programs, and the quality of worklife. The Institute does not sponsor foreign or international comparative studies, focusing instead on the local, state, and national scene within the U.S. The grants generally fall within a relatively modest range of funding, but the Institute is willing to consider joining with other foundations or private organizations or groups for support of meritorious proposals. One of the major purposes of the Institute is to disseminate the findings of useful research, so all proposals should be made with the prospect that the results will be published by the Institute.

```
120   LABOR (DEPARTMENT OF)
354      EMPLOYMENT AND TRAINING ADMINISTRATION
1428*      RESEARCH AND DEVELOPMENT PROPOSALS
```

Ms. Helen Thompson
Office of Research and Development
601 D Street, N.W.; Room 9108
Washington, DC 20213

AGENCY TYPE:
  Federal
TEMPORARY RELOCATION:
  Not Required
CITIZENSHIP REQUIRED:
  U.S. Citizen; Permanent U.S. Resident; Other.
ACADEMIC BACKGROUND REQUIRED:
  Doctorate/Professional.
SUPPORT:
  Research (may include Dissertation); Teaching or Curric/Prog Development.
DEADLINE(S) ANNOUNCED:
  None.

This program provides support for experimental, developmental, demonstration, and pilot projects for the purpose of improving techniques and demonstrating the effectiveness of specialized methods in meeting manpower, employment and training problems. Proposed projects should focus on potential solutions to significant employment and training problems. A preliminary statement describing the investigator's basic study ideas, subjects of research or proposals for experimental development and demonstration is required.

Source: University of Illinois at Urbana-Champaign, Board of Trustees, 1982.

Exhibit 7. Sponsored Program Information Network.

DATE
ESTABLISHED: 11/12/80

FOLLOW-UP
DATE: 10/01/82

DATE
REVIEWED: 03/15/82

R. F. PROGRAM NO: 0444

PROGRAM TYPE: NN

SPONSOR-ID: FF400

KEY WORD(S): 0062 1062

CONTACT ADDRESS: NATIONAL SCIENCE FOUNDATION
DIVISION OF INTERNATIONAL
PROGRAMS
U.S.–AUSTRALIA COOPERATIVE
SCIENCE PROGRAM
1800 G STREET, N.W.
WASHINGTON, DC 20550

CONTACT TELEPHONE NO.: (202) 357-9558

LAST POSTED DEADLINE DATE(S): 04/01/82

PROGRAM TITLE: U.S.–AUSTRALIA COOPERATIVE SCIENCE PROGRAM

CFDA: 47.053

Exhibit 7 (continued)

PROGRAM DESCRIPTION:

OBJECTIVES: THE U.S.–AUSTRALIA PROGRAM SUPPORTS THE WORK OF U.S. SCIENTISTS COOPERATING WITH SCIENTISTS IN AUSTRALIA IN RESEARCH AND RELATED ACTIVITIES IN ALL FIELDS OF SCIENCE. THREE TYPES OF ACTIVITIES MAY RECEIVE SUPPORT: (1) COOPERATIVE RESEARCH PROJECTS WHICH ARE JOINTLY DESIGNED AND JOINTLY CONDUCTED BY PRINCIPAL INVESTIGATORS FROM THE U.S. AND AUSTRALIA; (2) RESEARCH-ORIENTED SEMINARS OR WORKSHOPS WHICH ARE MEETINGS OF SMALL GROUPS OF SCIENTISTS FROM THE U.S. TO EXCHANGE INFORMATION, REVIEW THE CURRENT STATUS OF A SPECIFIC FIELD OF SCIENCE, AND PLAN COOPERATIVE RESEARCH; AND (3) SHORT-TERM (60-DAY) SCIENTIFIC VISITS.

RESTRICTIONS: U.S. SCIENTISTS INVOLVED ARE PRINCIPAL INVESTIGATORS/ PROJECT DIRECTORS AND MUST HAVE A DOCTORAL DEGREE OR ITS EQUIVALENT. NSF SUPPORT FOR SEMINARS AND WORKSHOPS IS LIMITED TO A MAXIMUM OF $20,000. THE MAXIMUM DURATION OF COOPERATIVE RESEARCH EXCHANGE PROJECTS IS TWO YEARS. NO CONTINUING AWARDS WILL BE MADE.

Source: Research Foundation of the State University of New York, 1982.

Exhibit 8. Report of Proposals Submitted or Funded.

THE UNIVERSITY OF TEXAS AT DALLAS
OFFICE OF SPONSORED PROJECTS

PROPOSALS SUBMITTED OR FUNDED PENDING	79 09 01 FIRST YR AMT	THRU 80 02 29 FUNDED	80 02 13 AMOUNT

HUMAN DEVELOPMENT

CALLIER CENTER FOR COMMUNICATION DISORDERS

| 6 | $257,261 | 2 | $140,553 |

PROGRAM IN PSYCHOLOGY AND HUMAN DEVELOPMENT

| 6 | $136,979 | 0 | $0 |

PROGRAM IN SPECIAL EDUCATION

| 2 | $214,268 | 2 | $102,700 |
| ***TOTAL 14 | $608,508 | 4 | $243,253 |

Exhibit 9. Report of Due Dates for Technical and Financial Reports.

THE UNIVERSITY OF TEXAS AT DALLAS
OFFICE OF SPONSORED PROJECTS   80 02 13

TECHNICAL & FINANCIAL REPORTS DUE 81 08 01 THRU 81 08 31

DUE DATE	ACCT NO	PRIN-INVESTIGATOR	AGENCY	KIND	TYPE	NUMBER
81 08 31	E1231	STEPHENS B.	OE	T	F	3
81 08 31	E1231	STEPHENS B.	OE	$	F	3
81 08 31	E1226	GOTTS E.	OE	T	F	3
81 08 31	E1226	GOTTS E.	OE	$	F	3
81 08 31	E1463-14	WINNINGHAM J.	NASA	T	F	3
81 08 31	E1463-14	WINNINGHAM J.	NASA	$	F	5
81 08 01	E1249-02	PESSAGNO, JR. E.	NSF	T	F	5
81 08 01	E1249-02	PESSAGNO, JR. E.	NSF	$	F	3

Exhibit 10. Report of Grants and Contracts Awarded.

THE UNIVERSITY OF TEXAS AT DALLAS
OFFICE OF SPONSORED PROJECTS

DATE:
TIME:

SCHOOL:

** GRANTS **

TYPE:	RESEARCH	TRAINING	EQUIPMENT	FACILITIES	STUD SUPPT	SERVICE
NUMBER:						
DIR. FUND						
INDIR. FUND						
TYPE TOTAL						

TOTAL DIR.   TOTAL INDIR.   TOTAL SCHOOL

** CONTRACTS **

TYPE:	RESEARCH	TRAINING	EQUIPMENT	FACILITIES	STUD SUPPT	SERVICE
NUMBER:						
DIR. FUND						
INDIR. FUND						
TYPE TOTAL						

TOTAL DIR.   TOTAL INDIR.   TOTAL SCHOOL

7

Developing Communication Systems and Information Sources

Two major roles of the office of sponsored projects are to facilitate the institution's interaction with all external sponsors (governmental, private, industrial) and to facilitate the search for external support of projects. As competition increases for funds from all sources, improved communication systems are essential. Figure 19 illustrates the matchmaking responsibilities of the office of sponsored projects and the need for excellent communication services.

The sponsored projects administrator is constantly involved with external and internal communications. External communications are those exchanges of information, written or oral, with individuals outside the institution; internal communications are those among individuals

Figure 19. Communications Network.

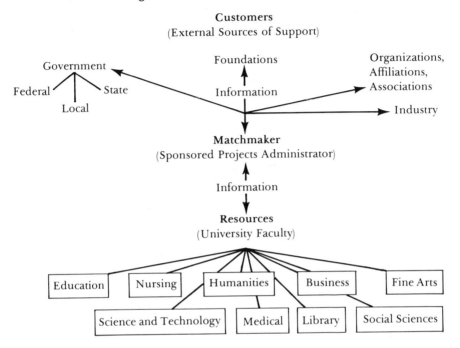

working within the institution. Let us examine each of these categories in turn. Exhibit 11 (page 110) offers a checklist of the components of an effective communication network, the importance of which cannot be overstressed. Communication skills, especially the ability to listen attentively and to state ideas clearly, are key ingredients to successful administration.

External Communications

The sponsored projects administrator interacts with many external individuals and organizations, including federal, state, and local government officials and employees; private and corporate foundation staffs; local community groups and industries; colleagues and researchers from other institutions; and various associations' personnel. Often the sponsored projects administrator is an outsider's major contact with the institution and the source of that individual's impression of the institution. Inasmuch as first impressions are often lasting, the sponsored projects office should carefully select and train receptionists, secretaries, and clerical staff who answer phones and greet visitors. Attention should be paid to their appearance, voice, knowledge, ability, enthusiasm, and mannerisms. The office cannot afford to overlook the key role these individuals play in external communications.

Similarly, each person who communicates with outsiders should develop a strategy for such interactions. Planning is critical: Take time to collect your thoughts and examine the key issues that need to be raised before a meeting or phone call. Have clearly in mind the issues that are negotiable and nonnegotiable. Be prepared to offer alternate solutions to the problem at hand. Good ideas require and merit organized presentations.

Developing Contacts. Personal contacts with agency representatives are essential to a sponsored projects administrator. The value of contacting an acquaintance at an agency to determine probabilities of funding, future trends, budget information, status, timing, and similar information cannot be overstressed. Agency officials are usually very busy; however, they are likely to take time from their busy schedules to return calls from individuals with whom they have had personal discussions. Of course, reciprocity is often necessary to maintain this rapport, and the sponsored projects administrator skilled in interpersonal relationships can be most effective.

Initial contacts with sponsor personnel can be developed in a variety of ways. Professional meetings, such as those held by the Society of Research Administrators and the National Council of University Research Administrators, where both sponsor and recipient organizations attend, are an excellent source of contacts. Alumni, former faculty and staff members now working for sponsors, or other contacts who have a keen interest in the institution should be approached. Also, the personnel of an agency that has awarded the institution several projects are familiar with the institution and its administration, and are ready reference sources for potential contacts.

Liaison with Sponsors. After the contacts have been made, visits to the sponsor are often quite helpful in acquiring additional contacts and maintaining those already developed. The itinerary of a visit depends on the administrator's purpose and style. Among the purposes of visits to sponsors are: to gather general information and facts, to market specific proposals, to solve particular problems, to maintain personal contacts, to express the institution's interest in sponsored activity, and to learn future priorities and plans of sponsors.

Some administrators prefer a whirlwind tour, making few formal appointments but informally visiting twelve to fifteen agency personnel each day for brief chats. Others prefer a more structured program and make appointments well in advance, with a concise agenda for each. They present program officers with a two- or three-page prospectus for a specific project and focus the discussion on that. Lunch and dinner meetings with program officials are often very helpful in obtaining information on an informal basis. There is no best method, and one's approach should depend on one's personality and familiarity with the sponsor personnel. Generally, advance planning and firm appointments assure a more productive and efficient trip.

To make the best use of limited time, especially in Washington, D.C., visits to sponsors can be clustered around location. As an example, one day may be spent in the southwest area of Washington visiting NASA Headquarters, DOT, DE, HUD, and congressional staff. Another day could be spent in the northwest area visiting the NSF Research Directorate, NIE, DOE, NEH, and NEA. A third day could be spent in the Bethesda area at the NSF Education Directorate, NIH (Westwood), NIH Campus and ADAMHA.

The frequency of visits depends on the type of institution one represents. However, as a minimum, four trips a year of approximately three days each are necessary to maintain Washington contacts. Many institutions have their office of sponsored projects staff visit Washington monthly. Then too, a few institutions with a large dollar volume of external funding have established Washington offices. The cost of such an office varies with responsibilities and staff, but the minimum cost for a director, secretary, and office facilities exceeded $100,000 annually in 1980. The value and services provided by these offices should be constantly reviewed, and the Washington staff must visit the home institution often in order to remain familiar with its research capability and needs.

It may be less costly for an institution to hire a Washington firm to represent it. This method, however, may have its drawbacks if the firm is not sufficiently familiar with the institution's employee and organizational needs or is not fully informed about the institution's current situation and future trends. Also, a firm that represents many other institutions may not have the time or staff expertise to be of real benefit to the office of sponsored projects. Another option for Washington-based contacts is the use of national organizations such as the Office of Federal Programs of the American Association of State Colleges and Universities to assist in making travel arrangements and appointments and to keep the office of sponsored projects informed of events in Washington. However, many institutions find that sending office of sponsored projects staff or project directors to meet with sponsor program officers is a more effective and efficient method than hiring a Washington representative.

Sladek (1977, pp. 36–37) concludes that agency contacts may be more important than previous research had indicated. Most important is the proposal-related contact with the sponsor's program officer prior to proposal submission, which helps the researcher tailor the proposal to the sponsor's requirements. Sladek's findings emphasize the value of personal contacts in determining the sponsor's needs in relation to prospective proposers' expertise.

Sources of Information

As mentioned earlier, matchmaking is a major responsibility of the office of sponsored projects. This office serves to help innovative researchers find the many possible resources available to enhance their creative activity. Successful matchmaking, of course, requires good information. Indeed, the office of sponsored projects is constantly deluged with brochures, newsletters, and reference materials regarding thousands of programs, regulations, legislation, deadlines, and the like. Selecting the information resources that will best keep staff abreast of current government and foundation activity is a formidable task for any director. Clearly, the type of institution determines which information is required by the office of sponsored projects. The needs of a small liberal arts college differ significantly from those of a large research institution or those of a medical center. Intelligent decisions to purchase reference books or periodical subscriptions must be based on specific institutional goals and objectives as they pertain to extramural funding.

Beasley (1976, p. 11) categorizes information sources into four groups: (1) basic library of reference sources, (2) periodicals from private and professional services, (3) periodicals from agencies and foundations, and (4) information services that provide basic information and optional periodic updates. The following listing of information sources— available to assist offices of sponsored projects in alerting researchers to funding opportunities and in keeping their institutions informed about legislative measures, federal programs changes, and foundation activities—is based on these categories.

1. Basic Library of Reference Sources

    The Art of Winning Government Grants (H. Hillman; New York: Vanguard Press, 1977)
    Budget of the United States Government
    Congressional Directory
    Congressional Record
    Congressional Staff Directory
    Corporate Foundation Profiles
    Developing Skills in Proposal Writing (M. Hall; Portland, Ore.: Continuing Education Publications, 1977)
    Federal Executive Directory
    Federal Register
    United States Government Manual

2. Periodicals from Private and Professional Services

    ACLS Newsletter
    ARIS Funding Messenger: Creative Arts and Humanities Report
    ARIS Funding Messenger: Medical Sciences Report
    ARIS Funding Messenger: Social and Natural Sciences Report
    The Chronicle of Higher Education
    Commerce Clearing House Reports
    Federal Grants and Contracts Weekly
    Federal Notes
    Federal Research Report
    Foundation News
    FRAS News Notes
    Fund Sources in Health and Allied Fields
    Government Contracts Reporter (Commerce Clearing House)
    Government Reports: Announcements and Index

Grants Magazine
The Grantsmanship Center News
Higher Education and National Affairs
Higher Education Daily
IRB: A Review of Human Subjects
Journal of the Society of Research Administrators
Medical Research Funding Bulletin
News, Notes, and Deadlines
Philanthropic Digest
R & D Management Digest
Research Management
Science
Science and Government Report
The Washington Post
Washington International Arts Letter
Wolff's Bulletin on College and University Regulation

3. Periodicals from Agencies and Foundations

American Education
Business America (Department of Commerce)
Commerce Business Daily
The Cultural Post (National Endowment for the Arts)
Ford Foundation Letter
Humanities
NIH Guide for Grants and Contracts
NIH Week
NSF Bulletin
Research Corporation Quarterly Bulletin
RF Illustrated (Rockefeller Foundation)
Science Resource Studies Highlights (National Science Foundation)
SRS Newsletter

4. Information Services that Provide Basic Information and Optional Periodic Updates

Annual Register of Grant Support
Catalog of Federal Domestic Assistance
College and University Reporter (Commerce Clearing House)

Foundation Directory
Foundation Grants Index
The Guide to Federal Assistance
A Guide to Federal Funding for Education
Taft Information System

Basic Library. It would be quite costly, time consuming, and re-
dundant to purchase and read all the resources in the preceding list.
Based on costs for 1982, a basic reference library would include:

Catalog of Federal Domestic Assistance	$ 20
The Chronicle of Higher Education	33
Commerce Business Daily	100
The Cultural Post	11
Federal Register	300
Foundation Directory	45
Humanities	7
NIH Guide for Grants and Contracts	free
NSF Bulletin	free
Federal agency directives and reports	free
Foundation newsletters and annual reports (Carnegie, Exxon, Ford, Rockefeller)	free
TOTAL	$ 516

For a more comprehensive library of reference materials, one would add
the following:

Developing Skills in Proposal Writing	$ 10
Federal Notes	72
Higher Education and National Affairs	30
Federal Executive Directory	96
ARIS Funding Messenger: Creative Arts and Humanities Report	68
ARIS Funding Messenger: Social and Natural Sciences Report	105
Journal of the Society of Research Administrators	25
Science and Government Report	119
Federal Grants and Contracts Weekly	143
Annual Register of Grant Support	58
Science	80
TOTAL	$ 806
GRAND TOTAL	$1,322

These materials are suggested for a reference library serving the needs of a comprehensive university, excluding a medical, dental, or nursing center. Of course, each office of sponsored projects must determine the information required to best serve its institution. For example, the University of Texas at Dallas, serving the Association of Higher Education Consortium, spent $2,560 in 1980 to purchase reference materials. In that same year, Southern Illinois University at Carbondale spent $2,100 for their Office of Research Development and Administration library.

State and Local Support Information. States vary in the amount of support and methods of distributing funds to higher education, but substantial funding is available from many state agencies. Federal flow-through funds administered by the states and direct state funding are available to support training, research, and demonstration projects. Information about such funding is usually not available from any centralized resource or commercial newsletter. Information on priorities and needs of these agencies is obtained by individual contacts and by being placed on the agencies' mailing lists. In some states, information on local foundation support is published in a statewide foundation directory; any such directory is an essential reference document for the office's library. Local foundations' annual reports and other information published about them are equally important. Also, the Foundation Center (with major offices in New York, Washington, D.C., and Chicago) has over fifty regional collections that detail the activities of local foundations.

Automated Information. As discussed in Chapter Six, computerized information systems are available to assist offices of sponsored projects in receiving timely external program information. The University of Illinois at Urbana–Champaign has a program information search system to which other universities may subscribe—Illinois Research Information System (IRIS). IRIS contains information on approximately 1,500 government, foundation, and association funding programs and is accessed by a 750-keyword glossary. The SUNY Research Foundation's computerized program information data bank, Sponsored Projects Information System (SPIN), is available to the 64 SUNY institutions, as well as to others on a subscription basis. The Foundation Grants Index, COMSEARCH, Federal Assistance Programs and Retrieval System (FAPRS), and the Individualized Grant Information and Search System are other computerized program systems currently available.

Internal Communications

The sponsored projects administrator has a pivotal role and position within the institution's administration as the focal point of information and contacts from sponsors regarding grants, contracts, pending regulations, legislation, and the like. The responsibilities of a typical sponsored projects administrator thus cut across all top administration levels. This unique position of the office of sponsored projects and its brokerage functions demand effective internal communication. Since the major responsibility of the office of sponsored projects is to serve the project directors of the institution, effective communication with these individuals is most crucial.

Communication with Faculty. Faculty members should be kept informed of the latest Washington activities and possible sources of support for themselves and their students. The office of sponsored projects must have information about each faculty member's expertise and be able to quickly inform individuals of specific opportunities and also keep them regularly informed of current events, program opportunities, and deadlines. Communications with faculty must be usable, accurate, timely and accessible. They should include both formal and informal types.

One type of formal communication that is essential and widely used by offices of sponsored projects is a newsletter, usually issued semimonthly. A newsletter can present the following types of information:

- office announcements
- information regarding legislation and new regulations
- brief description of program opportunities available during the next few months
- description of foundations
- special nonrecurring opportunities
- detailed analysis of specific programs
- list of deadlines of upcoming programs
- list of current proposals submitted and awards received by faculty
- list of faculty's publications or papers presented
- highlights of faculty research findings

Newsletters may be two pages or twenty; the length and amount of information depend on the needs of the specific institution. Typical is a newsletter of four to six pages published on a regular basis, but many institutions consider a brief two pages sufficient. Among the excellent newsletters that may be used as models are those published by Southern Illinois University at Carbondale, the University of Texas at Dallas, the University of Illinois at Urbana-Champaign, the SUNY Research Foundation, and Texas A & M Research Foundation. Specialized newsletters such as the University of Illinois (Chicago) Medical Center's Campus *Research Board News, Gerontology Newsletter,* and *Alcohol and Drug Abuse Newsletter* are also quite useful models. Individuals in research administration are usually willing to share their newsletters with other institutions upon request.

Effective informal techniques include news communiques directed to specific individuals. Unlike newsletter articles aimed at a wide variety of potential interests, these communiques are targeted to specific individuals whose interests or expertise are relevant to the specific announcements. Computerized faculty profile systems to assist in this targeting are discussed in Chapter Six. Regardless of the method used to match faculty and program announcements, the information on specific projects must be disseminated in a timely fashion.

Other forms of internal communication include: (1) a grants and contracts manual to assist project directors in proposal preparation and to explain services offered by the office of sponsored projects; (2) handout materials on specific services of institution and sponsor regulations, that is, budget preparation, indirect cost calculation, effort reporting, and audit disallowances; and (3) audio cassette tapes with a brief explanation of current topics.

Of course, personal contacts with faculty members are essential. A friendly acknowledgment in the hallway or a question about a research project in a meeting are important forms of oral communication. Such simple actions are often overlooked by administrators but are crucial in developing the proper environment for a service office. Similarly, if the sponsored projects administrator is too busy to visit the laboratories or offices of project directors, telephone calls can serve to inform directors of an opportunity for funding or congratulate them on a new award, paper, or article. Telephone calls provide effective internal communication.

If the sponsored projects administrator has the time, visits to individual project directors' offices or laboratories can be especially meaningful in promoting a personal relationship between project directors and administrators. Visits give project directors the opportunity to show their latest work and may make them feel that someone in the administration cares about their work. The sponsored projects administrator should also be prepared to receive project directors. The administrator should take time to determine their interests, the unit they are from, any funded or pending proposals they may have, and any relevant problems or concerns. Basic communication skills—making visitors feel at ease, being a good listener, and following up on any problems—are essential, especially in dealing with project directors. To be successful, the office must develop a good reputation for problem solving, following up on requests, and truly serving their patrons.

Communication with Academic Administrative Personnel. Horizontal and vertical communications within the academic administration are also crucial to a successful office. Deans, department heads, and center directors are influential and important individuals; good working relationships with this level of the administration are mandatory. Since these academic leaders are responsible for the workloads of faculty members, the sponsored projects administrator must be knowledgeable about their units. It is important that they promote meetings with academic leaders. Also, in proposal development and processing, these individuals are responsible for approving: (1) the availability of faculty time, especially released time or leave of absence; (2) facilities, equipment, or special services; (3) in-kind contributions; and (4) the congruity of the proposed project with goals and objectives of their department, school, center, or college. Thus successful proposal development depends on the knowledge, communication, and ability of the sponsored projects administrator in working within the institution's horizontal structure.

Communication with Vice-Presidents and President. The vertical communication channel is also quite essential. The vice-president for business affairs, vice-president for research and development, and the president must be aware of the role of the sponsored projects administrator within the total organization and must keep the office of sponsored projects well informed of the problems, priorities, and objectives of the institution. And sponsored projects administrators must communicate their needs for information to assist the university in achieving specific objectives. Such upward communications are important, and the sponsored projects administrator must keep superiors informed of program opportunities for external funding as well as new regulations and how they may affect the institution. The administrator must also be able to provide management reports detailing proposal submissions by project director, department, school; funded awards by sponsor, department, school; and comparisons of current and past external support. Good communication will enable the sponsored projects administrator to achieve such objectives as being part of the upper-level management team, setting priorities, being involved in planning, and helping to direct the future of the institution.

Communication with the Business Office. The office of sponsored projects usually deals daily with the business services division. The office of sponsored projects often serves as a buffer or mediator between faculty members and the business office, and effective communication skills are required to provide this service. Some staff members need to be reminded on occasion that the staff of the institution exists to serve students and faculty. "Wouldn't this be a nice place to work if it weren't for the faculty?" reflects a loss of perspective. The office of sponsored projects can assist both the business affairs employees and faculty by providing the skills necessary to satisfy specific needs of the faculty (purchasing, personnel, travel), and also by complying with the university, state, and sponsor regulations that concern the business group.

The first step is for the office of sponsored projects to appreciate and understand the responsibilities, duties, and needs of the business officials. The office's grant and contract handbook should be developed and revised with significant input from business affairs. Meetings to discuss such matters as purchasing procedures, personnel hiring, indirect costs, and audit disallowances should be ongoing and involve business affairs, faculty, and their support staffs. It is mandatory that the office of sponsored projects have good rapport with the office of business affairs if it is to provide services essential for faculty to conduct research.

The office of sponsored projects staff must also understand purchasing procedures and all the paperwork required—purchase requisitions, bids, purchase orders, invoice vouchers, justifications, equipment screening certifications—and be able to explain the necessity and value of the complicated system to project directors. Familiarity with personnel policies and procedures regarding advertising, screening, interviewing, hiring, appointing, budgeting, fringe benefits, and the like will improve communication and cooperation between the office of sponsored projects, business affairs, and project directors. Knowledge by the office of sponsored projects staff of the accounting functions and the rules and regulations that affect the administration of a grant or contract can prevent interruptions in research caused by delays in paperwork or requisitions for supplies and necessary equipment. Finally, communications with the business office must be honest and open.

Communication with Staff. Of course, communication between the director of the office of sponsored projects and office staff must be excellent. The timely communication of new regulations, programs, and problems to all staff is essential for effective administration. Weekly staff meetings and the routing of internal and external news to staff are two methods of keeping them abreast of current happenings. Seeking their assistance and involving them in the decision-making process are critical to their development and to the growth and capability of the organization. The people handling the daily problems in the office of sponsored projects, school, department, and center are excellent sources of ideas and information, and the director of the office of sponsored projects should not overlook them.

Exhibit 11. Checklist for Communication Systems and Information Sources.

External Communications

_____ Washington contacts, titles, addresses, phone numbers
_____ Agency visits (strategy)

Information Sources

_____ Basic library reference sources
_____ Periodicals from private and professional services
_____ Periodicals from agencies and foundations
_____ Information services that provide basic information and periodic update services
_____ Professional books
_____ Costs

Internal Communications

_____ Communication with faculty
       Newsletters:
       _____ Office announcements
       _____ Information regarding legislation and new regulations
       _____ Description of program opportunities
       _____ Description of foundations
       _____ Special nonrecurring opportunities
       _____ Detailed analysis of specific programs
       _____ List of deadlines of upcoming programs
       _____ List of current proposals submitted and awards received
       _____ List of faculty's publications and papers presented
       _____ Highlights of faculty research findings
_____ Communication with academic administrative personnel
_____ Communication with vice-presidents and president
_____ Communication with business office
_____ Communication with staff

8

Managing Proposal Preparation and Processing

The office of sponsored projects should develop a range of services to encourage researchers to seek external support. Three types of services need to be considered: (1) direct services for project directors in completing the application and preparing it for internal review; (2) an expeditious proposal review process that serves the concerns of project directors and the institution; and (3) information and reporting processes that allow project directors and the institution to meet required regulatory responsibilities. The nature and implementation of such services depend on the size of the institution, the number of proposals submitted or planned to be submitted, and the general philosophy of the institution. Some institutions centralize these services. In others, all or most of these services, with the exception of regulatory responsibilities, are conducted within the department or unit from which the proposal is being submitted. For purposes of this presentation, we assume that these services are offered centrally; however, the location of the service is not nearly as important as its effectiveness.

111

Proposal Preparation Services

Many essential activities precede the submission of a proposal to a sponsor; the submission is only the final act in a long chain of events. The process begins when a prospective proposer first contemplates the development and formulation of an idea; this stage is usually very lengthy and does not always yield a proposal. Proposals that do reach the submission stage usually differ greatly from the form in which they were first conceived.

A prospective proposer is guided in the formulation of an idea by several sources, principally the professional literature and faculty colleagues. Support in the development of a concept should also be available from the sponsored projects office. An individual in that office with experience in proposal development can offer two types of invaluable service to the prospective proposer. The first of these services takes the form of being a receptive listener and offering the prospective proposer a forum in which ideas can be freely discussed and shaped. Although the proposal developer may not share similar academic training with the prospective proposer, they can together discuss nontechnical questions that will be helpful in guiding the proposer. By asking probing questions and offering suggestions in a nonthreatening manner, the proposal developer can promote the expeditious maturation of a concept.

Second, the proposal developer can provide information about what sponsors have been doing or plan to do in specific areas. A proposal developer can provide information to a researcher about what an advisory committee is suggesting as the future program of a federal agency or what a board of governors says will be the future interest of a foundation. This type of information can be very important in refining an idea. The prospective proposer should not feel that someone is dictating a project to him, but rather that it is prudent strategy to develop a project proposal that will be attractive to a sponsor. Seldom are the needs of a sponsor and the desires of a project director irreconcilable. It is simply good management to be concerned with the direction and needs of a potential sponsor when finalizing the objectives and procedures of a project.

Once the idea reaches maturity, the proposer must work alone to complete a first draft of the proposal. Although the idea has matured conceptually, at this point further modifications are frequently undertaken. The idea may not seem as attractive as when first contemplated, or the written document may not adequately convey the idea. Review of the draft by colleagues is most helpful; however, there may also be a role for the proposal developer. The proposal developer should be aware of the proposal writer's frame of mind at this point. The writer may become impatient with regard to the proposal or be too close to see its flaws. At this critical time in the evolution of the proposal, the proposal developer can assist the writer in determining if the project has merit and should be continued.

What should the proposal developer do in this situation? Whatever needs to be done to assure the continued, timely development of the proposal. He or she can console the writer, offer advice on whom to talk to, or offer direct suggestions for improving the proposal. In determining what course of action to take, the proposal developer should be aware of the writer's attitude and be sensitive to the writer's concerns. It may be valuable simply to suggest that the writer leave the draft at the office and take a few days to do something far removed from the proposal. Time away from a proposal usually sharpens the writer's senses with regard to the proposal and invigorates him or her for the work that lies ahead. In a few cases, the revision of the first draft becomes a crisis point in the life of the proposal. The writer may form a strong mental block with regard to completing or revising the draft. In this case it is sometimes helpful for the proposal developer to actually rewrite or revise the draft and thus keep the proposal process on course. Such assistance should not be offered frequently, but at times it may be the only way to save a good idea and a capable researcher.

The Proposal and Its Parts

The proposal is the primary means by which a project director communicates an idea and plan to a potential sponsor. This document must convey to the sponsor the need for the proposed activity and the ability of the project director to conduct the work. Our discussion of the proposal and its parts is brief. More detailed information on proposal writing and content is available in many publications. Among these, especially helpful are: V. P. White, *Grants: How to Find Out About Them and What to Do Next* (New York: Plenum Press, 1975); M. Hall, *Developing Skills in Proposal Writing*, 2nd ed. (Portland, Ore.: Continuing Education

Publications, 1977); and C. W. Smith and E. W. Skjei, *Getting Grants* (New York: Harper & Row, 1980). In addition, many professional organizations and groups — such as the National Council of University Research Administrators and the Society of Research Administrators — hold workshops several times a year on the subject of proposal writing, as mentioned in Chapter Two.

Most funding organizations prescribe their own guidelines, but the substantial similarities make it possible to discuss the parts of the proposal and their purposes without specific reference to a funding agency. A typical proposal would include the following:

> Abstract
> Introduction
> Statement of the problem
> Objectives
> Methods
> Evaluation and dissemination
> Budget

Abstract: The abstract is a brief summary of the project. It identifies the applicant and the applicant's credibility, the problem to be addressed, the objectives to be achieved, the activities to be undertaken, and the costs. Although the abstract appears first, it should be written last. Proposal writers should remember that the abstract may be the only part of an application that is reviewed by some agency officials.

Introduction: The introduction describes the institution's and project director's qualifications for undertaking the proposed project, and it serves to enhance the applicant's credibility. The length of the introduction depends on how well known the applicant and institution are to the sponsoring agency. This could be the longest section of the proposal if the sponsoring agency is unfamiliar with the applicant and institution.

Statement of the problem: This section, sometimes called the needs assessment, should provide a brief, but complete and convincing description of the applicant's reasons for pursuing a particular problem.

Objectives: This section presents the specific expected outcomes of a project. Objectives should be reasonable and will be used to evaluate the effectiveness of a project. This part of the proposal should tell *who* is doing *what, when* it is being done, *how much* is being done, and *how* it will be resolved or assessed.

Methods: This section, sometimes called procedures, describes the steps to be undertaken in carrying out the objectives. Methods should flow naturally from the objectives of a project. It may be important or essential to justify why a certain method was selected rather than others.

Evaluation and dissemination: This section should present the applicant's plan for assessing the outcome of the project and the dissemination of its findings. In some proposals these issues are a critical component. The evaluation should be designed to determine to what extent the proposed objectives were met.

Budget: This section presents a detailed breakdown of the component costs of a project. (Budget development is discussed in the next section of this chapter.)

As mentioned earlier, many sponsors supply guidelines for the format of proposals, while others leave the organization to the project director. The guidelines and formats devised by the National Science Foundation (NSF) are widely known and frequently used; they can often be slightly revised and used in proposals for sponsors that do not prescribe a format. Resource C presents extracts from the NSF brochure *Grants for Scientific Research* and can be used as a guide in preparing a proposal.

Budget Development

Many proposal writers can easily describe their proposed work but require the assistance of the sponsored projects office in preparing the project budget. The proposal developer or budget specialist can provide the proposal writer with much-needed support and information, including an educated guess about the level of support available for a proposed activity from a given agency.

The experienced budget specialist usually has a checklist of budget categories to discuss with the proposer (see Resource D for sample budget checklist). The budget specialist aids the project director in recognizing the budget categories and amounts that need to be considered. Such discussions usually begin with the topic of personnel. For instance, the budget analyst might say: "Do you have summer salary support for the coming year? The sponsor will provide up to two months." Together the budget specialist and the project director work through the entire budget, being careful to include often-neglected items such as reprint costs, page charges, on-campus service charges, and computer time. The budget should also account for known and estimated salary increments as well as inflation between the time of submission and subsequent funding.

The budget is, in effect, a written description of the project in terms of its costs. The reader of a budget will gain a definite impression of the intent of the project. Any discrepancy between the budget and the proposal will be questioned by the sponsor during the review process; a serious discrepancy could lead the sponsor to immediately reject the proposal. Reviewers and project officers may hold that if a proposer cannot prepare an adequate budget, he or she cannot adequately conduct the project.

Sponsor Information

In developing proposals, researchers need basic information on the programs of sponsors. If an institution can afford to provide only one service, it must be this one. Chapter Seven presents a detailed account of the services and activities of this function, but suffice it to say here that the selection of the individual responsible for such basic information may well be the single most important decision made by the director of the office of sponsored projects. The information specialist must be an intelligent, independent individual with a strong desire to provide the best possible service to a diverse group of users of sponsor information. Information specialists must always be aware of what project directors are doing or planning and should spend some of their time encouraging individuals in disassociated units with similar information interests to talk about their mutual interests. As one might guess, the personality of the information specialist is critical to the success of this role.

Typing and Duplication Services–Office Automation

Project directors need adequate secretarial support in preparing proposals, and the importance of this support cannot be overemphasized. The appearance of the proposal significantly contributes to its reception by the sponsor and reviewers. A centralized typing service can help assure that proposals look professional and meaningful. Similarly, duplication of proposals on the best available word processing or duplication equipment will assure consistent high quality.

The use of word processing equipment in sponsored projects offices has increased rapidly in the last few years. Even offices that provide limited services should investigate the benefits of word processing systems. The advantages of such systems include increased efficiency and higher-quality output. For example, word processors reduce typing, revision, proofreading, and retyping time; they eliminate the retyping step for photocomposition input; and they offer increased productivity when repetitive typing is required.

In selecting a word processing system many options need to be explored; among them are decisions about: (1) mini- or microprocessors; (2) storage medium (paper tape, magnetic cards, floppy disks, hard disks); (3) storage capacity; (4) file organization; (5) number of supported key stations and printers; (6) display station features (type characters, cursor, highlighting, character pitch, underscore, subscript/ superscript, multicolumn page); (7) printer features (character types, character pitch and space, forms control); and (8) text editing features.

Proposal Processing and Coordination

The typical institutional review process begins with the departmental chairperson and ends with the institutional official authorized to commit the institution. The type and number of reviews that occur depend on the institution. In general, the fewer the number of review points, the shorter the time needed to get a proposal "cleared." The sponsored projects administrator must inform proposal writers of the need to start the review process early enough to meet their submission deadlines.

Role of the Chairperson and Dean

Each review official examines the proposal for very specific reasons, although occasionally two or more reviewers share similar concerns. In a college or university, the chairperson reviews a potential submission to see that it is within the mission of and will contribute to the advancement of the unit. The chairperson is also interested in the amount of faculty time allocated to a project and whether that time is to be provided on a reimbursement or contribution basis. The chairperson also reviews any other commitments to the project to ensure that those resources, including facilities, will be available once the project is funded.

The dean's concerns are similar to those of the chairperson, and the dean's review serves to keep his or her office informed about the kinds of activities that individual project directors are proposing. If the proposal requires a specific commitment from the dean's office, the dean must decide whether to commit the necessary resources. The dean may also be interested in seeing that collegewide policies related to sponsored projects are being carried out properly. Or if the dean is interested in recovering the maximum amount of faculty time on projects through reimbursement from sponsors, he or she may review the chairperson's earlier decision. At this stage there may be some conflict between the dean, chairperson, and project director if the institution's policy is not well understood or clearly articulated.

Role of the Office of Sponsored Projects

Since the review process can be very complicated, institutions must develop a systematic process that allows for the orderly and timely review of proposals. Many institutions use a checklist or proposal transmittal form in reviewing proposals. These forms are the official record of the review process and contain any specific commitments made by the institution for a given proposal. Exhibits 12 and 13, pages 123–126, present a sample checklist and transmittal form.

Each institution must decide which official is to be the final signatory for proposal submissions. This responsibility may be given to the president, academic vice-president, the financial vice-president, a dean, or an official in the office of sponsored projects. The individual selected must be accessible, and the institution should designate an alternate in the absence of the regular official.

The sponsored projects office must reconcile its several functions in proposal development. It must work in concert with proposers while maintaining control over the submissions process. While encouraging and supporting individual proposers, the sponsored projects office must enforce institutional, college, and departmental policies. The proposal development officer is important in this process because he or she can give needed procedural advice. Specific review responsibilities for proposals in the sponsored projects office include (1) compliance with institutional objectives, mission, and policy; (2) compliance with sponsor policies and guidelines; (3) obtaining of appropriate institutional approval; (4) obtaining of appropriate regulatory compliance approval; (5) verification of commitments from sponsors; and (6) verification of cost-sharing commitments.

Other Reviews

Once the dean and chairperson approve the submission of a proposal, the approval of various other institutional officers may be required. Some of these include: financial officer, legal officer, facilities officer, computer facilities officer, animal facilities officer, human subjects officer, and, of course, the sponsored projects administrator. The number of such reviews depends on the type of project. Each institution should have an orderly process for acquiring such approvals (see Figure 20) and a clear division of responsibilities for executing this process. For example, the project director can be responsible for obtaining any approval that is contingent on the specific activities of a project. Such approvals include a determination of the project's need for a specific service—for example, computer services, facilities planning, animal care services, and the like. Responsibility for obtaining other approvals— from the financial affairs office or the legal counsel, for example—is sometimes left to the office of sponsored projects. For approvals related to institutional regulatory responsibilities—such as human subjects, animal welfare, and biological hazards—there should be a standard review process that the project director can initiate.

Finally, some federal agencies require that regional and state planning committees review and approve a proposal before it is submitted to the sponsor. The office of sponsored projects should assist the project director in obtaining an external review by supplying pertinent information about the appropriate planning committee; for example, the project director will need to know how to contact the committee and the purpose of its review.

Figure 20. Flow Chart for Processing Proposals and Awards.

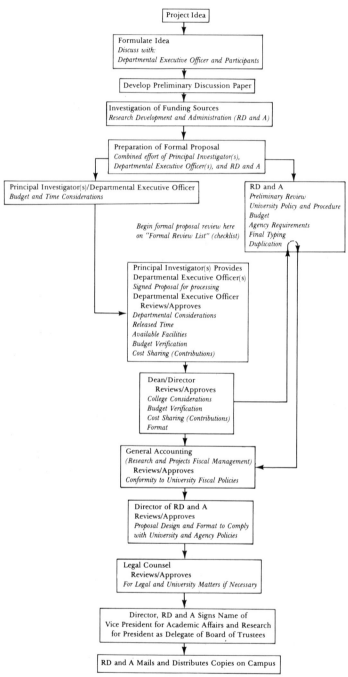

Note: Additional reviews may include information processing where computer time is indicated in the budget; dean of graduate school if tuition and fee waiver is requested or if graduate courses, graduate credit, or new graduate programs are involved. Also, the vice president for student affairs, the vice president for fiscal affairs, or the vice president for university relations may be indicated on the university checklist to formally review the proposal prior to submission if the proposal involves personnel or other commitments in their areas of responsibility.

Source: Original chart used by Office of Research Development and Administration, Southern Illinois University at Carbondale.

Deadlines

It is the responsibility of the sponsored projects office to keep the appropriate people informed of sponsor deadlines. Such information may be disseminated by letters, memos, phone calls, or through a newsletter or institutional publication. Proposers must be informed of institutional deadlines for submitting proposals for internal review. At least ten days in advance of sponsor receipt deadlines is suggested.

Sponsors usually have either a "postmark" or "receipt" deadline. A postmark deadline requires that the proposal be postmarked by a prescribed date; the date of its actual arrival is irrelevant. A receipt deadline, however, requires that the proposal be in the sponsor's office on the date prescribed. Some sponsors consider a proposal to be received on time, despite its arrival date, if it is postmarked at least five working days prior to the deadline. The office of sponsored projects should be familiar with such requirements and encourage proposers to plan ahead.

Proposals that are completed too late to be mailed to the sponsor can still meet their deadlines, although the means of delivery are relatively expensive. The first option is that the proposer personally deliver the proposal to the sponsor. The cost of round-trip transportation may be justifiable if the proposer can talk with sponsor officials or conduct other business on the trip. A second option is the use of a commercial delivery service that guarantees overnight delivery. The office of sponsored projects should have all the details about such services and stand ready to offer advice.

Regulatory Responsibilities

The sponsored projects office must support an expeditious process for satisfying the institution's responsibilities for compliance with federal regulations. Compliance concerns relate primarily to research, and, therefore, under the purview of the sponsored projects office, usually include such topics as the use of human subjects, the use of experimental animals, the use of biologically hazardous materials, and recombinant DNA research. Each of these areas is governed by specific federal mandates, and the institution's review procedures must assure compliance with federal regulations. In this section we address the review process; a more complete discussion of some of these topics is reserved for Chapter Fourteen.

Human Subjects. Institutions that conduct research with human subjects must comply with federal regulations to guarantee that a subject's rights, privacy, welfare, and civil liberties are protected. Each institution must submit a policy for approval by the National Institutes of Health and forward a list of its review committee members for similar approval. To aid its review committee, the institution should develop operational procedures and forms that project directors are to use in making applications for the committee's approval. A system must also be developed to delegate specific responsibilities for followup approval. Examples of these responsibilities may include assurances of termination of a project or assurances that a committee-mandated condition has been met. These responsibilities are usually simple and can be handled with a minimum of effort by the committee. The committee also requires administrative and clerical support, and the sponsored projects administrator should determine that the committee is acting according to policy and doing so in a timely manner.

Recombinant DNA and Biologically Hazardous Materials. Regulations related to recombinant DNA research and use of other potentially hazardous biological materials are also issued by the National Institutes of Health (1981), and compliance in any projects and experiments involving such materials is the responsibility of each institution. A campus-based committee must review research proposals and consider related questions concerning the conduct of research that involves such hazards. The National Institutes of Health prescribes a format for the campus review document; each participating institution must provide a memorandum of understanding and agreement for each type of activity. Again, it is the responsibility of the office of sponsored projects to see that this effort is conducted effectively and expeditiously.

Animal Welfare. Animal welfare regulations are very specific, and compliance is the responsibility of the institution. An animal welfare committee must be established and, depending on the institution's animal facilities, plays a role in assuring compliance. Specific guidance on this topic is presented in the National Institutes of Health's publication *Guide for the Care and Use of Laboratory Animals* (1980).

Exhibit 12. Checklist for Proposal or Grant Review.

Preproposal	☐	Proposal Revision	☐
Proposal	☐	Budget Revision	☐
Grant Award	☐	Supplement	☐

PRELIMINARY REVIEW (To be filled out by Research   Date: _____
Development and Administrative Personnel)

     Research ☐   Instruction ☐   Service ☐   Other ☐
               NSF Survey No. _____

Other _____ Other _____ Other _____

AGENCY: _____   PROPOSAL/AWARD REVIEWED BY: ____

DEADLINE DATE: _____   BUDGET PREPARED/REVIEWED BY: ___

PROJECT DATES: _____ to _____

AMOUNT REQUESTED: _____   _____ % of returned overhead to _____
SIUC CONTRIBUTED: _____   Dept/Unit

AGENCY ALLOWED IDC _____ %   _____ % of returned overhead to _____
of _____   Dept/Unit

GENERAL INFORMATION (To be filled out by Principal Investigator)
Title of Project: _____

Name(s) and Signature(s) of
Principal Investigator(s): _____ // _____

ITEMIZE *ALL* RELEASED TIME AND OTHER SIUC CONTRIBUTIONS INDICAT-
ING THE SPECIFIC SOURCE (See instructions following checklist)

_____

_____

_____

ADMINISTRATIVE REVIEWS
(See instructions following)

		A D DEPARTMENTAL EXECUTIVE	A D ASSOCIATE VICE-PRESIDENT
	☐	OFFICER(S) (Dept. Acct. No. _____)	FOR RESEARCH AND DEAN, GRADUATE SCHOOL
UNCERTAIN	☐ ☐	_____ (Date)	☐ ☐ _____ (Date)
	☐ ☐	_____ (Date)	
		DEANS	VICE-PRESIDENT FOR ACADEMIC AFFAIRS AND
NO	☐	☐ ☐ _____ (Date)	RESEARCH
	☐ ☐	_____ (Date)	☐ ☐ _____ (Date)

Exhibit 12 (continued)

GENERAL ACCOUNTING
OFFICE

☐ ☐ _____
(R&PFM—101 Small Grp. Hsg.,
Room 206)

DIRECTOR, RESEARCH
DEVELOPMENT AND
ADMINISTRATION

☐ ☐ _____
(Date)

PREFUNDING: YES

OTHER REVIEWS AS REQUIRED:

☐ ☐ _____
Academic Computing   (Date)

☐ ☐ _____
Legal Counsel   (Date)

☐ ☐ _____

☐ ☐ _____

☐ ☐ _____

☐ ☐ _____

XXXXXXXXXXXXXXXXXXXXXXXXXXXXXXXXXXXXXXXXXXXXXXXXXXXXXXXXXXXX

(For ORDA use only) Date Logged: _____ No. of copies to Agency: _____

Copies to: PI _____ R&PFM _____ Other: _____ File: _____

Date Mailed: _____ Type of Mail: HAND CARRY / COURIER / CERTIFIED / SPECIAL DELIVERY / FIRST CLASS / OTHER: _____

PROPOSAL PROOFREAD BY: _____
(Please read instructions before filling out this form)

GENERAL INSTRUCTIONS FOR FILLING OUT CHECKLIST:
1. A Program Development Specialist in the Office of Research Development and Administration (ORDA) will be responsible for completing the PRELIMINARY REVIEW section *prior* to the proposal/award being routed for ADMINISTRATIVE REVIEW.
2. The Principal Investigator will provide the following information:
   a. Under the section, GENERAL INFORMATION, please fill in the title of the grant application.
   b. Signatures of Principal Investigator(s) and date signed.
   c. Please itemize *all* university contributions that appear on the budget and in the proposal and indicate the specific source of each contribution—salaries, wages, travel, supplies, equipment, and so on.
   d. ADMINISTRATIVE REVIEWS. The Principal Investigator is responsible for obtaining the following signatures:
      (1) Departmental Executive Officer(s)—(of all DEO's whose faculty members are in the grant)
      (2) Dean(s)—(of each Dean of the School/College whose faculty are involved)
      (3) Academic Computing (if applicable)
      (4) Vice-Presidents (other than Academic Affairs —if applicable)
      (5) Legal Counsel (if applicable)
      Normally, ORDA will obtain the review signatures of General Accounting (R&PFM) and of the Vice-President for Academic Affairs and Research. Please note that ORDA sends proposals for review by General Accounting via *campus mail*. If an agency deadline is imminent, it is suggested that the Principal Investigator or a designated representative hand carry the proposal to General Accounting for review

Exhibit 12 (continued)

then hand carry it to the ORDA for final processing and signature of the Vice-President for Academic Affairs and Research.

3. ORDA will run the necessary copies for the agency, if so desired, and will furnish the Principal Investigator ONE copy of the complete proposal. Printed materials such as reports, monographs, manuscripts, pamphlets, and so on that are to accompany the proposal to the agency must be furnished ORDA in the agency-prescribed number of copies.

4. ORDA will mail all proposals via FIRST CLASS MAIL and/or CERTIFIED MAIL when a postmark deadline is indicated. Other types of special mailing or special courier service will be the responsibility of the Principal Investigator.

5. HUMAN SUBJECTS. It is the responsibility of the Principal Investigator to obtain human subjects clearance from the Carbondale Committee on Research Involving Human Subjects, if the proposed activity deals with humans. The appropriate forms may be obtained from the ORDA Office.

6. This checklist is to be returned to the Office of Research and Development and Administration as a permanent part of the proposal/grant file.

ADDITIONAL REVIEWS (when required) DEPARTMENTAL EXECUTIVE OFFICES	DEANS

Source: Southern Illinois University, Office of Research Development and Administration, 1980.

Exhibit 13. Proposal Transmittal Form.

The accompanying proposal is for the support of a program of ☐ research, ☐ building, ☐ instruction, ☐ equipment, ☐ summer institute, ☐ academic-year institute, ☐ international activity or study[1], or ☐ other, entitled[2] _____

_____ . This proposal is ☐ a new project, ☐ a renewal, ☐ a continuation, ☐ a revised proposal and/or budget. For renewal or continuation proposal please give previous grant number _____

Initiated by _____ of the department of _____

for submission to _____

for direct costs in the amount of .... $ _____

plus indirect costs of .... $ _____

total amount requested .... $ _____

The program, to start on _____ and terminate on _____ , will ☐ will not ☐ require an allocation of university funds (in the amount of $ _____). The need for these additional funds is explained on the attachment. Any other items listed *in the proposal as university contributions are available from the sponsoring department's own resources for the period indicated.*

Acceptance of the proposal will ☐ will not ☐ require that additional space be made available to the department or that existing space be renovated. Arrangements to meet this need have been made and are described on the attachment.

NEW [The work to be performed under this proposal will involve ☐ use of human subjects, ☐ use of warm-blooded animals, ☐ use of PLATO services, ☐ use of confidential, classified, or proprietary information, ☐ use of hazardous materials or procedures (☐ chemical hazard, ☐ biohazard, ☐ radiation hazard, ☐ other hazard _____), ☐ none of the above.]

This proposal will require approximately $____ for payment of charges at the Computing Services Office; amount provided for this purpose in proposed budget $____ .

The sums listed in the budget for consumable supplies, equipment, travel, personnel, and for any special purposes appear to be adequate.

It is understood that if a grant or contract results from this application, the principal investigator will perform the administrative duties normally associated with the project. The principal investigator assures that he makes this submission with the understanding that any resulting grant or contract will contain no provision restricting the university's right to publish research results, and that if any question of such restriction arises in subsequent negotiation he will assist in arranging the further review that will be required.

	_____	_____
	Date	Principal Investigator or Initiator of Proposal
	_____	_____
	Date	Executive Officer of School
Approved by	_____	_____
	Dean or Director[3]	for the Research Board
	_____	_____
	Business Affairs Office	Vice-Chancellor for Academic Affairs[4]

[1]All international programs and studies are to be approved by the Director of International Programs and Studies.
[2]If the complete title requires more than 34 typewriter spaces, please also supply, in the top margin, an abbreviated title within that limit for use in machine tabulation.
[3]Proposals that will require facilities or staff of several colleges are to be approved by the dean of each college concerned.
[4]Required if proposal is for a summer or academic year institute or if acceptance will require additional university funds, additional space as noted above, the construction of a building, or approval by Board of Trustees or by the Illinois Board of Higher Education.

Source: University of Illinois at Urbana, Grants and Contracts Office, 1976.

9

Determining
Indirect Costs
and Cost Sharing

Three broad cost categories are used for budgeting, expending, and reporting a sponsored project's financial status: direct costs, indirect costs, and cost sharing. Each category may be separately accounted for and further detailed by itemizing expenditures; however, not all three categories are always required or allowed by the sponsor. For example, an industrial grant to further a particular research effort may allow direct costs only and specifically exclude provisions for indirect costs and cost sharing. Direct costs are always present in sponsored projects, and are generally considered prior to indirect costs and cost-sharing requirements. Requirements for direct costs are discussed in Chapters Four and Eight (on proposal budgeting), Chapter Eleven (on allowability of costs), and Chapter Thirteen (on expenditure reporting). In this chapter we describe requirements for indirect costs and cost sharing.

Indirect Costs

Indirect costs are those costs associated with the conduct of sponsored projects that *cannot* be clearly identified and *cannot* be directly accounted for on an individual-project basis. The federal government defines indirect costs as those costs incurred for common or joint objectives that, therefore, cannot be identified readily and specifically with a particular sponsored project, an instructional activity, or any other institutional activity. Usually, the total amount of an institution's indirect costs is distributed among the four basic functions of the organization. The Office of Management and Budget (OMB circular A-21) defines these functions as: (1) instruction, including departmental research; (2) organized research (the federal government and industry are likely to be the major sponsors for this portion); (3) other sponsored activities; and (4) other institutional activities. At educational institutions, such costs normally are classified under the following indirect-cost categories: depreciation and use allowances, general administration and general expenses, sponsored projects administration expenses, operation and maintenance expenses, library expenses, departmental administration expenses, and student administration and services. Similar guidelines for state and local units of government are provided in OMB circular A-102, and nonprofit organizations' indirect-cost guidelines are presented in OMB circular A-122. The General Services Administration's guidelines for profit-making institutions are stated in Federal Procurement Regulation 1-15.2. Overall, the definitions and rate determinations are similar.

OMB circulars A-88 and FMC 73-6 established policies for coordinating the determination of indirect-cost rates and auditing in connection with federal grants and contracts with educational institutions. The federal government designates a federal agency with significant amounts of grants and contracts with an educational institution as the institution's "cognizant agency." This cognizant agency is assigned responsibility for conducting indirect-cost rate negotiations or carrying out the necessary audit, or both, at a particular institution. The cognizant agency's director appoints an indirect-cost staff within the agency's auditing department and delegates them authority for negotiating the indirect-cost rate with the institution. These staff auditors are usually located in one of the agency's regional offices. For example, the Department of Health and Human Services locates their division of cost allocations in regional administrative support centers. The director of the cognizant agency's auditing staff usually contacts the institution's auditor for an indirect-cost rate negotiation conference or audit.

The institution must prepare an annual indirect-cost proposal in accordance with the provisions of A-21. This proposal, its working papers, and summary data are submitted to the cognizant agency's audit staff for review. The cognizant agency's staff thoroughly examines the proposal, audits all costs, and arranges to discuss areas of disagreement about allowable indirect costs. Sometimes these discussions are short, but at other times they are rather lengthy. However, once the government and the institution's auditors reach an agreement on the indirect-cost rates, those rates are used for the designated year.

Allowable Indirect Costs

Allowable indirect-cost rates are of two types: agency-fixed rates and institution-negotiated rates.

Agency-fixed rates are determined by legislation or by the funding agency's regulations. For example, federal training grants may limit agency-fixed rates to 8 percent of the total direct costs, and other federal facility or equipment projects may exclude indirect costs. Nonprofit agencies and foundations frequently do not fully reimburse indirect costs. When seeking sponsor support, project directors must carefully consider restrictions on full reimbursements. Usually special permission must be obtained from the institution before accepting sponsored funding that involves fixed rates.

An institution-negotiated indirect-cost rate is an agreed-upon percentage that, when applied to a base of direct costs, results in the allowable indirect costs of the award. This negotiated rate is determined by the institution according to the applicable regulations and then approved by the cognizant auditing agency. For educational institutions, state and local governments, hospitals, and nonprofit institutions, the cognizant auditing agency is usually the Department of Health and Human Services. Negotiated indirect-cost rates vary greatly among institutions, as does the method of selecting rates.

The institutional confirmation of approved indirect-cost rates is usually a three- or four-page document that provides the various indirect-cost rates for each major function. In common practice, indirect-cost rates are usually reported according to the format shown in

Exhibit 14, page 140. The most common indirect-cost categories for each function included in the institutional confirmation document are shown in Exhibit 15, page 140.

The office of sponsored projects usually does not have the actual responsibility for determining indirect costs. That calculation is usually performed by the accounting or auditing office. However, the office should keep informed of the details of the indirect-cost calculation. As indicated in Table 5, the latest published data available, indirect-cost rates vary considerably.

Determining Indirect Costs

Determining indirect costs is a very complicated process, requiring an accounting system that prepares costs according to cost categories and institutional functions. There are two procedures for determining indirect costs within the regulations of OMB circular A-21. Small institutions may use a simplified method if the total direct costs covered by A-21 do not exceed $3 million in a fiscal year; section H of A-21 explains this simplified procedure. The regular procedure must be used by institutions that have more than $3 million of direct costs sponsored by the federal government and by institutions for whom the simplified procedure produces results that appear inequitable to the government or the institution. Here we provide only an overview of indirect-cost calculation. For a more thorough guide, the reader should refer to the guidelines presented in Sections E to K of circular A-21.

Six principal factors should be considered in selecting a distribution method for institutional costs:

1. The selection of an allocation base should be the one best suited for assigning the "pool of costs" to the "cost objectives" (instruction, organized research, and other sponsored activities) in accordance with benefits derived, a traceable cause-and-effect relationship, or logic and reason.
2. If a cost center can be identified directly with the cost objective benefited, it should be assigned to that cost objective.
3. If the expenses in a cost center are more general in nature, the distribution may be based on a cost-analysis study that results in an equitable distribution of the costs.
4. The order of distribution begins with depreciation and use allowances, and continues through operation and maintenance expenses and general administrative and general expenses.

Table 5. Indirect-Cost Rates by Geographical Region.

Location/Institution	Indirect Cost Base[a]	
	Salary and Wage	Modified Total Direct Costs
Northeast		
MIT	68.0%	
Columbia University		32.3%
Cornell University—state	69.0%	
Cornell University—endowed	61.8%	
Mid-Atlantic		
University of Maryland		51.0%
George Washington University	65.4%	
University of N. Carolina	48.13%	
Southeast		
Georgia Tech	68.0%	
Florida State University	50.0%	
University of Tennessee	73.0%	
Great Lakes		
University of Chicago	72.0%	
University of Illinois	66.0%	
University of Wisconsin	59.0%	
South		
Louisiana State University	46.0%	
University of Texas–Austin	54.0%	
Texas Tech University	44.0%	
Midwest		
University of Nevada	53.0%	
Colorado State University	64.0%	
Washington University	70.0%	
West		
University of California		29.0%
Stanford University		58.0%
University of Washington	50.0%	
University of Oregon	71.6%	

[a]These rates were compiled in December 1976 and therefore may not represent currently negotiated rates.

Source: Redecke and Darling, 1977, p. 24.

5. Cross-allocation of expenses between two or more indirect-cost pools may result in a more equitable allocation of costs for certain indirect-cost categories.
6. Indirect-cost pools must be closed once final assignation and cross-allocation have been made.

As mentioned earlier, cost objectives or major functions should be selected in a way that will best promote an equitable and accurate distribution of costs. Total direct costs associated with the major cost objectives of instruction, organized research, and other sponsored activities are placed in three bases:

- The *instructional base* should include all modified total direct costs related to instruction (including departmental research). Instruction means the teaching and training activities of the institution.
- The *organized research base* should include all modified total direct costs for research and development activities that are separately budgeted and accounted for. This base includes research and development that is sponsored by federal and nonfederal agencies and organizations as well as those that are separately budgeted by the institution under the internal allocation of institutional funds.
- The *other sponsored activities base* includes the modified total direct costs associated with all other activities of an institution except: (1) instruction, departmental research, organized research and other institutional activities; and (2) specialized service costs (see section J of OMB circular A-21 for a complete listing). Other institutional activities include operation of residence halls, hospitals and clinics, student unions, museums, and other auxiliary enterprises.

These three bases are assigned indirect costs from the indirect-cost pools. The number of pools depends on the institution; some universities use only one or two overhead pools, most use five, and some use seven or more (Balderston, 1973). The most frequently used overhead pools are: general administration, research and departmental administration, library, plant operations, and building and equipment usage.

Robert E. Gentry, vice-president for finance at Seton Hall University, devised a schematic in 1980 similar to the one shown in Figure 21 to explain the gathering of indirect costs into appropriate cost clusters and

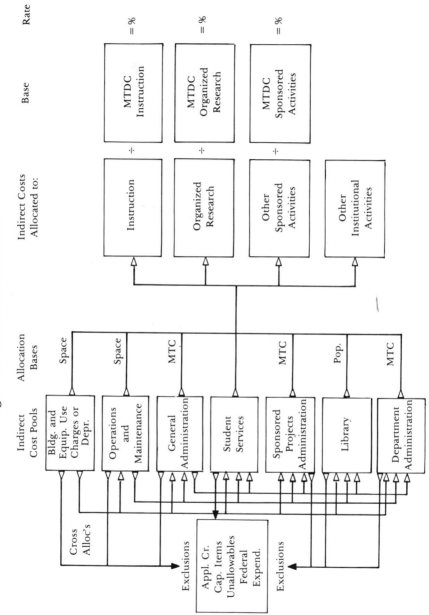

Figure 21. Indirect Cost Calculation.

subsequent reallocation and ultimate assignation to the appropriate base for the calculation of specific indirect-cost rates.

For many years indirect costs were figured according to a salary and wage base (S&W) under the cost principles of FMC 73-8. Beginning with an institution's first fiscal year after October 1, 1979, any rates negotiated under the provisions of circular A-21 must be expressed as a percentage of a modified total direct costs (MTDC) base rather than a percentage of S&W.

In Figure 21, the first indirect-cost pool, depreciation and use allowances, gathers together the portion of costs related to the institution's buildings, capital improvements to land and buildings, and equipment. The second indirect-cost pool, operation and maintenance expenses, includes those costs that have been incurred by a central service organization or at the departmental level for administration, supervision, operation, maintenance, and preservation and protection of the university's physical plant. The other indirect-cost pools are selected by the institution according to its needs and are defined according to its current cost-analysis studies. By dividing the institution's indirect-cost pools as allocated by their modified total direct cost base, the indirect-cost rate is determined.

Cost Sharing

Cost sharing, or matching, on sponsored projects is a relatively new concept that accounts for the portion of project costs not supported by the sponsor. Cost sharing began in 1966 when the House Appropriations Committee recommended that for the Department of Health, Education and Welfare the statutory limitation on indirect costs in research grants be eliminated and in its stead a cost-sharing provision be inserted. The intent of this recommendation was to encourage institutions to contribute to federally sponsored research. The committee instructed the Bureau of the Budget to draw up regulations to stipulate an appropriate level of financial cost sharing by recipient institutions. A cost-sharing provision was enacted in the Department of Health, Education and Welfare, the Department of Defense, and other agencies.

The office of sponsored projects must prepare an annual cost-sharing plan that: (1) shows the extent to which nonfederal funds contribute to the cost of research that is also supported by federal funds; (2)

provides the institution with maximum flexibility in the methods used to meet the established cost-sharing level; (3) simplifies the administration of proposal budget preparation by showing the institution's commitment to specific projects; and (4) facilitates review, award, and reporting procedures for both the recipient and sponsor. Unless an institution has few research grants and little nonfederal support for such projects, the cognizant audit agency will request a cost-sharing agreement.

For example, the Public Health Service requires cost sharing on every research project grant and encourages cost sharing on contracts. Its regulations provide two approaches to cost sharing: (1) the use of institutional cost-sharing agreements that cover the aggregate of all grants awarded by the agency to the institution, or (2) the use of separate cost-sharing agreements for each research project supported by grant funds (project-by-project cost sharing).

In preparing the institutional cost sharing agreement, the office of sponsored projects should consider the items discussed in this section.

Level of Contribution

The level of contribution toward research supported in part from federal funds varies among institutions. No fixed or arbitrary level is intended by the federal government. Instead, institutions are expected to establish a level consistent with experience and are to consider relevant current and projected data. These calculations involve determining the institution's average contribution to projects supported by each sponsor, stated on the basis of the grantee's fiscal year. During any given fiscal year the institution may make no contribution (or only a token contribution) to some grants, but its overall average contribution is maintained through higher contributions to other projects. However, in order to comply with the statutory provisions, the institution should contribute to every project at some time during the project's term.

Methods of Providing Contributions

The institution's contributions may be derived from most nonfederal sources, including nonfederal grants or contracts. Costs charged to federal funds may be counted as all or part of the institution's contribution only if the institution is a federal organization or a quasi-federal organization, a major part of whose support is from direct federal appropriations.

The contributions may be in the form of either direct or indirect costs, and their amounts may vary among individual projects as long as they are related to the grants. Cost-sharing amounts for a project are often obtained by calculating the project director's percentage of institution-contributed effort expressed in dollars, the applicable fringe benefits, and the corresponding indirect cost chargeable to the institution. This is an allowable cost-sharing contribution because a certain portion of faculty salaries are usually paid from sources other than federal agencies. The institution's contributions to all projects requiring cost sharing are aggregated for the fiscal year, and this total represents the actual institutional contribution.

Only those items that are allowable under the applicable cost principles if charged to the grant may be included in determining the institution's contribution. For example, the use of facilities and equipment already owned by an institution may not be counted as a contribution if the cost or value is reflected in the indirect cost rate as a depreciation or use charge, or if funded by federal monies. An exception to this policy may be made, however, for nonfederal third-party contributions made directly to a project without charge to the institution. While such costs may not be charged to the project, they may be counted toward the institution's contribution, provided that the costs are documented and relevant; and in all other respects the costs would have been allowable.

Universities are not required to obtain prior sponsor approval of the manner in which contributions are to be provided. The contributions may be in any allowable budget category or combination of categories. Special indirect-cost rates need not be developed to reflect cost-sharing agreements. If a university wishes to provide cost sharing in the indirect-cost category, it need merely reduce its claim for indirect costs to which it would otherwise be entitled and note that claim in the report of expenditures. Contributions from nonfederal sources may be counted as cost sharing toward federal projects *only once*. If, however, such contributions are related to grants supported by more than one federal agency, the institution may elect to make a proration among the agencies involved.

Negotiation of Institutional Plans

The responsibility for negotiating institutional cost-sharing agreements applying to research grants is assigned to a specific cognizant federal agency, often the Department of Health and Human Services (HHS). Institutional cost-sharing agreements for HHS research grants are negotiated by the Office of Administrative Management, Public Health Service. Institutions can request information on submitting proposals from: Chief, Cost and Audit Management Branch, Office of Administrative Management, Public Health Service, 5600 Fishers Lane, Rockville, Md. 20852. Plans or proposals may be submitted at any time, at the convenience of the institution.

The negotiation of an institutional cost-sharing agreement requires the agency and institution to discuss the actual base, proposed rate, scope of agreement, effective date, and period covered by agreement. For a detailed explanation of these elements, see, for example, the U.S. Department of Health, Education and Welfare's publication, *A Guide to Institutional Cost Sharing Agreements for Research Grants Supported by the Department of Health, Education and Welfare* (1975). This publication offers the following format for a proposal to provide cost sharing under an institutional plan. The use of this format is not mandatory; however, it combines the essential elements into a brief document, thus facilitating review:

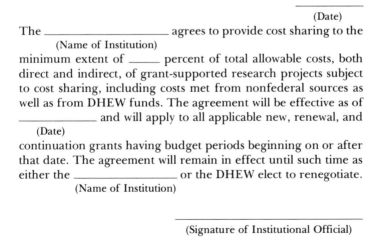

                                               (Date)

The _____ agrees to provide cost sharing to the
     (Name of Institution)
minimum extent of _____ percent of total allowable costs, both direct and indirect, of grant-supported research projects subject to cost sharing, including costs met from nonfederal sources as well as from DHEW funds. The agreement will be effective as of
_____ and will apply to all applicable new, renewal, and
  (Date)
continuation grants having budget periods beginning on or after that date. The agreement will remain in effect until such time as either the _____ or the DHEW elect to renegotiate.
    (Name of Institution)

                       (Signature of Institutional Official)

As an attachment to the proposal, the institution should submit the information on its actual cost-sharing rate for the previous fiscal year.

Administration of Institutional Agreements

To minimize the paperwork for institutional cost-sharing agreements, the federal government stipulates that the following procedures be used by the cognizant agency.

Applications. Once an institutional cost-sharing agreement is in effect, no additional paperwork on this subject is needed for individual applications. Institutions should present budgets in the applications that represent only the costs requested from the sponsor to whom the application is directed. No reference to cost sharing is needed unless the specific program guidelines require inclusion of an institution's matching funds in the proposal.

Awards. Awards issued by units of the cognizant agency are to specify that the grant is subject to an institutional agreement and give the effective date of the agreement.

Expenditure Report. On expenditure reports for projects subject to an institutional agreement, only the costs chargeable to the project are to be listed. The report need only state that an institutional cost-sharing agreement is in effect and give the effective date.

Amendments to Agreements. If an institution cannot meet the level of contributions stated in its cost-sharing agreement because anticipated funds from nonfederal sources do not materialize or for other valid reasons, the cost-sharing level may be amended retroactively to provide for a lower contribution. An amended agreement must also be submitted whenever the name or structure of the institution is changed through merger, novation agreement, or by any other means.

Documentation. No standard format or method for calculating and documenting the level of cost sharing under an institutional agreement is prescribed. Each institution may choose the method most consistent with its own procedures for maintaining, accumulating, and reporting financial information on research. Such information may be part of the formal accounting system or be maintained in memorandums or other institutional records. However, the following general requirements hold:

1. Institutional records must show the total costs, both direct and indirect, charged to sponsor funds provided for research, as well as the

total costs, both direct and indirect, expended from nonfederal funds on related research. The level of cost sharing is then computed by determining the percentage of the total nonfederal funds to the total funds expended. An alternate method, showing the percentage between all nonfederal and federal funds in applicable research, is permissible when there is a similarity between such research.

2. The records must show that the institution has provided at least some level of cost sharing on each applicable project at some time during the term of the project. For a grant related to research supported by nonfederal funds, it is necessary only to show the relationship. For a grant that has no related project supported by nonfederal funds, the legal requirement may be satisfied by charging some part of the costs to nonfederal funds. This may be accomplished by contributing some direct cost of the project (such as salaries, travel, or supplies) or by reducing the claim for indirect costs.

3. The records used to develop the information required by items 1 and 2 must be auditable. The information need not be submitted to the cognizant agency on a regular basis, but it should be available upon request to federal auditors and other appropriate staff.

Project-by-Project Cost Sharing. In the absence of an institutional cost-sharing agreement for each sponsor, it may be necessary to demonstrate cost sharing on each project. Consequently, the proposal budget should set forth the items to be paid for by the institution; that amount then is used in the negotiations. After the award, these costs must be separately accumulated and reported in order to satisfy requirements. Cost sharing on a project-by-project basis is a complicated procedure, and such an arrangement must be entered into carefully. Fluctuations in one project cannot be offset by other projects as is possible in institutional agreements.

Exhibit 14. Sample Format for Indirect-Cost Rates.

Research	Current Rates[a] 09/01/81–08/31/82
On-Campus	35.0%
Off-Campus	13.0%
Instruction and Training	
On-Campus	27.0%

[a]Based on modified total direct costs (MTDC). Total direct costs less subgrant and subcontract costs in excess of $25,000 each, capital equipment expenditures, alterations and renovations, stipends and tuition payments, and off-campus rent.

Source: University of Texas at Dallas, 1981.

Exhibit 15. Indirect-Cost Rates[a] for Research.

Research on Campus

Building-use charge	2.0%
Equipment-use charge	3.0%
Operation and maintenance	14.5%
General and administrative	9.0%
Library	2.5%
Departmental administration	1.5%
Research administration	2.5%
TOTAL	35.0%

[a]On-campus—best estimate of cost rates from negotiated rates.

Source: University of Texas at Dallas, 1981.

10

Negotiating and Accepting Awards

Several types of award documents are generally used between sponsors and recipients, and each major type is described in the first section of this chapter. Then we examine pre-award negotiations, and we suggest appropriate strategy and techniques. We conclude this chapter by discussing the acceptance of awards and the sponsored projects office's role in assisting the director following acceptance.

Types of Awards

A sponsored project award is a legal formalization of an agreement between parties. Sponsored project awards vary in their length and complexity—from a short award letter to a formal multiple-page contract with many clauses and regulations. The sponsored project award should specify: (1) the activity being supported or item(s) procured, (2) the period of performance, (3) the amount of money or value provided, and (4) the terms and conditions. All awards are legal instruments between sponsor and recipient that commit them to a relationship. Consequently, awards must be closely examined to determine whether they fulfill the agreements reached during negotiations and can be accomplished within the terms specified.

Sponsored project awards are usually made to organizations and not to individuals. Most awards require acceptance by the organization, either by the signature of an authorized official on the proposal document or by some other formal acceptance procedure once the award is made. Sponsored project awards are usually made by federal, state, and local governments, and by industry, foundations, and nonprofit agencies.

Three main types of legal instruments are used to convey sponsored project awards: grants, cooperative agreements, and contracts. Both grants and contracts have been widely used for many years to transact a broad range of assistance and procurement programs. Cooperative agreements date back to early agricultural research projects and extension activities supported by the federal government in land-grant colleges. In 1978 the U.S. Congress passed PL 95-224 (the "Federal Grant and Cooperative Agreement Act of 1977"), which sets forth criteria for selecting award instruments, defines their uses, and seeks to achieve uniformity in their use.

The Office of Management and Budget (1980) reports that over half of the federal budget is used to fund assistance programs and activities. Assistance takes such forms as direct payments, grants, cooperative agreements, subsidies, loans, loan guarantees, insurance, services, information, and property donations. There were over 1,100 federal assistance programs and activities in 1980.

Grants

Grant agreements are described in PL 95-224 (1978), section 5. They are to be used in a relationship between the federal government and a recipient whenever: "(1) the principal purpose of the relationship is the transfer of money, property, services, or anything of value to the state or local government or other recipient in order to accomplish a public purpose of support or stimulation authorized by federal statute, rather than acquisition, by purchase, lease, or barter, of property or services for the direct benefit or use of the federal government; and (2) no substantial involvement is anticipated between the executive agency, acting for the federal government, and the state or local government or other recipient during performance of the contemplated activity."

Grants are used to support those projects for which the sponsor awards funds or provides assistance with few or no restrictions. Most sponsors have grant manuals or grant conditions that are incorporated into the award agreement by reference. Even though these conditions may be lengthy, they are more flexible and provide the recipient with more discretion than cooperative agreements or contracts. Private foundations and nonprofit agencies usually use grant awards to support their programs.

There are many types of grants, each with its own purpose or method of award:

- *Research project grants* are the most common type; they provide sponsored support for investigation or experimentation in basic research or teaching methods.
- *Training grants* are used to support costs of training students, personnel, or the public in an area of interest to the sponsor.
- *Construction and equipment grants* are to assist the recipient in supporting the building, expansion, and remodeling of facilities, and the purchase and maintenance of equipment.
- *Planning and demonstration grants* are awarded to assist in planning, demonstrating, developing, designing, or accomplishing objectives of interest to both parties.
- *Institutional formula grants* are awarded on the basis of volume, population, enrollment, or some other factor related to the purpose of being supported.
- *Student financial aid grants* provide direct support to students based on financial need.

All awards usually require reports, such as fiscal, technical progress, and final status reports. However, for grants, the technical reports may be summaries and include copies of publication reprints derived from the grant support. More information on reports is provided in Chapter Thirteen.

Cooperative Agreements

Cooperative agreements are described in PL 95-224 (1978), section 6. They are to be used in a relationship between the federal government and a recipient whenever: "(1) the principal purpose of the relationship is the transfer of money, property, services, or anything of value to the state or local government or other recipient to accomplish a public purpose of support or stimulation authorized by federal statute, rather than acquisition, by purchase, lease, or barter, of property or services for the direct benefit or use of the federal government; and (2) substantial involvement is anticipated between the executive agency, acting for the federal government, and the state or local government or other recipient during performance of the contemplated activity."

The distinctive characteristic of cooperative agreements is that "substantial involvement is anticipated" between sponsor and recipient. This involvement may take such forms as directed performance, exchange of employees, frequent reporting, exchange of materials and test results, and specification of performance results. In any case, the sponsor stipulates the required involvement and the recipient agrees to comply. Frequently, both parties have an interest in the work sponsored under a cooperative agreement, and the award serves to segregate responsibilities and efforts. Therefore, the conditions and expected results are specified in more detail in a cooperative agreement than they usually are in a grant.

Several types of cooperative agreements are used to support sponsored projects, and their use is becoming more frequent:

- *Agriculture research agreements* are used to support basic and applied research in agriculture programs of interest to federal and state sponsors.
- *Extension agreements* provide support for public information activities through teaching, demonstrations, and publications of interest to the public and improvements desired by sponsors.
- *Personnel exchanges* are agreements whose terms include support for participants to exchange employees for specified periods of time.
- *Testing agreements* set forth the terms for a recipient to provide testing arrangements in specialized facilities of interest to the sponsor.
- *Consortium agreements* frequently involve many recipients and support programs of mutual interest and benefit. Occasionally, participating recipients may provide the funds necessary to conduct the effort.

Cooperative agreements usually require a more frequent, detailed reporting procedure than do grants, because the mutual interest and greater involvement of the parties entail the sharing of information.

Contracts

Contracts are defined in PL 95-224 (1978), section 4. They are to be used in a relationship between the federal government and a recipient "(1) whenever the principal purpose of the instrument is the acquisition, by purchase, lease, or barter, of property or services for the direct benefit or use of the federal government; or (2) whenever an executive agency determines in a specific instance that the use of a type of procurement contract is appropriate."

Contracts are part of the acquisition process used to procure tangible items and services; they specify the deliverables expected within the performance period. Government contracts include many clauses and regulations based upon statutory requirements or agency regulations. Some regulations such as the Armed Services Procurement Regulations (ASPR) and Federal Procurement Regulations (FPR) may be extremely lengthy and difficult to interpret. Contracts, as procurement instruments, are usually not used to support basic research. There are some notable exceptions to this, however, since the National Institutes of Health, Department of Defense, Department of Energy, and others increased their use of contracts to procure basic research during the 1970s. This trend may be reversed by the enforcement of PL 95-224. In addition, applied research is frequently supported by contract awards when the sponsor desires to restrict the range of effort, performance period, reporting requirements, or other aspects of the project.

The main types of contracts are:

- *Fixed-price contracts* require the contractor to deliver specified items or perform work at a specified time and place for a fixed price agreed upon in advance.
- *Cost reimbursement contracts* provide that the contractor be paid for costs incurred to supply the service or product at agreed-to component rates; a ceiling amount is stated in the contract.
- *Cost-plus-fee contracts* provide the contractor with a cost reimbursement and an additional fee. Usually the fee represents the contractor's profit for completing the contract or serves as an incentive to encourage timely completion or product quality.
- *Fixed-price contracts with price revision(s)* are fixed-price contracts with a provision for negotiating the final price within set limits after the work is completed.

Contracts awarded for sponsored programs require frequent, detailed reporting. In some cases, the sponsor may provide an on-site representative or have its staff frequently visit the performance site to observe progress. Contracts may require lengthy bidding procedures, competitive negotiations, and detailed pricing information prior to the award.

Part of the sponsored efforts on awards may be subcontracted to other organizations by the recipient organization. A subcontract is a legal instrument that has most of the provisions of a contract. In most cases, subcontracts must be approved by the sponsor and the intent to subcontract a portion of the sponsored effort must be included in the proposal and negotiation process. Subcontracts must be signed by both parties and usually include the following provisions: scope of work, period of performance, allowable costs and payments, incorporation of provisions of prime award, and special provisions.

An example of a subcontract showing essential provisions is presented in Exhibit 16, pages 155–156.

Other Awards

Other types of awards, used for various purposes, include fellowships, prizes, gifts, and seed grants. Some do not require applications or have no reporting requirements.

Fellowships are awards sponsored by many sources and are usually to an individual rather than an institution. Fellowships are commonly used to support advanced study and training. The competition is usually based on individual applications, and awards are made on the basis of potential achievement. Fellowships may have a term of several weeks to several years and support only a small fraction or the entire cost involved. Reporting requirements are minimal, but the recipient may have to meet a few requirements in order to continue the award.

Prizes are usually awarded to convey distinction and recognize certain achievements. They are usually unsolicited and have few restrictions. Some may be awarded directly to an individual or deposited into an institution's account in support of its programs.

Gifts and bequests are awards given to a recipient with few or no conditions specified. Gifts may be provided to establish an endowment fund or to provide direct support for existing programs. Frequently, gifts are used to support developing programs for which other funding is not available. The unique flexibility, or lack of restrictions, makes gifts extremely desirable sources of support.

Internal allocation awards, also known as "seed" grants, are important forms of awards for sponsored programs. They are usually awarded based on an application and internal review process. Awards may be made to support entire projects, begin new projects, support a portion of a project, or match other support sources. Most institutions have internal allocation programs; however, few have sufficient support levels. Internal allocation awards restrict the recipient to the purpose proposed and may require a report after the project is completed.

Whatever the type of award, it is important to remember that an award is a legal instrument binding upon the recipient. Care must be exercised to fulfill the requirements honestly and to protect the interests of the sponsor, including those of authorities to whom the sponsor must report. The recipient should be aware of an award's conditions and must meet its requirements.

Exhibit 17, pages 157–158, summarizes the basic differences between the most common award types.

Negotiations

The successful negotiation of external awards requires that the recipient institution designate the office of sponsored projects, or a similar office, as the responsible agent to conduct negotiations with external sponsors and that the institution provide a policy statement to govern negotiations. Without such a policy, it is quite difficult to conduct successful negotiations with a sponsor. A typical policy statement reads as follows (adapted from the University of California at San Diego):

> Representing the principal investigator [project director] and president [institution], the Office of Sponsored Projects will negotiate the proposal budget and award as to the cost, work statement, and terms and conditions of the award. The Office of Sponsored Projects will work in conjunction with the principal investigator during these negotiations. If requested by the funding agency [sponsor], the principal investigator should submit a revised budget and proposal face sheet through the appropriate school dean [official] to the Office of Sponsored Projects for review and transmittal to the agency.

The project director must be fully aware that the sponsored award is made to the institution, not to the individual. As the institution's representative, the office of sponsored projects serves as clearinghouse for all contacts, communications, and negotiations with funding sponsors—both governmental and nonprofit—in proposal negotiations. The office of sponsored projects must not become a bottleneck; rather it must coordinate recipient-sponsor relations, presenting a uniform position and maintaining a record of commitments.

The office of sponsored projects staff should recognize, however, that personal relationships develop between individual project directors and sponsor staff members. Such contacts should be encouraged and maintained. But all parties must remember that informal discussions do not represent either sponsor or recipient commitments. It is also important that the project director understand the benefits of having a sponsored projects staff member negotiate the award. For example, a project director may be so excited about receiving an award that he or she merely accepts the budget revisions of the sponsor's program officer or grants manager. In doing so, the project director may accept a budget that is far too low to cover the work outlined in the proposal. In contrast, a sponsored projects administrator can be more objective and can negotiate with the sponsor, noting that the budget in the proposal was carefully calculated and should not be reduced. Budget negotiations usually require verification of salaries, fringe benefits, indirect costs, and other line items. This can be handled quickly and professionally by the sponsored projects administrator.

Although sponsor officials might prefer to negotiate the budget with the project director, the project director should refer any questions about the budget to the sponsored projects office. The project director should also inform the office about any discussions with the sponsor concerning nonbudgetary matters. All official negotiations, budget revisions, and the like should be made by the office of sponsored projects in consultation with the project director.

Many times a proposal is considered eligible for an award, but the funds requested exceed what the sponsor's reviewers feel is necessary or what the sponsor has available to support the proposed work; a reduction in the budget is then necessary. The office of sponsored projects should contact the project director to discuss possible reductions in line items and corresponding reductions in the scope of the work. Indeed, to maintain the institution's credibility with the sponsor, substantial budget reductions require corresponding reductions in the scope of work, revisions which must be made by the project director. Most negotiations go very smoothly and there are no problems if handled according to the procedures outlined.

All budget revisions must be approved by the office of sponsored projects before they are submitted in writing to sponsors. If the programmatic or budget revisions are extensive, they may need to be reviewed by the department head, director, dean, or other appropriate administrative officials. If budget reductions, changes, or revisions are minor, the institution's policy may be to allow submission directly to the sponsor by the office of sponsored projects.

Strategy

Most routine negotiations are handled quickly and require little strategy or planning. A sponsor's contract or program officer may request confirmation of fringe benefits, indirect-cost rates, current salaries, effective dates, terms and conditions, and reporting requirements, or may suggest minor budget revisions. The office of sponsored projects routinely checks for hold-harmless clauses, third-party insurance, equipment title, proprietary rights, and other special considerations during these negotiations.

However, negotiations for large contracts, center grants, and the like may require the sponsored projects administrator and the project director to visit the sponsor, or the sponsor's representative to visit them. These negotiations require careful planning; meetings between the project director, dean or director, and the office of sponsored projects are necessary to discuss the negotiating strategy. (See Chapter Seventeen for a discussion of on-site visits.) At these meetings the participants establish the parameters for the negotiations: the minimum budget acceptable and a corresponding work statement. They also decide who is to be responsible for the various aspects of the negotiations.

Normally, the strategy is to defend the work statement and costs submitted in the original proposal. The proposed budget should not be increased unless there are unusual circumstances—for example, increases in fringe benefits or the indirect-cost rate, new salary figures, or additional work requested by the sponsor. The negotiating team, which usually consists of the project director, dean or director, and the office of sponsored projects, should also decide on an appropriate budget range. Any informal information that has been picked up by the team members should be discussed in these planning sessions—for example, names of other bidders, average price of similar awards, and the like.

Finally, all members of the negotiating team must realize that the office of sponsored projects representative is the chief spokesperson for the team.

Techniques and Principles

All members of the negotiating team should understand the following basic techniques and principles of negotiating:

- Control the environment, especially if the sponsor is making a site visit to the institution.
- Control the number of participants—try to have at least as many people at the negotiation meeting as the sponsor has, if not more.
- Watch body language; facial expressions, movements, and the like can convey very important information.
- Control the group by use of questions; do not counterpunch the entire time.
- Use breaks (lunch, coffee) when the discussion is not going smoothly or when team members disagree; breaks are useful in settling differences.
- Take the responsibility for summarizing the understanding to date; summaries both clarify the present status of the discussion and strengthen the offensive position of the summarizer.
- Remember that a compromise is not a loss; negotiation is by definition a give-and-take situation.
- The objective is "win the war, not the battle"; concentrate on the overall objectives.

Above all, careful preparation is essential. Surprise, indecision, and lack of information reduce confidence and hamper successful negotiation. Also, remember, in the successful negotiation of an award, both sides are winners.

Acceptance of Awards

After a successful negotiation, an award is made to the recipient. Whether it is a grant, cooperative agreement, or contract, the project director, the sponsored projects office, and the institution all have certain responsibilities, as outlined in this section.

Provisional Account. The institution should adopt a policy to address delays in the receipt of executed awards. If sponsor verification of intent to fund is sufficient, the project director should be able to request the office of sponsored projects to approve the establishment of a provisional account against which to charge expenses. An example of an advanced approval form is shown in Exhibit 18, page 159.

Award Examination. When an award is received, the office of sponsored projects should examine the document for possible administrative errors and omissions. All documents are reviewed for conformance to the initial proposal, agency negotiations, revised budget, award terms and conditions, and recipient policies. Grants usually do not require a recipient signature for execution and establishment of an account. However, for contracts, cooperative agreements, and some grants, a copy of the award should be sent to the project director for technical review and approval before the document is sent to an authorized official for signature. Exhibit 19, page 160, shows a sample form for the notice of award and approval.

In some instances the project director or office of sponsored projects may find that the award contains objectionable terms and conditions. It is then the responsibility of the office of sponsored projects to seek comments or changes through the institution's administration and to resolve the questionable conditions with the sponsor before acceptance.

Acceptance and Account Assignment. After the project director approves the award document, it is signed by the appropriate institutional official and returned to the sponsor for the signature that fully executes the award. Only then does one have an official executed copy of the award. Prompt project director attention is therefore required in approving the document so that an account can be established and work can commence on the sponsored project. A notice of award allocation may be used (see Exhibit 20, page 161).

After an award is received by a recipient, a specific account number must be assigned for expenditures and accountability. The account number may be assigned by the office of sponsored projects or the accounting office, but it is recommended that the former have this responsibility. The sequencing of characters in the account number or other identifiers can indicate the type of award (grant, cooperative agreement, contract), year, department, center or school, independent identifiers, and continuation years. For example, G=grant, 78=year, 01=business school, A=accounting department, 001=independent identifiers, -01=first year (G7801A001-01). The account number should be sent to the project director, unit officer, and accounting office. Also, pertinent information should be added to an active projects file for all other administrative units, including purchasing, dean's office, personnel, and service units.

Orientation. If this award is the first for a project director, an orientation session should be scheduled, ideally while the award is being processed by the office of sponsored projects. For this session the project director meets with the postaward specialist to review the institution's and sponsor's requirements. The project director bears the primary responsibility for successful completion of the project and must administer the funds in accordance with both the terms of the award agreement and the institution's policies and regulations. The project director should also be provided with the necessary information on affirmative action policy and personnel, purchasing, and accounting procedures. This orientation session thus is a critical introduction to fiscal and administrative duties; a good orientation can save the office of sponsored projects from having to spend time in correcting project directors' mistakes.

Award Notification Brief. After the office of sponsored projects has an executed agreement, a brief of the award is then prepared (see Figure 22). The brief and a copy of the award are then forwarded to the project director and appropriate institutional personnel. The sending of briefs serves to systematically notify the appropriate individuals regarding all new sponsored projects. In addition to the business office, the department chairperson, director, dean, and vice-president should routinely be made aware of all new and continuing awards. The news and information service of the recipient institution should receive a copy of the notice and a layman's abstract of the work; that office should be encouraged to call the project director for additional details. Recognition of the award by the recipient institution is an important source of gratification for the project director. If the office of sponsored projects has a close relationship with the news and information service, much goodwill and publicity can be generated with little effort.

Budget. The budget received from the sponsor usually contains categories and codes that differ from those of the institution's system. Therefore, the office of sponsored projects prepares a project budget authorization form that translates the agency budget into the correct recipient accounting codes (see Figure 23). This form could be completed at the new project director's orientation session. Once approved, the form and a copy of the award budget are forwarded to accounting to be input into the computerized accounting system.

Checklist. Exhibit 21, page 162, presents a checklist of the main considerations for the office of sponsored projects in negotiating and accepting an award.

Figure 22. Information Provided in Award Notification Brief.

Account No.:
Proposal No.:
Cost Sharing Account No. (if appropriate):
Contract or Grant Award No., Modification or Amendment Nos.:
Date Issued:
Title:
Program or School or Center:
Project Director:
Sponsor:
Effective Date and Duration:
Amount:
Cost Sharing (Amount):
Funding and Expiration Date:
Reporting Requirements (if required):
Equipment (if required):
Other Pertinent Information:

Figure 23. Budget Project Authorization Form.

Agency: _____ Project A/C No. _____

Agency No.: _____ Budget No. _____

○ Contract ○ Grant

Awarding Agency Approval
Required? _____ Yes _____ No

○ New Budget ○ Revision

	Exp. Code	NEW/ PRESENT BUDGET	INCREASE (DECREASE)	REVISED BUDGET	PERIOD OF PERFORMANCE: From: Thru:
Labor (Salaries/Wages):					
					REMARKS:
SUBTOTAL S&W					
Fringe Ben.: . % S&W	220				
Unused SLv/V: . % S&W	210				
Supplies	310				
Subcontracts	320				
Purchased Services	330				
Equipment	340				
Consultants: Fee	351				
Travel	352				
Postage/Frt/Customs	360				
Communications	370				
Reproduction Services	380				
Bks/Periodcls/Reprints	391				APPROVED:
Travel: Domestic	411				
Foreign	412				
Computer: Internal	430				
External	960				
Sup. Serv.	961				Principal Inv. Date
Publications: Costs	511				
Page Costs	512				
Equipment/Repair/Maint.	903				
Equip. Rent/Demurrage	912				Dean/Master/ Date Director/Head
Vehicle M & O	915				

Figure 23 (continued)

					Adm. Serv. Ofcr.	Date
TOTAL DIRECT COST					Ofc. Sponsored Proj.	Date
INDIRECT COST						
% S&W						
% S&W						
% S&W						
% S&W						
TOTAL						

Source: University of Texas at Dallas, Office of Sponsored Projects.

Exhibit 16. Sample Subcontract Form.

This subcontract is between _____ ,
hereafter called the *recipient,* and _____ , hereafter
called the *sponsor.*

Witnesseth that for the consideration stated herein the parties mutually agree
to the following:

1. *Scope of Work.* The recipient shall furnish the necessary personnel and
   facilities to perform the following tasks: _____
   _____
   _____
   _____

2. *Period of Performance.* The period of this subcontract is from
   _____ to _____ . The performance may be ex-
   tended by mutual written agreement between parties.

3. *Allowable Costs and Payments.* The recipient may incur costs up to
   $ _____ and be reimbursed by the sponsor with _____
   payment frequency. The parties agree to the subcontract budget, specifying major object categories as follows:

Salaries and Wages	$ _____
Equipment	_____
Supplies	_____
Travel	_____
Other Direct Costs	_____
Indirect Costs	_____
Total Budget:	$ _____

Exhibit 16 (continued)

4. *Incorporating the Provisions of the Prime Award.* The subcontracted effect being performed under this agreement is part of the award received from the prime sponsor _____ , number _____ . Consequently, the terms and conditions specified by the prime sponsor award _____ becomes a part of this agreement by reference.

5. *Special Provisions.* The following special provisions are a part of this subcontract effort:

    _____
    _____
    _____
    _____

6. *Principal Parties and Subcontract Approvals.* The following principal parties are:

Sponsor	Project Director	Authorized Representative
Name	_____	_____
Address	_____	_____
	_____	_____
Phone	_____	_____
Recipient:	Project Director	Authorized Representative
Name	_____	_____
Address	_____	_____
	_____	_____
Phone	_____	_____

Subcontract Approval:

_____   _____
                  Sponsor Signature   Date

_____   _____
                  Recipient Signature   Date

Exhibit 17. Basic Types of Awards.

	Grant	Cooperative Agreement	Contract
Basic Purpose	Provide assistance with few restrictions	Provide assistance with substantial involvement between parties	Procure tangible goods and services
Solicitation Method	Application kit or guidelines	Request for proposal	Request for bid or quote
Award Instrument	Short, may refer to general conditions	Describes involvement, party relationships	Long, detailed specs, clauses, regulations, and expected results
Award Acceptance	Usually not required	Usually required	Requires signature of authorized official
Involvement by Sponsor	Generally none	Substantial involvement	May be extensive
Rebudgeting	Flexible	Usually allowed	Occasionally allowed within restrictions

Exhibit 17 (continued)

Equipment Title	Grantee	Varies based upon agreement	Contractor
Performance Period	Flexible	May be specified with flexible dates	Specified in contract
Patent Rights	Generally liberal	May be involved	Provision in contract
Publications	Unrestricted	May ask to be informed	Maybe prior review and approval
Technical Reports	Annual summary reports	More frequent (quarterly) reports	Detailed reports, maybe monthly

Exhibit 18. Advance Approval Form.

○ CONTRACT ○ GRANT Date _____
  ○ Fixed Price ○ New
  ○ Cost Reimbursement ○ Renewal Contract or Grant No. ____
  ○ Other ____ ○ Continuation Previous Acct. No. ____

Principal Investigator ____ Department ____
School or College ____
Sponsoring Agency ____
Program Title ____
Expiration Date of Current Project (if applicable) ____
Anticipated Award ____ ____ Total Amount ____
  Start Date Expiration Date
Amount Herein Requested ____ For Period ____ ____
  From To

DESCRIPTION OF REQUEST

(Use additional page if necessary)

APPROVALS: (Must be signed by all appropriate personnel.)

Initiated By Date Principal Investigator Date

Department Chair Date Dean/Provost/Director Date

OCGA USE ONLY: ○ Disapproval Recommended
  ○ Amount Recommended ____ For Period ____ ____
  From To

Approved By ____
  Manager, OCGA Date

CHANCELLOR'S USE ONLY: ○ Disapproved
  ○ Approved Amount ____
  Date

ACCOUNTING USE ONLY:
Account and Fund No. ____ Assigned By ____ ____
  Date

Source: University of California at San Diego, 1977, p. AE 3.

Exhibit 19. Notice of Award and Approval.

Proposal No. UTD _____

_____
Date

To:

From: Office of Sponsored Projects, Mail Stop FO-3.2, Extension 2211

Subject: Agency and Award No. _____

Amount _____ Period _____

AWARD CONDITIONS AND OBLIGATIONS FOR WHICH THE PRINCIPAL IN-
VESTIGATOR IS RESPONSIBLE:

Title to property vests in the: Sponsoring Agency _____ ; University _____ .

Patent Obligations: A possibly patentable idea which is developed during the term of this
award must be disclosed promptly to the Office of Sponsored Projects for determination
of patent potentiality and/or disclosure to the sponsoring agency.

Other Special Conditions/Obligations (including reporting requirements):

APPROVAL: Please indicate your approval or disapproval of the award by initialing Item 1
or 2 below, provide any desired comments under Item 3, and *promptly return this form with a
copy of the attached award to the Office of Sponsored Projects so that final acceptance of the award can
be expedited.* A copy of this form is enclosed for retention by the principal investigator.
Upon final acceptance, copies of the award will be transmitted to the principal investigator
and pertinent administrative office.

1. The award meets with my approval _____
Signature

2. I disapprove the award _____
Signature

3. Comments:

Source: University of Texas at Dallas, 1979, p. 52.

Exhibit 20. Notice of an Award Allocation.

TO: File No.:
•   Date:
•

        Re: _____
The university has received an award which names you as principal investigator.

        No.:   Amount: $
Effective Dates: Execution Date:
Account Name:
Purpose:
Amendment or Modification No. _____ , which brings the total funding of
this contract or grant to: $
Prior Fund No.:
Budget Adjustment Journal No.:
DHHS Transaction No.:
Report of expenditures required?   If "Yes," due date:
The effective date for incurring expenditures or commitments is the date of execution of the award or
the beginning date specified, whichever is later. The award has been allocated to the following sub-
accounts; these allocations will appear on the monthly appropriation ledger:
    Cost Sharing Requirements: Amount _____ (_____ %) Dept. No. _____

Sub-Account Name	Special Provisions	Account Number	Amount (Credit)
Academic Salaries	(_____)	6– – –0	$
General Assistance	(_____)	6– " – " –2	
Supplies and Expense	(_____)	6– " – " –3	
Equipment and Facilities	(_____)		
	(_____)	6– " – " –4	
Travel (Domestic $ _____)			
(Foreign $ _____)		6– " – " –5	
Employee Benefits		6– " – " –6	
Other Expense		6– " – " –7	
•		6– –	
•		6– –	
•		6– –	
•		6– –	
Overhead (_____ %) Ref. No. _____		6– –	
Overhead (_____ %) Ref. No. _____		6– –	
From: (Debit)			_____
From: (Debit)		Total	$ _____

As principal investigator you hold the prime responsibility for adherence to the terms of the contract/
grant (including expiration date) and for ensuring that expenditures made are acceptable under the
terms of the contract/grant.
Cost Sharing Forms Attached _____
                             By _____

Source: University of California at San Diego, 1977, p. AE 2.

Exhibit 21. Checklist for Negotiations and Awards.

Negotiation

_____ Institution policy
_____ Office of sponsored projects' responsibility to negotiate award
_____ Award made to institution, not project director
_____ Negotiating team
        Negotiating techniques
            _____ Control environment
            _____ Control number of participants
            _____ Watch body language
            _____ Control group by use of questions
            _____ Use breaks to own benefit
            _____ Take responsibility to summarize the understanding to date
            _____ Remember, compromise is not a loss
            _____ Overall objective is "win the war, not the battle"

Acceptance of Award

_____ Policy for provisional account
        Award review and approval
            _____ Office of sponsored projects' responsibility
            _____ Project director's responsibility
_____ Notice of award
_____ Orientation meeting with project director
_____ Establish account
_____ Highlight the award
_____ Establish budget

⊡⊡ 11 ⊡⊡

Financial Management
of Projects

⊡⊡⊟⊡⊟⊡⊟⊟⊟⊟⊟⊟⊟⊟⊟⊟⊟⊟⊟⊟⊟⊡⊡

Financial management is important
to the sponsor, the recipient organization and the project director. These
parties share the responsibility for managing funds within guidelines
and accomplishing the purpose for which the funds were awarded. The
relationship between sponsor, organization, and project director should
be one of cooperation and trust in maintaining accountability and utilizing limited resources effectively; however, the relationship can also have
areas of disagreement. Figure 24 illustrates the dynamics of cooperation
and disagreement. The outer ring depicts the desirable phases of cooperation: the sponsor awards a project to a recipient organization, the
recipient institution helps the project director manage the funds, and
the project director reports progress to the sponsor. But legitimate dis-
agreements can enter the relationship, as illustrated by the inner
triangle. The sponsor may impose many regulations and audit results;
the institution may overreact to such regulations and audits and restrict
its financial management process more than necessary; and the project
director, who is primarily interested in project performance, may un-
willingly become entangled in an endless web of regulations and red
tape. The key to improving the process lies in shrinking the inner
triangle.

Figure 24. Project Management.

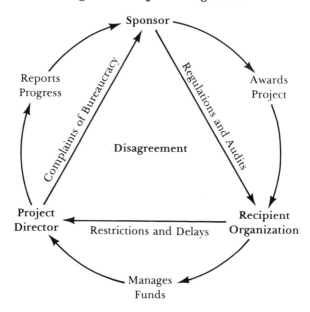

Many sponsors, recipient organizations, and project directors are successfully working together to improve mutual trust and understanding of each other's position. Everyone in sponsored projects administration has an obligation to join in this effort and help improve the process by example.

Allowability of Costs

The allowability of costs to a sponsored project is set forth in the award document as part of the terms and conditions. Each award identifies specific regulations, manuals, and guidelines that are applicable. The number and type of restrictions usually depend on the type of award, as discussed in Chapter Ten; grants are the least restrictive, and contracts the most. The degree of restrictiveness is usually proportional to the sponsor's involvement in the project.

Some basic considerations of cost allowabilities are set forth by the federal Office of Management and Budget (1979). Costs must be reasonable, must be allowable to the sponsored project, must be consistently treated in like circumstances, and must conform to any award limitations. Let us define each of these criteria in turn.

A *reasonable* cost is one that a prudent person would incur for goods or services at the time the cost decision is made. The goods or service must be necessary to carry out the performance of the sponsored project, and the cost must conform to appropriate laws and regulations. Prudence in such matters must reflect responsibility to the organization, the sponsor and the public. Reasonable costs must also be consistent with established recipient policies and practices.

An *allowable* cost is one assigned to a project based on the benefit to be received by the project. An allowable cost may be directed to a single project receiving sole benefit or several projects receiving mutual benefit, or it may be allocated through the indirect-cost assessment for common costs not readily identified with a particular project or group of projects.

Consistent treatment of costs within a budgetary unit involves the consistent identification of what is being benefited by the costs and the use of a consistent rate or price. Thus a cost for a sponsored project must be treated the same as a cost benefiting other organizational activities under like circumstances.

Special award limitations may occasionally govern some costs because statutory requirements set forth limits in the program legislation. These limitations must be observed and take precedence over any general principles.

OMB Regulations

The OMB issues regulations, guidelines, and principles determining the costs applicable to federally sponsored projects. In addition, management requirements, indirect-cost rate determinations, audit guidelines, and the like are set forth in OMB circulars. These regulations are based upon legislative actions, legal interpretations, sponsor and recipient suggestions, and management principles. They provide a generally accepted and consistent basis for determining appropriate costs. If there is a discrepancy between the OMB circulars and the sponsored agreement, the sponsored agreement would govern; however, this seldom happens. Thus the OMB guidelines are a good source of information on allowable costs for all projects. Every sponsored projects administrator should be aware of these regulations and keep them handy for reference purposes (an annotated listing of current circulars is included in Resource G, "Federal Regulations Pertaining to Sponsored Projects"). When the OMB intends to revise its policies, it requests all interested parties to suggest changes and clarifications. The sponsored projects administrator should take this opportunity, and perhaps obligation, to make any concerns and suggestions known.

An example of an OMB circular is A-21, *Cost Principles for Educational Institutions,* effective October 1, 1979. This circular provides principles for determining the costs applicable to research and development, training, and other sponsored work performed by colleges and universities under grants, contracts, and other agreements with the federal government. It defines the major institutional functions (that is, activities) that are used for allocating costs, and the distribution between direct- and indirect-cost groups. Procedures for identifying and determining indirect costs are presented as are principles applying to the allowability of cost items. The circular also discusses activity reporting and documentation for employees charged as direct or indirect costs, and the allowability of direct and indirect costs. Exhibit 22, pages 177–180, summarizes the costs presented in OMB circular A-21. Other circulars cover such topics as management principles in similar detail.

Sponsor Regulations

Each sponsor has regulations, guidelines, and manuals that must be used in project management. These may be included in the award agreement or made a part of the agreement by reference. Individual sponsor differences, many of which may be the result of enabling legislation or past practices, must be understood. For example, Department of Defense agency agreements may refer to Defense Acquisition Regulations, Armed Services Procurement Regulations, Cost Accounting Standards Board Regulations, and many others. In addition, reference may be made to other government departmental regulations or executive orders.

The National Institutes of Health (NIH) and National Science Foundation (NSF) have published their own *Grants Administration Man-*

ual and *Grants Policy Manual,* respectively. These manuals set forth the normal requirements relating to their programs and are generally easy to follow and use for reference. The manuals are available at a slight cost either through the sponsor or from the Superintendent of Documents, Government Printing Office, Washington, D.C. 20402. These sponsors usually inform all persons on their mailing lists about updates to the reference manuals. Also, brochures summarizing the information and how to apply for sponsored projects are available, usually at no charge, from the agencies.

Audits

Various types of audits are conducted on recipient institutions by different auditing groups. In addition to the usual financial audit, increased emphasis is now being placed on operational and systems audits to measure and evaluate the effectiveness of activities and jobs. These audits include both analysis and examination of the recipient's entire activities and the relationships between activities, including sponsored projects.

In most cases, audits are conducted by more than one group and can include internal or external auditors. A sponsor's auditors may visit the institution at intervals during the year or, if the volume of support is substantial, they may audit continuously throughout the year. Federally sponsored projects are usually handled by one cognizant federal audit agency to avoid duplication and wasted effort.

Audits should be viewed as a constructive activity from which both sponsor and recipient can benefit. Most auditors have a wealth of experience with many divergent organizations and may have beneficial suggestions to improve institutional procedures. The institution should have a policy and procedures that describe and govern its members' relationships with sponsored projects auditors; essential are elements such as:

- A stated policy to cooperate fully with sponsored projects auditors
- The designation of a liaison officer to be notified prior to audit
- A request for prior notice and scope of audit so appropriate information may be prepared
- A procedure to maintain contact with auditors through a liaison officer and to provide them with appropriate work space

- A procedure for the provision of records requested by the auditors and prompt scheduling of interviews requested
- An arrangement for a conference on the auditors' preliminary findings and an exit interview to answer any final questions or to correct erroneous perceptions
- A procedure to review the audit report once received and to prepare an appropriate response

This audit policy should be widely distributed throughout the institution. All members of the organization should be courteous and responsive to the auditor's requests, and the designated audit liaison officer should strive to make the audit a constructive and pleasant experience.

The vast number of regulations and restrictions make it unlikely that an institution will avoid audit disallowances. All disallowances should be investigated, and the appropriate actions should be taken to correct any unallowed practice. If an institution feels the disallowance is inappropriate or unfair, it should initiate an appeal as prescribed in the sponsor's regulations or audit agency's guidelines. Institution officials should not hesitate to correct immediately any misunderstandings or misinterpretations.

A list of practices that may lead to audit disallowances is presented in Exhibit 23, page 181. General guidelines for allowable costs are presented in Exhibit 24, page 182.

Prior Approval System

Sponsors of grants usually prefer a prior approval system, operated by an officer of the recipient organization, to approve certain costs before they are incurred. The award constitutes prior approval for the expenditure of funds as approved in the award budget. In addition, the organization may be permitted to reallocate funds among budget categories when a project has unanticipated requirements not provided for in the original award budget. Other rebudgeting must be requested from the sponsor's program or grants officer *prior* to incurring the costs. Typical examples of costs not in the award budget that need prior approval include: (1) Special-purpose equipment that costs $1,000 or more; (2) general-purpose equipment; (3) equipment costs that exceed the budget by 25 percent; (4) domestic travel that exceeds $500 or 125 percent of the budget; and (5) foreign travel. In addition, prior approval is required from sponsors to change the scope of the project or the project director.

Responsibility for some of these prior approvals may be delegated by the sponsor to the institution upon agreement by both parties. The institution must designate an appropriate official who does not have direct responsibility for the conduct of the project activity. For NSF projects this official may review and approve certain rebudgeting requests as designated under the Organizational Prior Approval System (OPAS); a similar approval method for NIH projects is called the Institutional Prior Approval System (IPAS). In order to execute a prior approval system, the institution must notify the sponsor of the institutional official responsible for the system. Exhibit 25, page 183, illustrates the OPAS devised by the NSF.

Budget and Expenditure Control

The need for timely, responsive financial information for project management has become increasingly important during the last decade. Sponsors have placed greater emphasis on accountability and reporting. The sponsors' more stringent regulations necessitate that institutions improve their financial management systems. Many organizations now use computerized programs for basic financial systems and management information systems for centralized administration.

Some centralized automated financial systems are developed only to report expenditure information to the sponsor, and do not meet the needs of the project director. These central financial systems handle the annual reporting functions of the entire organization, allowing the historical reporting of receipts and expenditures by major fund groups. But the project director needs information on the project's budget, obligations, and expenditures. One way to meet these needs is to have a separate accounting that project directors can maintain and understand. However, this is quite time consuming and does not allow for quick access to timely information needed in the administration of sponsored awards.

Another way to meet the project director's needs is for the institution to implement a user-oriented on-line accounting system. There are three general types of systems. The first is to have a centralized accounting system that is an on-line, interactive system. This system would meet the needs of project directors, the office of sponsored projects, and the sponsors; as the institution's central accounting system, it would handle all the institution's needs, including state funds, gifts, auxiliary enterprises, and tuition.

A second option is for the recipient to purchase or develop a user-oriented system that would interface with and be a subsystem of the centralized accounting system. This subsystem would be used strictly for sponsored funds administration and would be controlled by the office of sponsored projects. The subsystem would use data from the centralized accounting system's data base (for example, payroll, purchase orders, expenditures, and fringe benefits), and it would be reconciled monthly with the major system. This plan provides the project director with a tailored system that is easy to use and provides timely information for sponsored projects administrators.

A third option, usually for larger organizations, is to develop a unit financial management system that serves both project directors and unit managers. Such a project accounting system would interface with the organization's central financial system to avoid duplication of data entry and to ease reconciliations.

The system described in detail in this chapter is a user-oriented financial management system that meets the needs of project directors. Depending on the volume of an organization's sponsored programs and its present financial system, our model could be implemented within the organization's central accounting system, as a subsystem at the office of sponsored projects, or as a subsystem at a unit level. Our model places special emphasis on the user's needs and understanding of financial requirements. For example, the project director needs detailed budget, obligation, and expenditure data to plan and monitor daily project operations. Unit managers need summary and special information statements to coordinate and manage their responsibilities. This project accounting system should interface with the institution's central financial system to avoid duplication of data entry and to ease reconciliations.

General Description. This project accounting system was designed for use by project directors—specifically, it is easy to use, flexible, and readily understandable for users with little financial experience (Hess and Waters, 1979). While a CRT terminal is the main method of data input, information may also be submitted into the system on punched cards, magnetic tape, or magnetic disc (see Figure 25). The system's input flexibility, illustrated in the figure, allows one to input the automated billing system (see Chapter Twelve) and other computerized systems directly into the project accounting system's data files. Changes to the data base, such as the addition or deletion of accounts, are made by simple routines on a CRT terminal and can be done by anyone who can use a typewriter. The operator simply keys in the appropriate routine and the computer prompts the operator for more information by placing questions on the CRT screen.

The system allows users to define their own expenditure object codes and to break down accounts by subproject codes that can be totaled in an easy-to-read master account summary. A section of each statement is provided for free-form notes, which can be used to remind the project manager of proposal deadlines, special restrictions on project expenditures, companion projects, and the like. The statement format is as uncluttered by special symbols as possible; it presents data in an orderly, progressive format. Thus project directors and sponsored projects administrators can quickly determine the project's financial condition.

Statement of Account. The main financial document produced by the system is a *detailed statement of account* (Figures 26–28). The statement is divided into five sections: account description, notes, budget summary, obligations, and expenditures.

The *description* section contains information to identify the project and usually remains unchanged throughout the life of the project. This section includes the account number, title, project director, unit, total budget award, and current fiscal period.

The *notes* section has nine lines available of up to sixty characters each. The descriptive information to be placed in the notes section is entirely the user's decision. Figure 26 shows the composition of the total budget, indirect-cost rate, cost-sharing effort, any additional project years recommended, and deadlines for renewal or continuation proposals.

The *budget summary* section presents a picture of the financial condition of the project. Sixteen object classifications are available for major budget breakdowns; Figure 26 uses nine categories for federally sponsored projects. Object class 010 is used for salaries and wages, object class 100 for fringe benefits, and object class 950 for indirect costs. The remaining object codes, 200–900, in increments of 50, may be defined by

Figure 25. Project Accounting System Flow Diagram.

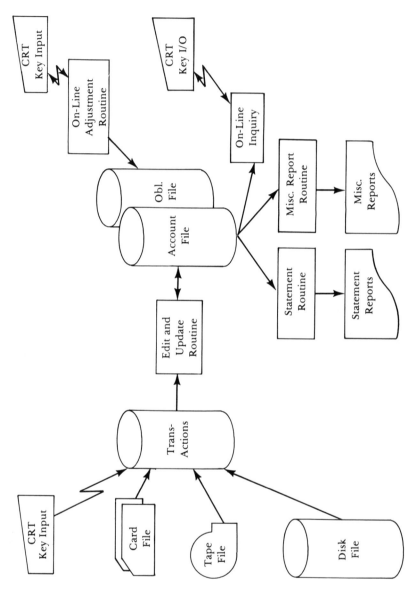

Figure 26. Detailed Statement of Account—Description and Notes.

```
110033455              STATEMENT OF ACCOUNT AS OF 12-31-81          PAGE   1    169

DIRECTOR        P/I NAME                    ACCT NUMBER    11 00 33 455
DIVISION        ORGANIC                     TOTAL BUDGET      $107,846
TITLE           NEW PHS GM 123              INDIRECT COST  68.00% SAL--, BALANCE REST
FISCAL PERIOD   04-01-81 TO 03-31-82        FRINGE BENEFIT WK: 0.40 HI: 3.30 RT:12.00

*****************          NOTES              *******************
BUDGET = $99,277 AWARDED AND $8,569 CARRYOVER
COST SHARING = 10%, ADDNL YEARS RECMD = 2
CONTINUATION PROPOSAL DUE 02-01-82
RENEWAL PROPOSAL DUE 06-01-82
PROGRAM OFFICER IS JOHN DOE AT 301-496-7181
PRIOR YEARS IC $3,296 RESTRICTED

*****************       SUMMARY STATEMENT      *******************

OBJ   DESCRIPTION   BUDGETED   EXP-MONTH   EXP-TO-DATE   OBLIGATED   BALANCE

010   PERSONNEL      46,246      4,553       32,622       11,342      6,282
100   FRINGE BENEFITS 1,480        124          969          354        157
300   EQUIPMENT       1,500          0            0          331      1,169
400   SUPPLIES       21,313      1,230       15,758           79      5,484
500   TRAVEL          1,000          0          833          328        161-
600   PUBLICATIONS        0         29          369           74        443-
700   COMP,COMM,OTHER 1,500          0           21            0      1,479
950   INDIRECT COSTS 32,307      3,096       20,960       11,347          0
***   GRAND TOTAL   107,846 *   9,031 *      69,724 *     24,355     13,767 *

*****************        OBLIGATIONS        *******************

OBJ    NAME         APPT PERIOD   LAST PAY PE   RATE TYP %   AMOUNT   TOTAL

010 PERSONNEL
011 ASSOC-1         09-16-81 03-31-82 12-20-81 C 1,083.330 M 100    3,574
011 ASSOC-1         04-01-82 09-15-82 03-31-82 C 1,083.330 M 100
011 ASSOC-2         08-21-81 02-22-82 12-22-81 C   917.000 M 100    1,834
012 NON-ACC-1       08-31-81 03-31-82 12-11-81 1   105.140 H  25      826
012 NON-ACC-1       04-01-82 06-29-82 03-31-82 1   105.140 H  25
013 ASST-1          03-21-81 03-31-82 12-20-81 3   595.000 M  50    1,963
013 ASST-1          04-01-82 05-20-82 03-31-82 3   595.000 M  50
013 ASST-2          08-21-81 03-31-82 12-20-81 3   476.000 M  50    1,572
013 ASST-2          04-01-82 07-20-82 03-31-82 3   476.000 M  50
013 ASST-3          08-21-81 03-31-82 12-22-82 3   297.500 M  25      930
013 ASST-3          04-01-82 05-20-82 03-31-82 3   297.500 H  25
013 ASST-4          09-21-81 01-20-82 12-20-81 3   595.000 M  50      595
**   TOTAL OBLIGATIONS FOR OBJ 010                                 11 342 *
FB CODES  1=RETIRE,HLTH INS,WK COMP   3=WK COMP   A,B,C=HLTH INS
```

the user, with up to fifty separate subobject classes within each major class. The following totals are kept for each major object class: project budget, expended-this-month, expended-to-date, current obligations, and free budget balance. Each of these totals is automatically updated when transactions are posted against the project. The budget summary statement is the most widely used section of the statement. Many project directors look at this section first; if it appears to be in order, they need not spend additional time reading the entire statement.

The *obligations* section uses the same object classes as the preceding section. Personnel is the first class, and each employee on the project

Figure 27. Detailed Statement of Account — Budget Summary and Obligations.

```
110033455              STATEMENT CF ACCOUNT #S CF 12-31-81      PAGE   2   170

OBJ       DESCRIPTION     NAME          RECUISITION  DATE  STATUS  AMOUNT      TOTAL

100 FRINGE EENEFITS
    RETIREMENT                                                      104
    HEALTH INSURANCE                                                205
    WORKMANS COMP                                                    45
**      TOTAL OBLIGATIONS FOR OBJ 100                                          354 *


300 EQUIPMENT
30E NEW BRUNS SCI    ASST-4       114045      10 06 81   0       331
**      TOTAL OBLIGATION FOR OBJ 300                                           331 *

400 SUPPLIES
404 WILMAD GLASS     ASST-1       527-0829    09 29 81   0         8
412 ALDRICH          ASSOC-1      636-1005    12 14 81   0        18
412 SIGMA            ASST-1       790-1016    10 15 81   0        14
412 FISHER SCI       ASST-4       914-2612    09 29 81   0        25
420 ANALABS          ASST-4       SCS223645   10 17 81   0        14
**      TOTAL OBLIGATION FOR OBJ 400                                            79 *

500 TRAVEL
503 LAS VEGAS        F/I NAME     TF2980      09 03 81   0       328
**      TOTAL OBLIGATION FOR OBJ 500                                           328 *

600 PUBLICATIONS
606 UNIV MICROFILM   ASST-4       113945      12 01 81   0        15
606 AM CHEM SOC      P/I NAME     133-0545    08 28 81   0        59
**      TOTAL OBLIGATION FOR OBJ 600                                            74 *

950 INDIRECT COST
**      TOTAL OBLIGATION FOR OBJ 950                                        11,847 *

*** TOTAL OBLIGATION FOR FISCAL PERIOD                                      24,355 **
```

is identified by name, period of appointment remaining, monthly rate, and dollars obligated. If an employee's commitment goes beyond the budget period of the project, a separate entry shows the dates and rate, but does not obligate any amount against the current project period. As payments are made to individuals, the entries are automatically updated. The obligations section also shows fringe benefits (see Figure 27). For each fringe benefit—retirement, health insurance, and workmen's compensation—the rate and dollars obligated are automatically calculated and entered. Then the obligations are listed for each major object class with the following information: object class, description or vendor, requisition or reference number, date of the obligation, individual incurring the obligation, and the amount of the obligation. The system handles all forms of obligations, and each obligation is appropriately reduced when payments are made.

Finally, the appropriate indirect-cost funds are obligated in one of two ways. In Figure 27, the indirect-cost budget funds are not restricted in the project, so only the actual committed portion is listed. If the indirect costs budgeted were restricted, a second entry would show the

Figure 28. Detailed Statement of Account—Expenditures.

```
110233455            STATEMENT OF ACCOUNT AS OF 12-31-81      PAGE   3    171

*******************         EXPENDITURES            *******************

OBJ      NAME/DESCRIPTION       FB   %TIME    STAT  DATE     AMOUNT        TOTAL

010 PERSONNEL       EXPS BROUGHT FORWARD                               26,268.26
  011 ASSOC-1                    C    100      P   12-26-81   1,053.33
  011 ASSOC-1                    C    100      P   09-20-81     130.56
  011 ASSOC-2                    C    100      P   12-22-81     917.20
  012 NON-ACC-1                  1     25      P   12-11-81     105.14
  012 NON-ACC-1                  1     25      P   09-27-81     165.14
  013 ASST-1                     3     50      P   12-20-81     525.00
  013 ASST-2                     3     50      P   12-20-81     476.22
  013 ASST-3                     3     25      P   12-26-81     297.00
  013 ASST-4                     3     50      P   12-20-81     525.00
  013 ASST-5                     3             *   12-26-81     193.33
    ** TOTAL EXPENDITURES FOR MONTH FOR OBJ 010                         4,553.20 *
  **** TOTAL EXPENDITURES FOR FISCAL PERIOD FOR OBJ 010               30,822.26 **
FB CODES:  1=RETIRE,HLTH INS,WK COMP    3=WK COMP   4,5,6=HLTH INS,WK COMP

OBJ    DESCRIPTION      NAME    REQUISITION VOUCHER STAT DATE    AMOUNT      TOTAL

100 FRINGE BENEFITS  EXPS BROUGHT FORWARD                              845.49
      RETIREMENT                                            26.62
      HEALTH INSURANCE                                      76.92
      WORKMANS COMP                                         18.21
    ** TOTAL EXPENDITURES FOR MONTH FOR OBJ 100                        123.75 *
  **** TOTAL EXPENDITURES FOR FISCAL PERIOD FOR OBJ 100                969.22 **

400 SUPPLIES        EXPS BROUGHT FORWARD                              14,522.32
  404 BIOCHEM 308    ASST-1        C809977E  N  12-31-81      2.81
  404 ORGANIC 371    ASST-1        CS020976  N  12-31-81    277.86
  404 NMR SERVICE    ASST-2        NS020281  N  12-31-81     12.25
  412 ALDRICH        ASST-2   936-1000  DI113456  C  12-31-81     61.93
  416 ORGANIC 371    ASSOC-1       CS020976  N  12-31-81    749.37
  416 ORGANIC 371    ASSOC-2       CS020976  N  12-31-81    175.10
  416 ORGANIC 371    ASST-4        CS020976  N  12-31-81    471.29
  416 ORGANIC 371    ASST-5        CS020976  N  12-31-81    466.06-
    ** TOTAL EXPENDITURES FOR MONTH FOR OBJ 400                        1,229.83 *
  **** TOTAL EXPENDITURES FOR FISCAL PERIOD FOR OBJ 400               15,752.15 **

500 TRAVEL          EXPS BROUGHT FORWARD                              832.53
    ** TOTAL EXPENDITURES FOR MONTH FOR OBJ 500                            .00 *
  **** TOTAL EXPENDITURES FOR FISCAL PERIOD FOR OBJ 500                832.53 **

600 PUBLICATIONS    EXPS BROUGHT FORWARD                              340.72
  618 SER SCS COPY   ASST-5        CC046632  N  12-31-81     27.02
  618 SER SCS COPY   ASST-4        CC046632  N  12-31-81      1.61
    ** TOTAL EXPENDITURES FOR MONTH FOR OBJ 600                         28.63 *
  **** TOTAL EXPENDITURES FOR FISCAL PERIOD FOR OBJ 600                369.33 **

700 COMP,COMM,OTHER  EXPS BROUGHT FORWARD                             21.18
    ** TOTAL EXPENDITURES FOR MONTH FOR OBJ 700                            .00 *
  **** TOTAL EXPENDITURES FOR FISCAL PERIOD FOR OBJ 700                 21.18 **

950 INDIRECT COST   EXPS BROUGHT FORWARD                              17,863.57
      INDIRECT COST CALCULATION FOR MONTH                  3,096.04
    ** TOTAL EXPENDITURES FOR MONTH FOR OBJ 950                        3,096.04 *
  **** TOTAL EXPENDITURES FOR FISCAL PERIOD FOR OBJ 950               20,959.61 **

  *** TOTAL EXPENDITURES FOR MONTH                                     9,031.23 **

  *** TOTAL EXPENDITURES FOR FISCAL PERIOD                            69,724.33 **
```

entire balance of the indirect-cost category; if the indirect-cost category is overcommitted, a negative balance would be shown.

Expenditures are the last section of the statement (see Figure 28). For personnel expenditures listed are the names, document number (payment date), and amount of each payment. Payments are entered, and the appointment is automatically updated as in the obligations section. Listed for each nonpersonnel expenditure are the object classification, vendor, voucher number, date paid, name of individual incurring the expenditure, and amount. For those expenditures incurred by a requisition, the requisition number is listed and the corresponding requisition is removed from the obligations section. Because the name of the person who made the expenditure is listed, the project director can monitor the spending habits of individuals in the research group and easily identify expenses. The appropriate fringe benefits and indirect-cost expenditures are automatically generated by a separate program and posted to the accounts. The accompanying obligations are adjusted accordingly.

Other Reports and Uses. The *summary statement of account* (Exhibit 26, page 184) is identical to the first three sections of the detailed statement of account. This shortened financial statement is sent to the unit manager and is used by the project director to check project funds before incurring additional obligations. This summary gives a short but comprehensive report of each account.

The *consolidated summary* (Exhibit 27, page 185) lists all accounts for a given operating unit and subdivides the statement into five groups. For each project it lists the account number, title, director, fiscal period, and the totals from the summary section of the detailed statement; that is, the total budget, amount expended current month, cumulative amount expended to date, amount obligated, and free balance for each project.

The system can also prepare an aged obligation list, a trial balance, and a comparison of charges in the project system with those in the central accounting system. An on-line inquiry displays the summary statement for a given account, and it can be accessed daily, enabling users to monitor the status of an account throughout the month on a CRT.

Finally, the system allows the user to assign subproject codes to a given account. Depending on the number assigned, a subproject code may be used for identification only or in a totaling arrangement. When used for identification only, a separate statement is produced with no other effect. When used in a totaling arrangement, the totals line is inserted into a master account (Exhibit 28, page 186). Thus, an account can be proportioned to various individuals, yet the director or manager and the office of sponsored projects can monitor the status of the entire account.

Exhibit 22. Checklist for Allowability of Costs.

| | Usually Allowable as: | | | |
Type of Expenditure	Direct Cost	Indirect Cost	Unallowable	Special Conditions
Advertising	X			
Air conditioning	X	X		Budgeted or approved
Alterations, nonconstruction	X			
Animals				
Bad debts			X	
Bonding	X			
Bonus payments	X			If part of compensation
Books	X			
Child-care costs	X			
Civil defense		X		
Commencement and convocation			X	
Communication costs	X			
Computer costs	X			
Conferences	X			
Construction			X	Unless specifically authorized
Consultant services	X			
Contingent reserves			X	
Custom and import duty	X			
Depreciation		X		
Donors	X			

Exhibit 22 (continued)

Type of Expenditure	Usually Allowable as:		Unallowable	Special Conditions
	Direct Cost	Indirect Cost		
Drugs	X			
Dues	X			
Entertainment			X	
Equipment	X			Budgeted or approved
Equipment maintenance and repair	X			
Equipment rental	X			
Fines and penalties			X	
Fringe benefits	X			
Fund raising			X	
Honorariums			X	When considered award
Human subjects	X			
Insurance	X			
Interest			X	
Investment-management costs			X	
Labor relations		X		
Legal costs	X			
Library		X		
Licenses and permits	X			
Losses			X	
Maintenance	X			
Materials	X			
Meals	X			For subjects and participants

Exhibit 22 (continued)

Type of Expenditure	Usually Allowable as: Direct Cost	Indirect Cost	Unallowable	Special Conditions
Memberships	X			
Moving costs	X			
News releases	X			With specific approval
Overtime	X			
Patent costs	X			
Patient costs	X			
Periodicals	X			
Plant-security costs	X	X		
Postage	X			
Preaward costs			X	
Proposal costs—new awards		X		
Proposal costs—renewals and continuations	X			
Public information costs		X		
Publication costs	X			
Rearrangement costs	X			
Recruiting costs	X			
Registration fees	X			
Relocation costs	X			
Renovation costs	X			Within budget limits
Rental or lease of facilities and equipment	X			

Exhibit 22 (continued)

Type of Expenditure	Usually Allowable as: Direct Cost	Indirect Cost	Unallowable	Special Conditions
Repairs	X			
Royalty costs	X			
Sabbatical-leave costs		X		
Salaries and wages	X			
Scholarships and student aid		X		
Service charges	X			
Severance pay	X			If institutional policy
Specialized service costs	X			
Student activity costs			X	
Subject costs	X			
Supplies	X			
Taxes	X			
Transportation costs	X			
Travel costs	X			
Tuition and fees	X			Within budget limits

Exhibit 23. Potential Causes of Audit Disallowance.

- Submitting cost proposals that greatly exceed probable costs.
- Incurring costs prior to the starting date of the grant or contract without permission.
- Buying office furniture or general-purpose equipment such as calculators, refrigerators, or air conditioners without prior approval of the sponsoring agency.
- Delegating the signing of monthly effort reports to others.
- Delaying the return of the effort reports.
- Making late charges to grant, particularly after sixty days.
- Transferring funds from one grant to another to avoid cost overruns or underruns, or for reasons of convenience.
- Spending money for major equipment during the last month or two of the grant.
- Using a residual balance in the last month of the grant account to stockpile supplies for coming year, or for other excessive spending.
- Charging costs to the grant that are not related to the grant; for example, travel costs of faculty not named on grant, or reimbursing a department for deficits incurred on an earlier grant.
- Charging more effort to the grant than actually committed to the grant.
- Charging foreign travel to the grant without prior permission of sponsor.
- Exceeding allowed travel by more than $500 or 125 percent of awarded travel budget item, whichever is greater, without permission.
- Subcontracting without recipient and sponsor approval.
- Absence of the project director for more than three months without notifying the sponsoring agency thirty days prior to departure.
- Incurring costs after termination of the sponsored project.
- Transferring indirect costs to direct costs without recipient and sponsor approval.
- Spending more than $1,000 for equipment or remodeling without recipient and sponsor approval unless authorized to do so in the award.
- Paying overtime without checking sponsor rules.
- Using funds to generate income without prior sponsor approval and an agreement as to the disposition of those funds.
- Changing the objective of the project without notifying the sponsor.
- Excessively rebudgeting funds without sponsor approval; tolerance for rebudgeting generally ranges from 5–20 percent depending on sponsor rules.
- Spending in areas specifically restricted by sponsor.
- Paying consulting fees to recipient staff. Rules vary with sponsor, some require prior approval from sponsor for all consulting.
- Changing the project director without requesting permission of the sponsor.

Exhibit 24. Checklist for Allowability of Costs.

- Keep the sponsor informed of significant changes in scope of the project.
- Proposal costs cannot be charged to a project; however, they may be part of the indirect-cost pool (new awards only).
- Project's financial statement should show all expenditures and obligations compared to budget to truly reflect the funds available.
- Do not charge honorariums to federally sponsored projects. They are considered awards and as such are not allowable. However, consultant fees *are* acceptable.
- Award documents should reflect terms and conditions. Read referenced regulations closely to avoid problems.
- Treat similar costs alike within a budgetary unit for funding purposes.
- If guidelines conflict with specific regulations set forth in the award agreement, the award agreement takes precedence.
- Depreciation is allowed on recipient equipment and buildings and, within specific limits, becomes part of the indirect-cost pool.

Exhibit 25. NSF Prior Approval Requirements.

Type of Expenditure	*Prior Approval Required By*
1. Alterations and renovations	
a. Under $1,000	OPAS
b. $1,000 or more	Grants officer
2. Capital expenditures for land, buildings, or repairs	Grants officer
3. Contractual (third-party) costs	Grants officer
4. Equipment	
a. special purpose: $1,000 or more	Grants officer
b. general purpose	Grants officer
c. cumulative expenditures that exceed budgeted amount by more than 25 percent	OPAS
5. News release costs	Program officer
6. Participant support costs: transfer of funds to other categories of expense	Program officer
7. Preaward costs	Grants officer
8. Production or distribution of books, films, etc.	Grants officer
9. Rental or lease of facilities	Grants officer
10. Travel	
a. Each foreign trip and its costs	Program officer
b. Cumulative domestic travel expenditures that exceed budgeted amount by $500 or 25 percent, whichever is greater	OPAS
c. Dependent foreign travel	Program officer

Source: National Science Foundation, 1979, p. V-11.

Exhibit 26. Summary Statement of Account.

```
463286316 ***** STATEMENT OF ACCOUNT AS OF 03 31 81 *****      PAGE 01 ******723

********IR INVESTIGATOR                ACCT TITLE  NSF PCM 12-34567 A01
ORGANIC                                ACCT NUMBER 46 32 86 316
TOTAL BUDGET $86,480                   CUR FIS PER 01 01 81 TO 12 31 81

************************       NOTES      ****************************

BUDGET = $77,990 AWARDED AND $8,580 CARRYOVER
IC RATE = 66% S&W, COST SHARING = 10%, ADDNL YRS RECMD   0
RENEWAL PROPOSAL DUE 07-21-81, SUBMITTED   - -

************************  SUMMARY STATEMENT  ****************************

CODE DESCRIPTION          BUDGET   MON-EXP   TOT-EXP   OBLIGATED  BALANCE
100 PERSONNEL             37,807    3,425    10,882    18,291     8,636
202 FRINGE BENEFITS        1,474       81       265       832       377
300 EQUIPMENT              2,846                                   2,846
400 SUPPLIES              13,288    1,561     4,212     3,030     5,996
500 TRAVEL                   516                                     516
600 PUBLICATIONS           3,692       38       105       332     3,255
702 COMP,COMM,OTHER          100       13        33                   67
800 RMDL,REPR,MAINT        1,805       94     1,969               164-
990 INDIRECT COST         24,952    2,260     7,181    12,072     5,699

    TOTAL                 86,480    7,472    24,645    34,607    27,228

.............................................................................

463286319 ***** STATEMENT OF ACCOUNT AS OF 03 31 81 *****      PAGE 01 ******728

********JONES/SMITH                    ACCT TITLE  HEW PHS CA 12345
ORGANIC                                ACCT NUMBER 46 32 86 319
TOTAL BUDGET   $6,000                  CUR FIS PER 04 01 80 TO 03 31 81

************************       NOTES      ****************************

BUDGET = $3,000 AWARDED AND $3,000 CARRYOVER
IC RATE = NONE, COST SHARING = NONE
INSTITUTIONAL ALLOWANCE FOR G SMITH

************************  SUMMARY STATEMENT  ****************************

CODE DESCRIPTION          BUDGET   MON-EXP   TOT-EXP   OBLIGATED  BALANCE
400 SUPPLIES              6,000                 230                5,770
500 TRAVEL                                    2,056               2,056-
600 PUBLICATIONS                      22         29                  29-
702 COMP,COMM,OTHER                           1,260               1,260-
750 STUDENT                                      15                  15-

    TOTAL                 6,000       22      3,590               2,410

.............................................................................
```

Exhibit 27. Consolidated Summary of Account.

ACCOUNT	PERIOD	BUDGET	MON-EXP	TOT-EXP	OBLIGATED	BALANCE
44 32 86 391						
JOHNS UNRESTRICTED						
DR JONES	01 01 64/12 31 82	23,500	0	10,131	5720	12,797-
80 32 86 912						
AGCY ACS ORG CHEM						
DR BAAK	07 01 77/06 30 82	12,700	306	4,037	0	8,307-
*** TOTAL ***		392,398 *	8,274 *	255,841 *	20,202 *	116,355*

SUMMARY OF GOVERNMENT GRANTS AND CONTRACTS – ORGANIC   ** 12 31 81

ACCOUNT	PERIOD	BUDGET	MON-EXP	TOT-EXP	OBLIGATED	BALANCE
46 32 86 145						
HEW PHS AM 44444-01						
KITZEN/PAZNE	05 01 81/04 30 82	3,000	1,899	3,363	729	1,092-
46 32 86 302						
NSF PCM 76-00000 A03						
DR KITZEN	07 01 81/06 30 82	41,405	3,371	27,312	9,214	4,879
46 32 86 303						
HEW PHS A177777-23						
DR JONES	12 01 81/11 30 82	85,323	5,672	23,831	41,625	17,867
46 32 86 304						
HEW PHS GM 33333-07						
DR BAAK	08 01 81/07 31 82	55,002	3,882	30,716	23,793	493
46 32 86 316						
NSF PCM 99-98766						
INVESTIGAT	01 01 81/12 31 82	86,480	7,472	24,645	34,607	27,228
46 32 86 319						
HEW PHS CA 12345						
JONES/SMITH	04 01 81/03 31 82	6,000	22	3,590	0	2,410
46 32 86 326						
HEW PHS CA 22222-09						
DR JONES	05 01 81/04 30 82	83,835	4,423	78,190	8,288	2,643-
46 32 86 328						
HEW PHS GM 11111-14						
DR WALL	03 01 81/02 29 82	98,591	969	969	39,283	58,339
46 32 86 337						
NSF CHE 77-99999						
DR CHIME	05 01 81/04 30 82	20,000	2,147	13,898	2,576	3,526
*** TOTAL ***		479,636 *	29,662 *	206,514 *	160,115*	113,007 *

Exhibit 28. Subproject and Master Account Summary Statement.

```
46328518E ***** STATEMENT OF ACCOUNT AS OF 12 31 81 *****      PAGE 01 ******55

********DR HAIER                        ACCT TITLE   HEW PHS GM9999-04
BIOCHEMISTRY                            ACCT NUMBER 46 32 85 185     626
TOTAL BUDGET  $27,203                   CUR FIS PER 07 01 80 TO 06 30 81

****************************      NOTES      ****************************

BUDGET = $27,203 AWARDED
IC RATE = 8% DC
BIOCHEMISTRY PORTION OF TRAINING GRANT
SUB-PROJECT CODE 626

***********************      SUMMARY STATEMENT      ***********************

CODE DESCRIPTION          BUDGET     MON-EXP    TOT-EXP   OBLIGATED   BALANCE

 300 EQUIPMENT                0          0          0       1,607     1,607-
 400 SUPPLIES            25,188        990      4,970       3,612    16,606
 600 PUBLICATIONS             0         45        711           0       711-
 700 COMP,COMM,OTHER          0          0      1,028         881     1,909-
 800 RMDL,REPR,AMINT          0        129      3,001           0     3,001-
 990 INDIRECT COST        2,015         93        777       1,238         0

     TOTAL              27,203      1,257     10,487       1,338     9,378

...............................................................................

46328518E ***** STATEMENT OF ACCOUNT AS OF 12 31 81 *****      PAGE 01 ******55

********DR HAIER                        ACCT TITLE   HEW PHS GM9999-04
BIOCHEMISTRY                            ACCT NUMBER 46 32 85 185     699
TOTAL BUDGET  $86,670                   CUR FIS PER 07 01 80 TO 6 30 81

****************************      NOTES      ****************************

BUDGET = $86,670 AWARDED
IC RATE = 8% DC, COST SHARING = NONE, ADDNL YRS RECMD = 1
CONTINUATION PROPOSAL DUE 12-01-81, SUBMITTED 10-31-81
MASTER ACCT PROJECT CODE 699

***********************      SUMMARY STATEMENT      ***********************

CODE DESCRIPTION          BUDGET     MON-EXP    TOT-EXP   OBLIGATED   BALANCE

     DENNIS/DORNER        8,165          0      1,388         502     6,275
     DR APLE             6,804         246      6,590         364       150-
     DR BAKER           16,330         391      7,583         648     8,299
     DR CHARLIE          9,526         751      4,062         938     4,526
     DR HAIER           27,203       1,257     10,487       7,338     9,378
 100 PERSONNEL           8,000         585      4,808       1,756     1,436
 200 FRINGE BENEFITS     1,262          24        145          72     1,045
 300 EQUIPMENT           2,000           0          0           0     2,000
 400 SUPPLIES                0          25        306          46       352-
 500 TRAVEL                  0         126        614           0       614-
 600 PUBLICATIONS            0           0          0           6         6-
 700 COMP,COMM,OTHER     6,000           0      3,095           0     2,905
 800 RMDL,REPR,MAINT         0           0         85           0        85-
 990 INDIRECT COST       1,380          60        725         655         0

     TOTAL              86,670       3,465     39,888      12,325    34,457
```

12

Administering Facilities and Equipment

Facilities and equipment available for sponsored projects are an important consideration in the sponsor's proposal review. Often their availability determines whether a project can be accomplished successfully in a cost-efficient manner. These tangibles are also very important in recruiting and retaining staff. Consequently, the acquisition, maintenance, and funding of facilities and equipment play an important role in sponsored projects. The extent of the facilities and equipment are somewhat determined by the size and type of institution. In this chapter we describe their nature, how they may be funded, and make suggestions regarding useful services. We also present a computer-automated system for a stores inventory and billing procedure, and a shared-use and automated equipment inventory system.

Facilities

Facilities needed for sponsored projects include real property and support services. Sponsored projects require facilities of diverse sizes and complexities, but the facilities may frequently be used for other programs. Our discussion of facilities focuses on buildings, stores, copying and printing services, shops, computers, and specialized service facilities. While this list is not exhaustive, it represents the major facilities ordinarily associated with sponsored projects.

Buildings. The costs of buildings, including the improvement costs, may sometimes be funded through sponsored projects. Occasionally, when specifically authorized by program legislation, buildings may be considered a direct cost of a sponsored project. In some cases, lease and rental costs may be appropriate. Generally, however, sponsored projects pay for building facilities through depreciation and use allowances recovered through the indirect-cost assessment. This recovery includes the original building's cost and capital improvements, or the value of donated real property at the time of the donation.

The recovery of building costs allocated to sponsored projects is set out in Sections F and J-9 of OMB circular A-21 (Office of Management and Budget, 1979). Depreciation or use allowances that are based on the acquisition costs (including subsequent improvements) less land costs are the costs portions supported by the government. The depreciation rate is determined by the expected useful service or life and is usually calculated on a straight-line depreciation method. To change the depreciation method, the sponsor's permission must be obtained. Component parts of the building (that is, shell, plumbing, heating, air conditioning, and the like) may be treated separately and depreciated over their estimated useful lives. The use allowance for buildings and improvements is computed at an annual rate not to exceed 2 percent. The building may not be broken down into component parts for use charges. Reasonable use charges may be made after an asset has been fully depreciated, taking into account the previous government-supported depreciation and the remaining useful life. Therefore, for older buildings that have outlasted their ordinary depreciation lives, recovery may be possible through use allowances.

Depreciation and use allowances for buildings used for more than one institutional activity are allocated to each activity based upon square footage excluding common areas. Where the space is used jointly for more than one activity, the allocation is the proportion of total salaries and wages applicable to the space. Depreciation and use allowances on other capital improvements, like sidewalks and parking lots, may be allocated based on the number of full-time equivalent employees allocated to the activity.

Operation and maintenance expenses are allocated on the same basis as described in the two preceding paragraphs. These expenses include utility services, janitor services, repairs, grounds care, and maintenance. Usually the building facilities are administered by a central services organization that reports to the vice-president for administration or business. Care must be exercised when proposals are prepared for sponsored projects to ensure that adequate building facilities are readily available to house the projects.

Stores. Stores are those facilities, centralized and decentralized, that procure supplies and equipment, store them until needed, and then issue them to researchers. Items in stockrooms include everything from pens and pencils through laboratory chemicals, gases and apparatus, hardware, electronics, and metal supplies. Stores provide important support for sponsored projects. Especially in basic research, the need for uncommon supplies and short lead times to procure special items make a substantial stores facility extremely valuable. Unlike a retail or wholesale business inventory, which should turn over several times a year, service storeroom stock may have slow-moving items, and the stock value may turn over only every two to five years. The important principle is access to needed stock, not frequency of turnover.

Another issue in storeroom organization is the use of centralized and decentralized stores. Although quantity purchases reduce unit costs and large facilities can realize economies of scale, both centralized and decentralized stores are needed in large organizations. Centralized stores should be used for those items needed in large quantities throughout the institution that can be stocked and issued at reasonable costs. However, the sponsored projects staff need ready access to stocks unique to their effort. If these stocks are not readily available, the staff will purchase excess supplies and stock them in their immediate areas. Good service and economy in a stores operation require an understanding of users' needs, including accessibility.

The administration of stores facilities depends on location and clientele serviced. Central storerooms are usually administered by the vice-president for administration or business. Decentralized stockrooms usually report to their unit administrator. Funding for storeroom operations usually comes from an overhead charge added to the unit price.

This overhead should recover the cost of direct personnel, supplies, and operating costs incurred in the stockroom. Costs that are charged to an indirect-cost pool are recovered through charges to sponsored projects, but all users of stores facilities must be charged consistently.

Copying and Printing. Copying and printing facilities are an essential part of most organizations that conduct sponsored projects. The issue of centralized and decentralized services arises here, too. Most institutions have decentralized copying facilities, but their printing facilities are centralized under the jurisdiction of the vice-president for administration or business. Decentralized printing units usually are administered by the organizational units in which they are located, although in some organizations they are controlled by the central administration. But locating the administrative responsibility as close to the user as possible improves service and enables problems to be more rapidly solved.

Costs incurred by these service facilities are usually charged to sponsored projects based on the operating expenses incurred by the facilities. These costs may include the rental and maintenance of copying machines. The costs of purchasing copying and printing equipment may be recovered through the indirect-cost provision for depreciation and use allowances. Whatever method is used must be equitable and consistent for all users.

Shops. Shop facilities serve development, construction, repair, and maintenance functions. They are as varied as the sponsored projects they are organized to serve; examples include glass-blowing shops, machine shops, electronics shops, instrument shops, and foundry shops. The sophistication and creative talents of their staff are extremely important to the success of many sponsored projects. These facilities represent not only substantial expenses for technical and professional staff but also sizable investments in specialized equipment and stock. Most shops are tied closely to the organizational units they serve. However, when their expertise is needed by another unit, they may perform the needed service.

Funding for shop facilities is difficult because they usually require large capital expenditures and overhead, including the costs to remodel facilities, acquire equipment, and train staff. These costs are difficult to fully recover as direct or indirect costs to sponsored projects. Equally troublesome is the funding for replacement and new equipment, additional staff, and expanded space. The development of new, more sophisticated equipment and changes in technology make the ordering of priorities for limited resources a difficult and recurring task. Usually these improvements are funded from institutional resources rather than charged to sponsored projects. However, identifiable costs for labor, materials, and operating expenses for jobs may be directly charged to sponsored projects. Here again, it is essential to charge all users consistently. Depreciation of equipment may be included through the indirect-cost rate, but maintenance charges may be recovered as part of the direct-cost calculation. Rates established for these types of service facilities should be reviewed periodically and adjusted accordingly for subsequent periods. Underrecovery or overrecovery may be shifted to the next period rather than making adjustments to prior charges.

Computers. Computer use has probably grown more than any other facility in the last decade. Currently, large central installations are giving way to decentralized units for distributed processing, which in turn may be connected to the central units. Here we address multiuse computers and exclude those that are dedicated to one piece of equipment or perform operational and computational functions for only one unit.

Computers require substantial investments in hardware, software support, and program maintenance. Usually a central computer center's director and staff are funded as a specialized service facility. Costs for computer services are normally recovered through direct costs and their allocatable share of indirect costs. The costs are charged directly to users based on actual use and a schedule of rates that apply consistently to all users. Since costs vary widely and annual recovery cannot be accurately projected, costs and recovery may be spread over more than a single fiscal period. The administration of central computer facilities is usually handled by a center director who reports to the vice-president for academic affairs or sponsored projects.

The development of smaller but powerful computers allows for more decentralized use. It seems that interconnected decentralized facilities (distributed processing) may be more effective and efficient than large centralized units. Decentralized facilities are usually under the administration of the units in which they are located. Many times they are organized, staffed, and funded in a manner similar to the larger central installation. Other decentralized units are funded as part of the sponsored projects costs included in the award budget. Whatever charge system is used must be consistent in charges to all users and must not charge sponsors for costs already being supported by them.

Specialized Service Facilities. Specialized service facilities are those that provide support specifically for the needs of sponsored projects. Examples of such facilities include labs with highly specialized analytical instrumentation (such as mass spectrometers, molecular spectroscopy equipment, lasers, and x-ray equipment) and microanalysis service facilities; more sophisticated facilities include reactors, wind tunnels, or materials engineering research labs. Frequently, the presence of these facilities and their capabilities directly determine the outcome of a sponsored project award. Reputations of excellence in many physical and biological sciences are dependent on specialized service facilities. Because of their critical nature and sophistication, they are usually administered closely by the disciplinary unit they represent and serve. If the specialized facility cuts across many disciplines, it may be administered centrally by an oversight committee of staff from the appropriate disciplines.

Funding for specialized service facilities, like funding for shops, involves substantial start-up costs. However, a portion of these costs may often be funded by sponsors; the National Institutes of Health (NIH) and the National Science Foundation (NSF) have special programs to help fund specialized equipment and remodeling. Usually the organization must supply a portion of the funding on a matching basis. That portion of the equipment not paid by sponsors may be recovered through the indirect-cost rate charge. Direct charges to users may be made to recover personnel, supplies, equipment maintenance, and operating expenses. Here again, all users must be charged on a consistent basis. Provision must be made for periodic reviews of costs and rates, with the appropriate adjustments made in subsequent rates.

Occasionally, sponsors support a portion of the operating costs if they have sufficient interest in the work being done or in the contemplated improvements, or if they are sponsoring many projects that use the service. For example, an NSF program, which began in 1978 and is being phased out in 1982, supports regional instrumentation facilities. This program is designed to extend specialized facilities by funding additional personnel, upgrading equipment, and making the facilities available to all regional users. In such cases, rates may be established to recover those expenses not supported directly by the sponsor. The operating policies and rate structure must be approved by the sponsor's program officer.

Facilities Automated Inventory and Billing System

An inventory control and billing system is important to a facility's ability to serve and recover proper costs from sponsored projects and other users. Regardless of staff talents and sophisticated equipment, facilities must be supplied and resupplied with materials needed to operate. Frequently these supply and material needs may be overlooked or given low priority when compared to broad organizational business functions such as accounting or payroll. However, automated inventory and billing systems have been developed to operate successfully in a facility of any size. The system described and illustrated here was developed at the University of Illinois, Urbana-Champaign campus, School of Chemical Sciences. It currently handles inventories in ten locations, and supplies and services issued from more than twenty-five locations. Supplies and services include issuing laboratory gases, liquid nitrogen, and dry ice; recovering mass spectrometer, NMR, laser, and microanalytical sample costs; charging for copying and printing services; and charging gas cylinder demurrage.

Since computer cards are reasonably inexpensive and easy to handle and replace, and people are quite accustomed to using them, computer cards were chosen as the input form. Another noteworthy system of recording input information was developed at the University of California–Berkeley, Department of Chemistry (Matteson and Smiriga, 1976). They built a point-of-entry magnetic-card controller with magnetic-tape storage to record the data. The cassette-tape records are automatically fed into the main computer for preparing inventory and billing reports.

Figure 29 shows the illustrated stores inventory–document list flow chart for the University of Illinois system. The issue cards are placed in the service areas or storeroom either next to the item to be issued or in a card file. Upon issue, the quantity is written onto the card and initialed by the user. Issue cards are then filed behind header cards and become a transaction deck; this deck and the order and receipt cards and adjustment cards are fed into the computer. Basically, the computer

Figure 29. Stores Inventory/Document List.

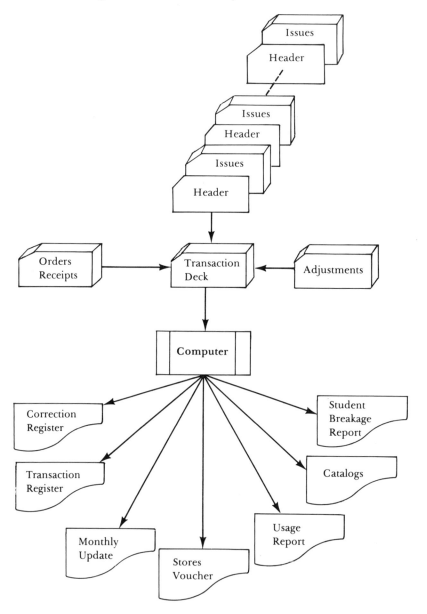

Source: Hess and Waters, 1975, p. 39.

maintains a master file by stock number showing the description, unit of issue, and current price for each item in stock. Each storeroom has its own separate inventory file. The various report documents — such as the transaction register, monthly update, stores vouchers, and usage report — are prepared on the computer at whatever interval is requested by the storekeeper responsible for that storeroom. Some documents are prepared monthly, while catalogues are prepared semiannually or annually. Thus the system is quite flexible, adjustments are quite easy to make, and it is relatively simple for the storekeepers to be responsible for their own inventory. The systems personnel schedule their workload to meet the storekeeper's needs for information; they can usually respond to requests within two days. Therefore, the reports are up-to-date and enable the storekeeper to order the supplies necessary to maintain a predetermined stock level.

The input documents for the stores inventory and billing system are all basic card formats with the issue cards prepared in groups by gang-punching. The four principal types of input documents are the issue cards, return cards, header cards, and transaction cards.

Issue cards are prepared in groups of 25 to 100 as specified by the storekeeper. The issue card shows the item's stock number, description, and the unit of issue. Only one issue card is needed to record whatever quantity is being issued to the storeroom user. When the supply of issue cards becomes low, the storekeeper removes one card from the bin or file and sends it to the computer systems group, noting the quantity of additional cards needed.

The header card identifies the user's name, account number, and work area. One card is made for each user of the storeroom; the cards are maintained by the storekeeper in alphabetical order. Issues are filed behind a user's card after the quantity and initials are recorded on the card. An infrequent user for whom a header card is not available simply records his name, account charged, and unit directly onto the top issue card.

The issue and header cards are periodically given to keypunch operators for processing. The information on the header cards is punched onto the issue card along with the quantity issued. The issue card is then a transaction card that contains all the information for the transaction: the stock number, the description of the item, unit of issue, the account charged, the user's name, and the quantity issued.

Three additional documents used by the storekeepers to maintain their storeroom inventory are the order, receipt, and correction cards. As inventory reports are printed out, the storekeeper needs to know what is to be ordered. Therefore, each time a storekeeper places an order for an item, the requisition number, the date, the stock number of the item, the quantity ordered, and the cost are recorded. As items are received, the storekeepers record this information on a receipt card, thus automatically updating the store's inventory of that item. Correction cards are used to change a price, enter a new item into the inventory, adjust the balance on hand, or change a quantity on order.

The output document for the stores system is printed as frequently as needed by the storekeeper to maintain control of the storeroom. The transaction register (Figure 30) is the most important and useful document for the storekeeper. It describes all the items in the stockroom that have shown some activity since the last transaction report. It gives the stock number, description, unit of issue, balance on-hand at the beginning of the period, units added to stock, units issued from stock, unit cost, balance on-hand at the end of the reporting period, value of stock on-hand at the end of the reporting period, messages, orders received, and number of units received. Typical messages shown on this report include: FR—full receipt of an outstanding order; PR—partial receipt of an outstanding order; OS—items out-of-stock; and RO—reordering point has been reached. This document enables the storekeeper to determine what items need to be ordered. In addition, items on order are reported showing the order number and quantity requested. From this report, the storekeeper can find whether an order is delinquent and check to see why the item has not been received.

The monthly update report (Figure 31) contains the same information as the transaction register but lists all items available in the stockroom regardless of activity. It also lists the maximum stock level and reordering point so that if an item has not moved, the storekeeper can decide to adjust those values. Messages on the monthly update report, like those on the transaction register, give the storekeeper an easy guide for bringing stock up to the predetermined level. Also, the monthly update shows the shelf number or location of the item in the storeroom. From this information the storekeeper can easily check the balance on-hand to see if it is appropriate.

Another output document prepared from the information is the

Figure 30. Weekly Transaction Register.

SERVICE-SCS   ORGANIC 317 RAL   DATE FROM 06 17 81 TO 08 24 81

STOCK NO LOCATION	DESCRIPTION	UI	BAL BEG	ADD UNITS	UNITS ISSUE	COST	DATE COST UPDATED	BAL O/H	VALUE BAL O/H	MESSAGE	ORDER RECVD	UNITS
30 78 4600 A22-3	FUNNEL BUCHNER FRITTED 150M GCS	EA ORDER DATE AMOUNT	2	4	1	16.41	03 24 81	3	49.23	IR	13152	4
30-78-5700 A22-4	FUNNEL BUCHNER FRITTED 200M GCS	EA ORDER DATE AMOUNT	1	13153 061781 12	1	47.67		0	.00	OS	1	
30-99-6001 S11-5	FIBER PX GLASS WOOL 8 OZ GCS	EA ORDER DATE AMOUNT	7		4	6.94	04 21 81	3	20.82			
31 NI 0235 A8-4	COLUMN CHROMATOGRAPHY W/TEFLON PLUG STOPCOCK 16 MM OD X 120 MM LONG 2MM PLUG GLASS SHOP	EA ORDER DATE AMOUNT	5		1	6.77		4	27.08			
31 NI 0055 A8-4	COLUMN CHROMATOGRAPHY W/TEFLON PLUG STOPCOCK 25 MM OD X 300 MM LONG 2 MM PLUG GLASS SHOP	EA ORDER DATE AMOUNT	3	13140 061081 12	1	6.37		3	20.61	HT		
31 NI 0060 A8-4	COLUMN CHROMATOGRAPHY W/TEFLON PLUG STOPCOCK 25 MM OD X 500 MM LONG 2 MM PLUG GLASS SHOP	EA ORDER DATE AMOUNT	6		2	7.25		4	28.22			

Figure 30 (continued)

```
31 ML 0085  COLUMN CHROMATOGRAPHY W/TEFLON      EA           5    1   10.43      4   41.72
            PLUG STOPCOCK 51 MM OD 600           ORDER
            MM LONG 3 MM PLUG GLASS SHOP         DATE
A8-6                                             AMOUNT

31 ML 0101  COLUMN CHROMATOGRPHY 10 MM ID        EA           8    5.90 09 01 81  10  59.00   FR   6043   10
            X 30MM LONG (ECONO-COLUMN)           ORDER
            BIO-RAD 737-2282                     DATE
                                                 AMOUNT

31 02 0401  AMPUL TRIMMED STEM COLOR-            EA          33    3    .22      30    6.60
            BREAK 10 ML 6/MIN                    CRIER
            GCS                                  DATE
S28-3                                            AMOUNT

31 14 2000  BOTTLE GAS WASH DRESCHEL 250ML       EA           3    2   15.50      1   15.50
            GCS                                  ORDER     13148  12982
A5-4                                             DATE     061581 051581
                                                 AMOUNT       12     12

31-35-2750  CYLINDER SING SCALE EXAX 10 ML       EA          19    1   2.62 03 24 81  18  52.76
            GCS                                  ORDER
A11-5                                            DATE
                                                 AMOUNT
```

Figure 31. Monthly Update Report.

***** ORGANIC 371 BAL *****   VALUE *26 15 61-TO-09 14 61*

STOCK-NO	DESCRIPTION	UI	UNIT PRICE	BAL BEG	AFL UNITS	UNITS ISSUE	ON ORDER	UNIT LEVEL	REORD POINT	BAL O/H	VALUE BAL O/H	MESSAGE	$UPDTE	TYPE
37 60 6701 D58	TEFLON SHEET 1/32IN THICK (6X6 IN MIN SOLD BY SQ INCH) GCS	S1	.32	247		12		144	12	235	79.04		03 24 81	C
37 60 7001 D58	TEFLON SHEET 1/16IN THICK (6X6 IN MIN SOLD BY SQ INCH) GCS	S1	.17	57				144	12	57	9.69		06 16 81	C
37 60 7701 D58	TEFLON SHEET 1/8IN THICK (6X6 IN MIN SOLD BY SQ INCH) GCS	S1	.07	244		112		144	36	132	17.03		11 04 80	B
37 60 8001 D58	TEFLON SHEET 3/16IN THICK (6X6 IN SOLD BY SQ INCH)	S1	.11	36				144	12	36	3.96			C
37 60 8401 I58	TEFLON SHEET 1/4IN THICK (6X6 IN MIN SOLD BY SQ INCH) GCS	S1	.15	144				144	12	144	21.60		11 04 80	C
37 60 9101 I58	TEFLON SHEET 1/2IN THICK (6X6 IN MIN SIOD BY SQ INCH) GCS	S1	.29	70		10		36	9	60	20.32			B
37 60 9210 I45	TEFLON SLEEVE TAPERED 14/35 GCS	EA	2.59	7		4		12	4	3	18.13	RO	04 21 81	A

Figure 31 (continued)

Item	Description	Unit	Price						Total		Date	Code
37 60 9230 D45	TEFLON SLEEVE TAPERED 24/40 GCS	EA	3.43	10	2	24	0	8	34.30		29 30 80	A
37 60 9240 D45	TEFLON SLEEVE TAPERED 29/42 GCS	EA	3.48	10	1	6	1	9	34.80		04 21 81	B
37 60 9250 I45	TEFLON SLEEVE TAPERED 34/45 GCS	EA	3.16	4	3	0	1	1	12.64	RO	24 21 81	A
37 60 9500 A33-6	TEFLON STOPPERS 14/20 FISHER	EA	4.31	2		3	3	2	8.62	RU	04 21 81	A
37 60 9600 A33-6	TEFLON STOPPERS 24/42 FISHER	EA	6.65	5		6	1	5	33.25		07 29 60	C
37 62 2400 A30-5	TRAY POLYETHYLENE 14X12X6IN DISHPAN YELLOW GCS	EA	1.20	7	2	12	2	5	6.00		04 07 81	A
37 62 2800 A30-4	TRAY POLY 13.5X 11.5X 5 5/3 IN GCS	EA	6.50	7	3	6	1	4	45.50		04 21 31	P
37 63 5850 I53	TUBE CENT POLYPROD CON 15ML GCS	EA	.46	36	6	34	5	30	13.80			B
37 63 9500 A33-7	TUBE SUPPORT POLYPROD 23MM GCS	EA	8.09	8		4	1	8	64.72		11 18 80	C

stores voucher, shown in Figure 32. Essentially this is an account-transfer document that charges the items received by the user to the user's account and credits the storeroom account. It lists the receiver, the quantity received, the catalogue number, description, unit cost, total extended price for each item, and a total for the voucher. This voucher is prepared once a month, and summary information is prepared for the financial system. A copy of the voucher is returned to the unit of the individual receiving the supplies.

A storeroom catalogue, as shown in Figure 33, is prepared periodically, depending on variations in the inventories of the storeroom. Two types of catalogues are prepared. The catalogues for each storeroom contain a numerical list and an alphabetical list of all items in the storeroom. The master catalogue shows the stock number, description, unit price, unit of issue, and the storeroom in which the item is located. Items that are used in several areas may be stocked in several storerooms readily accessible to users. The catalogue then shows the storerooms in which an item is stocked and the level of inventory. In addition to the hard-copy catalogue, microfiches are prepared for reference.

Several types of special reports are prepared from the computer files to be used for storeroom management. For example, a monthly issue-usage report (Exhibit 29, pages 210–211) shows the item stock number, item description, unit price, unit of issue, balance on-hand, location, maximum level, and reordering point for each item in the storeroom. It also gives a historical, month-by-month pattern of usage. This report is usually prepared annually for each storeroom. The storekeeper can easily compare the monthly usage to the minimum reordering point and adjust the maximum level and reordering point according to the past year's operations. If an item has been unused for several years, the storekeeper may consider taking it out of the active stock and transferring it into inactive status in a special storeroom.

One module of the inventory and billing system can have several uses. The programming used to generate the stores voucher (transfer document) can be used to automatically generate the billing for service facility charges, copy machine usage, and other special commodities issued to sponsored projects.

The input document is, again, the punched card. Areas on the card are used to record the name, account number, and units. Units may be the number of copies, liters of nitrogen, number of samples, number

Figure 32. Stores Voucher (Transfer Document).

University of Illinois at Urbana-Champaign

STORES VOUCHER

STOREROOM SER SCS CONSOLIDATED 256 NL   DATE 10 05 81   ACCOUNTING DIVISION CY 1046892 PAGE 01

QTY.	CATALOG NO.	DESCRIPTION	NAME	ECC	REQ. NO.	CL	UNIT COST	EXTENSION
50	32844201	SCREW CAP VIAL 13 x 63MM 4ML	LETKOWITZ A	41		04	.04	2.00
1	34418400	GREASE APIEZOM H 1 UZ TUBL	LETKOWITZ A	40		04	21.04	21.04
6	37665501	TUBING POLY PEZ09 055x075 1H	LETKOWITZ A	40		04	.17	1.02
19	37667001	TUB VINYL CLR 1/4 ID 1/16 FL	LETKOWITZ A	40		04	.10	1.90
24	37966801	STOPPER SERUM HOODED 16 MM	LETKOWITZ A	40		04	.10	2.40
2	53401062	FUSE 3 AG 5 A Z/F661	LETKOWTIZ A	41		04	.11	.22
/ / /	/ / / / / /	/ / /S U B ** T O T A L ** F O R ** LETKOWITZ A					/ / / /	28.58 *
****	T O T A L	** C H A R G E 40 32 83 434 DINGY FOUNDATION UNRESTRICTED - HENDERSON					****	28.58 *

CODE NUMBER	CLASS	VOUCHER NUMBER	CL 4 AMOUNT	CL 6 AMOUNT	TOTAL AMOUNT
1-40-32-83-434	04	CY 1046892	28.58		28.58

APPROPRIATION CHARGED: DINGY FOUNDATION/UNRESTRICTED

APPROVED BY

CODE NUMBER 1-15-32-83-950 SER SCS CONSOLIDATED

Form 530A Rev. 2 81

Figure 33. Master Catalog of Stock Items.

MASTER CATALOG -PAGE 0368

STOCK NUMBER	DESCRIPTION	UNIT PRICE	UNIT ISSUE	ECC SCS	ECC UI	371 RAL	104 RAL	303 RAL	GLASS SHOP	MACH SHOP	469 NL	4 CA	204 CA	304 CA	256 NL
30-18-8100	DESICCATOR COVER ONLY 250MM VAC GCS	41.47	EA	42	4	1	2	2	1	10 / 7	1 / 8			1 / 1	3 / 10
30-18-9000	DESICCATOR SLEEVE ONLY 200MM & 250MM GCS	21.34	EA	42	4	2 / 1	2	* / 3		12 / 6		* / 2	15 / 14		2 / 8
30-22-1400	DISH CRYSTALLIZING 50 X 35 MM	2.43	EA	42	4	5		13 / 6					8 / 9	3	31 / 16
30-22-1500	DISH CRYSTALLIZING 70 X 50 MM GCS	1.67	EA	42	4	1 / 32	4 / 5	4 / 2	2	* / 5	3				19 / 23
30-22-1700	DISH CRYSTALLIZING 80 X 40 MM GCS	1.42	EA	42	4	26 / 8	7 / 1		50 / 114			3 / 2			23 / 10
30-22-2000	DISH CRYSTALLIZING 90 X 50 MM GCS	2.00	EA	42	4	13 / 19	7 / 7	4 / 6	25 / 200		12		6 / 1		25 / 14
30-22-2500	DISH CRYSTALLIZING 100 X 50 MM GCS	2.52	EA	42	4	23 / 24	* / 5	7 / 2	15 / 65					* / 5	1 / 48

Figure 33 (continued)

Item Code	Description	Price	Unit																
30-22-3000	DISH CRYSTALLIZING 125 X 65 MM GCS	3.82	EA	42	4	3 52	6 9	4 10	10 25		3	*	4 7		6 51
30-22-3500	DISH CRYSTALLIZING 150 X 75 MM GCS	5.23	EA	42	4	6 34	1 8	4 15	5 30		*		3	1	7 46
30-22-4000	DISH CRYSTALLIZING 170 X 90 MM GCS	5.55	EA	42	4	8 23	6 2	3 10	5 17		1		* 12	*	2 38
30-22-4500	DISH CRYSTALLIZING 190 X 100 MM GCS	6.76	EA	42	4	12 17	2	3 8	12 9		1		1 3	5 1	17 26
30-22-5000	DISH CULTURE PETRI COMP 60 X 15 MM GCS	15.48	EA	42	4		48		11 9	1 7		6 6	1 3	1	12 9
30-22-5001	DISH CULTURE PETRI COMPLETE 60X15 MM (12UNITS/PKG) GCS	1.25	EA	42	4	11 16	55 134	17 6	15 12		5		1 4		58 77
30-22-5500	DISH CULTURE PETRI COMP 100X15 MM GCS	12.20	EA	42	4	22 6	21	5 2		2 8	13 14			5	14 6
30-22-5501	DISH CULTURE PETRI COMPLETE 100X15 MM (12UNITS/PKG) GCS	.97	EA	42	4	15 33	14 43	26 23	6			*			36 103

of hours, or any other measure for which the user is to be billed. The programming simply multiplies the rate for that facility times the number of units and generates a stores voucher as it does for storeroom purchases. The information printed on the stores voucher is similar to the stores issue voucher.

Several types of computer-generated reports are used to administer the services and supplies involved in the billing system. For example, from the inventory and location of gas cylinders, monthly rental costs are charged to sponsored projects. Computer-generated notices of cylinder locations and rental costs are periodically sent to inform project personnel of their costs and possible returns. Records of service facility usage, both in terms of materials and hours recorded, are accessible through the billing system data base. In all cases, cost centers, sponsored projects, or individuals using the services may be easily determined, and trends projected. This type of management information is essential in providing services and supplies to sponsored projects.

Equipment

OMB circular A-21 (1979) defines equipment as an article of nonexpendable personal property having a useful life of more than two years and an acquisition cost of $500 or more per unit. However, an institution may establish lower limits to be consistent with its policies. Rapidly changing technology compels institutions to pay attention to equipment acquisition, use, and management. Therefore, sponsored projects administrators need to be thoroughly familiar with equipment regulations, funding programs, and management systems. Also, managers must be careful to continually analyze new developments and aging equipment. Most sponsored projects depend heavily on adequate equipment.

Shared Use

Shared use is simply the sharing of equipment among two or more parties. Federal regulatory and sponsoring agencies have recently focused a lot of attention on the shared use of moveable equipment. The avoidance of unnecessary equipment purchases, the proper maintenance and accountability for existing equipment, and the multiple and shared use of expensive special-purpose equipment have been addressed by congressional committees, agencies, and recipient institutions. Sponsoring agencies have not yet imposed additional regulations and equipment reports; they continue, in most cases, to transfer equipment title to the recipient institution. However, the recipient community has been asked to improve its equipment records and utilization.

Responding to this voluntary request, many recipients have developed systems to manage and increase utilization. One such model system was developed at Iowa State University and reported by Ditzel (1976). The system described in this chapter was developed at the University of Illinois at Urbana-Champaign, School of Chemical Sciences. The school has automated its moveable-equipment records and has initiated a shared-use procedure to encourage and document equipment utilization. The implementation of such systems may contribute to postponing or avoiding the imposition of mandatory inventory recordkeeping for all grant property.

Procedure for Shared-Use Equipment. The procedure used at the School of Chemical Sciences has three components. First, the traditional unstructured, informal sharing of equipment continues to be encouraged. However, it is desirable to record such cooperation so that informal sharing can be documented for reports to federal agencies concerning equipment utilization. The inventory system also records location changes when equipment is moved. The school's business office prepares the appropriate records and a shared-usage agreement (Exhibit 30, page 212) if desired by either party. This informal sharing procedure also governs unused equipment; if the equipment is still serviceable, it is transferred to an equipment pool for use by other sponsored projects as needed. Project directors are encouraged to check with the school's business office to see what equipment is available in the pool to meet their particular needs. This record of informal sharing and the establishment of a pool of useful equipment are substantial measures to improve utilization of existing equipment and to avoid duplication of equipment purchases.

The second component of the procedure governs equipment screening for items costing $1,000 to $10,000. When equipment items in this price range are requisitioned, the school's business office screens the equipment inventory listing to see if it shows similar equipment that might be used in place of the purchase. A copy of the screening certificate (Exhibit 31, page 213) is prepared and sent to the project director, who may then initiate a request for shared use. The equipment requisition processing through the campus purchasing office is not held up, and, if similar items are identified, the project director has ample time to initiate the shared-usage agreement before a purchasing commitment is made. A copy of the screening certificate is filed with the requisition in the project file, and another copy is put into the shared-use screening file in the school's business office.

The third procedure is the screening for equipment costing more than $10,000, a procedure similar to that for less costly items but which involves the active participation of the project director. The screening certificate (Exhibit 32, page 214) is prepared by the business office in conjunction with an actual review of the existing equipment by the project director. This screening takes place whenever an item costing more than $10,000 is to be requested in a sponsored project budget or whenever such an item is to be purchased. The screening certificate is signed by the project director and approved by the director of the school. Copies of this certificate are filed in the proposal file for sponsored projects, and in the business office's shared-use procedure file.

When equipment is budgeted from grant funds, a budget certification form (Exhibit 33, page 215) accompanies the proposal and becomes part of the budget justification for the equipment requested. The equipment budget certificate and accompanying proposal must be signed by the project director, the school's director, and an institutional official.

Inventory Management

Equipment inventory management systems have received increased attention in the past few years. As inflationary pressures and technological sophistication have dramatically affected prices, the need to manage equipment assets and resources has increased. Like shared-use agreements, equipment management systems improve accountability, utilization, and productivity.

OMB circular A-110 (1976), attachment N, prescribes uniform standards for the management of property. However, recipients may use their own property management standards and procedures, provided they observe the following standards: (1) the records must include a description of the property; manufacturer's serial number, model number, or other identifying number; the funding source(s); in whom the title is vested; acquisition date and cost; and location, use, and condition of property; and (2) the inventory must be verified every two years. While these requirements seem relatively minor, many recipients have had to place more emphasis on inventory management. In the following section we present an example of a system for automated equipment inventory.

Equipment Automated Inventory System

The equipment automated inventory system presented here is used at the University of Illinois, Urbana-Champaign campus, School of Chemical Sciences. The system meets data requirements for internal use and for federal accountability and shared-use requirements. The flexibility of the system and its ease of use make it far more efficient than manual systems. Thus automated inventory benefits the overall management of equipment and resources.

This automated system consists primarily of one main disk file and index file. The basic data contained in the file are inventory number, item description, vendor, date purchased, cost, voucher number, funding account, purchaser, location code, present location, prior location, and sort key.

All or any part of the moveable-equipment data file may be listed in whatever order the user desires. For example, a user may request a list of all items costing more than $2,500 purchased between 1970 and 1973 for any sponsored project. Users can request hard-copy reports from the file, and they have immediate access on a CRT to all the data elements in the file.

Corrections and additions to the equipment data file are recorded using a CRT terminal. After the annual physical inventory is taken, the present location codes are updated and the previous year's locations are stored as prior locations.

Inventory Report—Numerical Order. The basic inventory report lists the entire data by inventory number in numerical order (Exhibit 34, page 216). It is prepared annually as the basic reference source. This report is frequently used to identify the date of purchase and supplier of a particular piece of equipment, information that is required when equipment needs maintenance or repair parts. This report also makes it easy to identify who purchased a particular piece of equipment, what project group utilizes the equipment, and where the equipment is presently located.

Project Group Equipment. The inventory data system can prepare a listing of all the equipment purchased by a project group (identified by project director) or for courses or for the school's service facilities; for example, a user can prepare a list of all the equipment purchased by a project director during employment at the school. From this list and information about the source of funds, subsequent needs within the school are determined and decisions are made on the amount of equipment released for transfer to another unit.

Alphabetical List–Shared-Use Equipment. Specific items can be readily identified from either an alphabetical listing (Exhibit 35, page 217) or on-line access to the data base. This information is used to compare an item to be purchased with items already available within the school. The sort key identifies an abbreviated field of items that contain similar data and may be considered like items. Therefore, when a user needs to know whether equipment is available in the school for possible shared use, it is easy to find out who has similar types of instruments, where they are located, and from what funds they were purchased.

Annual Physical Inventory Verification. In preparation for a physical verification of inventory, a numerical inventory listing by rooms (Exhibit 36, page 218) is requested. Inventory takers check off those items that are still in the room and add those items that have been moved into the room, a procedure that is substantially easier than listing all the items in a room or checking off the items on a master list in numerical order. The room list serves as a worksheet for the school's annual check; it simplifies the recording of items verified and also updates the location on all equipment.

Exhibit 29. Monthly Issue—Usage Report.

STOCK NUMBER	DESCRIPTION	UNIT PRICE	UI	BAL O/H	LOCATION	UNIT LEVEL	REORDER POINT				ISSUED THIS MONTH
34 37 7400	IONEX NO 1X12 220-400 MESH CL- FORM 1#	36.21	EA	1	52-88	***	***	1****	1	2	0
	HISTORY		1	0	1	0	0	2			0
34 37 7500	DOWEX NO 2X8 52-100 MESH CL- FORM 1#	26.72	EA	1	52-88	***	***	1****	1	2	MONTH 1
	HISTORY		1	2	2	2	0	2			0
34-37 7800	DOWEX NO 50WX8 50-100 MESH H FORM 1#	17.14	EA	3	52-88	***	***	1****	2	1	MONTH 1
	HISTORY		1	0	1	0	0	0			0
34 37 8100	DRIERITE WHITE 1S	1.15	EA	37	52-4B	***	12****	12****	2	1	MONTH 2
	HISTORY		6	9	11	4	0	0			2
34 37 8400	DRIERITE INDICATING 8 MESH 1S	2.31	EA	9	52-4B	***	36****	12****	5	3	MONTH 5
	HISTORY		5		6	2	11	7			6
34 41 0600	ETHER ETHYL ANHY REAG 1S	1.16	EA	434	533	****	288****	144****	177	162	MONTH 130
	HISTORY		208	271	237	129	154	148			125
34 41 0750	ETHER ETHYL NF 27S CAN	10.17	EA	3	536	***	3****	1****	1	1	MONTH 1
	HISTORY		0	2	1	0	0	1			0
34 41 1000	ETHER ETHYL NF 5S CAN	3.44	EA	9	533	***	30****	12****	17	19	MONTH 12
	HISTORY		32	38	26	13	29	16			13
34 41 1200	ETHER PET 30-60 SKELLY F 1 GAL	1.68	EA	146	536	***	160****	54****	3	1	MONTH 1
	HISTORY		7	3	2	3	12	3			2

Exhibit 29 (continued)

34 41 1350 ETHER PET 60-68 SKELLY B 1 GAL 1.66 HISTORY	EA 34	76 E31	31 30	20	*** 19	106*** 35	*** 37	E4*** 33	56	34	26	16	MONTH 25
34 41 1500 ETHER PET 90-112 SKELLY C 1 GAL 1.63 HISTORY	EA 6	123 530	3	1	*** 2	106*** 35	*** 6	5*** 1	2	3	7	1	MONTH 2
34 41 1550 ETHER PET REAG 30-60 8 PT 2.62 HISTORY	EA 3	24 E41	4	9	*** 9	36*** 19	*** 17	12*** 7	9	11	5	7	MONTH 6
34 41 1800 ETHYL ACETATE REAG 1 FT .75 HISTORY	EA 7	10 541	6	9	*** 1	72*** 10	*** 5	24*** 5	9	3	6	5	MONTH 4
34 41 1350 ETHYL ACETATE REAG 8 PT 3.44 HISTORY	EA 8	15 541 12	11	*** 0	48*** 15	*** 22	12*** 16	6	9	4	6	MONTH 8
34 41 1860 ETHYL ACETATE SPECTRO AR 1 PT 1.66 HISTORY	EA 0	16 541 2	2	*** 2	24*** 4	*** 3	6*** 0	1	2	1	2	MONTH 1
34 41 1950 ETHYL ACETIC ACETATE PRACT 500 3.45 HISTORY GE	EA 0	1 C3-1R 0	0	*** 0	1*** 1	*** 0	0*** 1	0	0	0	0	MONTH 0
34 41 1951 ETHYL ACETO ACETATE PRACT .71 HISTORY 500 GH	GM 0	500 C3-1R 10	0	*** 0	500*** 0	*** 100	300*** 50	0	0	0	300	MONTH 50
34 41 2300 ETHYL BROMIDE REAG 1 PT 5.83 HISTORY	EA 0	2 C8-1R 2	0	*** 0	12*** 0	*** 1	4*** 2	3	1	0	0	MONTH 2
34 41 2400 ETHYL CELLOSOLVE 1 PT .22 HISTORY	EA 3	2 CE-2A 0	0	*** 0	8*** 0	*** 1	1*** 0	0	3	2	0	MONTH 1

Exhibit 30. Shared-Usage Agreement.

Date: _____

Equipment Description: _____

_____

Model No.: _____ Manufacturer: _____

Tag No.: _____ Acquisition Cost: _____

Present Location: _____

Location to be Used by Borrower: _____

Period of Shared Use: From _____ To _____

Schedule of Shared Use (if less than 24 hours a day): _____

_____

_____

Special Conditions Relating to Cost, Upkeep, Equipment, Condition, and so on:

_____

_____

_____

_____

_____

_____

_____

_____

_____

_____

_____

_____   _____   _____

Equipment Lender   Equipment Borrower   Director

Source: University of Illinois at Urbana-Champaign, School of Chemical Sciences, 1980.

Administering Facilities and Equipment

213

**Exhibit 31. Shared-Use Equipment Screening Certification
(for items costing between $1,000 and $10,000).**

Date: _____

Requisition No.: _____

Account No.: ___ ___ ___ _____

Principal Investigator: _____

Approximate Value(s): _$_____

Equipment Description: _____

_____

_____

_____

_____

The above item(s) of equipment has/have been screened against the SCS equipment inventory.

_____ No similar item(s) exist(s) within the school or is/are conveniently available.

_____ A copy of similar items is attached and has been sent to you, the PI, for determination of shared use.

_____   _____
Date   Authorized Signature

PLEASE CHECK THE LIST AND MARK THE APPROPRIATE RESPONSE:

_____ Similar items exist but are not available for shared use.

_____ Similar items exist and are available for shared use.

_____ The equipment that appears similar does not, in fact, have the same specifications as we need.

_____   _____
Date   Principal Investigator

Source: University of Illinois at Urbana-Champaign, School of Chemical Sciences, 1980.

Exhibit 32. Shared-Use Equipment Screening Certification
(for items over $10,000).

Date: _____

Requisition No.: _____

Account No.: _____ — _____ — _____ _____

Principal Investigator: _____

Approximate Value(s): __$_____

Equipment Description: _____

_____

_____

_____

_____

_____

The above item(s) of equipment has/have been screened against the SCS equipment inventory.

_____ No similar item(s) exist(s) within the school or is/are conveniently available.

_____ Apparently similar items exist but are not available for shared use (see attached explanation).

_____ Items similar to the above described equipment exist and are available for shared use (see attached Agreement).

_____   _____
      Principal Investigator   Director

Source: University of Illinois at Urbana-Champaign, School of Chemical Sciences, 1980.

**Exhibit 33. Equipment Budget Certification
(for unit acquisition costs exceeding $10,000).**

Date: _____

Agency: _____

Proposal Title: _____

_____

Proposal Effective Period: _____

Grant No. (for continuations, renewals): _____

Principal Investigator: _____

Approximate Value(s): $_____

Equipment Description: _____

_____

_____

_____

_____

_____

The above item(s) of equipment has/have been screened against the SCS equipment inventory.

_____ No similar item(s) exist(s) within the school nor is/are conveniently available.

_____ Apparently similar items exist but are not available for shared use (see attached explanation).

_____ The equipment described above is essential to the project and, if funded, will be subject to reasonable inventory controls, maintenance, and organizational policies designed to enhance multiple or shared use on other projects.

Principal Investigator	Director	Assistant Director
		Business Affairs Office

Source: University of Illinois at Urbana-Champaign, School of Chemical Sciences, 1980.

Exhibit 34. Moveable Equipment Inventory.

INVENTORY NUMBER DESCRIPTION	LOCATION PAST	PRESENT	$ VALUE	DATE PURCHASED	ORDERED FOR	ACCOUNT CHARGED CONTROL GROUP	VENDOR
701561 PUMP VACUUM	3650 NL	3650 NL	$100.30	07-72	GLENN	46-32-86-342 MILLS	HG EQUIP
701562 STIRRER MDL 101	263 RAL	261 RAL	$42.30	07-72	ANDERSON	15-32-84-950 COOPER	TALBOYS INST
701563 TELETYPE WRITTER MDL 33AR-3320	227 NL	41 NL	$14,299.42	23-73	FRANFR	15-32-84-969 GATES	DATA COLL CORP
701564 ILLUMINATOR	LOST	359 RAL	$74.00	07-72	GARY	46-32-85-346 WILLIAMS	MATHESON
701565 METER URVEY MDL 2652 S 3456N	500 RAL	503 RAL	$477.22	07-72	KRAUSE	46-32-85-357 JONES	NUCLEAR CHICAGO
701566 REGULATOR 2 STAGE STRINGNT	309 RAL	346 RAL	$64.96	08-72	SMITH	44-32-86-320 ROSS	CENTRAL STORES
701568 REGULATOR 2 STAGE STRINGNT	450 NL	450 NL	$64.96	08-72	BROWN	15-32-86-950 AIRWAN	CENTRAL STORES
701569 FILE LETTER GRAY STL 4 DR	125 NL	125 NL	$52.08	03-72	KAHN	40-32-84-100 KELLMAN	CENTRAL STORES
701570 THERMO-LIFT SER 42926	314 RAL	427 RAL	$177.14	07-72	GATZ	46-32-85-320 DEARTH	BUCHLER INST
701571 SENSOR PRESSURE MDL 550 SER 2447	262 RAL	262 RAL	$1,377.50	07-72	MCDADE	46-32-86-359 PRIMM	CENTRAL STORES
701572 CALCULATOR POCKET MDL HP S1143A-38737	213 RAL	213 RAL	$399.95	07-72	HASTINGS	46-32-86-363 MCDADE	HEWLETT-PACKARD
701573 MIXER SUPER VORTEX GENIE	500 RAL	570 RAL	$65.52	10-72	ALCORN	46-32-85-357 SNYDER	CENTRAL STORES
701574 RECORDER X-Y W ACCESS SER 1204A-03676	179 RAL LOST	LOST	$2,356.97	27-72	LOWNEY	46-32-86-371 YOUNG	HEWLETT-PACKARD
701575 AIR CONDITIONER 25000 BTU SER E217-68720	221 RAL	221 RAL	$266.53	09-72	HUTCHISON	40-32-84-100 SANDS	PHYSICAL PLANT
701576 AIR CONDITIONER 25000 BTU SER E217-68731	221 RAL	221 RAL	$266.53	09-72	DORAN	40-32-84-100 NELSON	PHYSICAL PLANT

Exhibit 35. Alphabetic Listing of Inventory Master.

DESCRIPTION INVENTORY NUMBER	ROOM HELD	$ VALUE	DATE PURCHASED	CONTROL GROUP	ORDERED FOR	ACCOUNT CHARGED	VENDOR
INCUBATORS SS MDL E2-17PH SER 1897175 723448	495 RAI	$2,626.00	02-75	CONNERS	CONNERS	46-32-85-334	WEDCO INC
INCUBATOR WATER JACKETED 723741	442 RAI	$1,999.00	06-75	STANFORD	STANFORD	46-32-85-362	KEY ASSOCIATES
INCUBATOR WATER JACKETED MDL 3212 AN MAE 443112	LOST	$1,041.64	02-71	CASTLE	CASTLE	46-32-18-315	CENTRAL STORES
INCUBATOR WATER JACKETED 3149 703231	317 RAI	$1,205.85	11-74	PATERSON	PATERSON	40-32-85-125	FORMA SCIENTIFIC
INCUBATOR WEICO SINGLE CHAMBER SER 213512 704167	317 RAI	$1,526.20	01-76	REICHARD	REICHARD	46-32-85-347	WEDCO INC
INSTRUMENT BASE SERVOMATIC SN17452 442767	365E NL	$2,220.00	06-74	STONE	STONE	46-32-19-358	RUSKA INSTR
INTEGRATOR BOXCAR PAR MDL 160 SER 126 441860	203 RAI	$3,250.00	03-69	KIRBY	FISHER	46-32-19-342	PRINCETON RES
INTEGRATOR COMPUTING MDL SP4100-01 751114	425 RAI	$5,975.00	11-79	PANDLER	HANDLER	46-32-85-378	SPECTRA PHYSICS
INTEGRATOR ELECTRONIC VARIAN SER 134 274965	425 RAI	$1,984.16	12-64	MAST	MAST	40-32-86-365	VARIAN
INTENSIFIER FOCUSED MICROCHANNEL IMAGE 725214	405 RAI	$8,750.00	11-77	WRIGHT	WRIGHT	40-32-86-105	ITT
INTERFACE COMPUTER FOR CHROMATOGRAPH 721596	0026 RAI	$1,256.44	03-72	BARNES	HAULK	46-32-95-378	HEATH

Exhibit 36. Physical Inventory—Room and Building Listing of Equipment Items.

ROOM & BUILDING: 51 NL

PAGE 1**

INVENTORY NUMBER DESCRIPTION	PREVIOUS LOCATION	$ VALUE	DATE	ORDERED FOR	ACCOUNT CHARGED	CONTROL GROUP	VENDOR
366120 DESK LAB GRAY METAL DEL PEDESTAL	51 NL	$150.20	09-63	JONES	46-32-20-137	SMITH	APPLIED PHYSICS
372615 SPECTROPHOTOMETER CARY SER 367 & ACCESS	51 NL	$13,246.59	01-66	LEE	46-32-20-137	CARSON	APPLIED PHYSICS
701653 MIXER DELUX 115V	51 NL	$77.00	07-72	DOLAN	46-32-66-137	HOFFMAN	SCIENTIFIC PROD
701662 RYSE HOT AIR M EG501	51 NL	$44.01	01-73	ALIMS	15-36-86-950	ASHER	NEWARK ELECT
702724 MIXER SUPER VORTEX GENNIE	50 NL	$65.00	05-74	CARTER	46-32-66-366	MCDOWELL	CENTRAL STORES
702726 MIXER SUPER VORTEX GENIE	51 NL	$65.00	05-74	JACKSON	46-32-36-366	COWELL	CENTRAL STORES
722786 EVAPOMIX ROTARY	528 MSB	$474.65	04-74	HARTMAN	46-32-86-366	FISHER	SCIENTIFIC PROD
703048 PUMP VACUUM LITTLE GIANT	51 NL	$119.00	06-74	FALK	46-32-86-391	HASLER	GELMAN INST
703194 BALANCE HARVARD	51 NL	$44.00	10-74	BUTLER	46-32-66-366	SMITH	SCIENTIFIC PROD
704469 BATH ASSEMBLY SER 2234	51 NL	$575.00	06-75	REDFORD	46-26-18-326	NEWMAN	SCIENTIFIC PROD
704661 WATER BATH LAUDA MDL K-2/RD SER 614010	52 NL	$816.00	14-76	EASTWOOD	46-32-66-366	BROWN	SARGENT-WELCH
725120 STIRRER MAGNETIC HEAVY DUTY	48 NL	$156.42	05-77	LEAKE	46-32-86-306	SPENCER	BELLCO GLASS

TOTAL 15,842.87

13

Preparing Reports for Sponsors

When organizations accept awards, they also accept the responsibility for submitting reports to sponsors. There are many kinds of reports, and requirements vary among sponsors. Recently, much attention has been paid to activity reporting, which serves to distinguish staff paid directly from sponsored projects funds from those included in the indirect-cost pool. These reports are also used to demonstrate the recipient's commitments to cost sharing. Activity reporting is the subject of the first section of this chapter.

The second group of reports discussed are those that describe a sponsored project's progress and are used to judge the project's worthiness for continued support. Progress reports may be required monthly, quarterly, or annually. Most sponsors, including those for basic research, also encourage recipients to report their results in professional journals. The right to disseminate project findings is always a topic in the award negotiations between an institution and a potential sponsor.

The third group of reports covered in this chapter are financial reports. The concluding section of the chapter concerns such other reports as the invention statement and certification.

Most reports are sent to the sponsor, but the institution should, of course, retain a copy that can be supplied for audit if requested. All reports should be legible, timely, and accurate. Illegible or inaccurate reports may be returned as unacceptable by sponsors, and the failure to submit required financial reports on time may result in the sponsor's withholding of future support.

Activity Reports

Activity reporting is the reporting of an employee's distribution of activity expended during a specified period. In the past, activity reporting (or time-and-effort reporting) was simpler because only those staff paid from sponsored projects were reported. But the 1979 revision of OMB circular A-21 requires that the report account for all employees who are paid directly from sponsored funds and also for all employees whose earnings are part of the indirect-cost pool or are used as evidence of cost sharing. The *total* activity, or time, of those staff included in the indirect-cost computation must be accounted for, a requirement that has raised concern from recipients, especially professorial staff. The new reporting requirements also tie the reporting system to the payroll distribution system by organizational unit. Recipients may choose between two reporting methods: personnel activity reporting or monitored workload. Most recipients choose the first method since, in many cases, it approximates their own time-and-effort reporting system.

Personnel activity reporting is the listing of the distribution of salary and wages reflecting the activity expended by each employee during the preceding reporting period. Each report must account for all the time for which the employee is compensated and reasonably reflect the percentage of activity to each sponsored project, each indirect-cost category, and each major function of the recipient institution. Each report must be signed by the employee or a responsible official who has first-hand knowledge of the work performed. Reports must be prepared at least each academic term for professional and professorial staff and at least each month for other employees. Time cards that show the activity percentage can be used to meet the requirements if properly signed and if they account for total time. Institutions are encouraged to report nonprofessional employees under the personnel activity reporting system.

The monitored workload system for professional and professorial employees is a report of projected activity percentages. Assigned workloads, as projected, must be changed if significant changes in effort occur during the reporting period. However, although the system must include the project workload, it only requires annual certification by the employee and responsible official having first-hand knowledge. This system, because of the longer reporting period, tends to allow fluctuations to smooth out over the total reporting period.

These reports are not routinely submitted to sponsors. Rather, the recipient institution retains them, and they are subject to audit by the sponsor's auditors or cognizant audit agency. Activity reporting became a controversial part of the revised A-21 and will probably undergo revisions as experience suggests workable changes.

Project Results

Project results are reported in various forms and with diverse frequency. These progress reports in many cases have a direct effect on continued support. For example, the National Science Foundation (NSF) and National Institutes of Health (NIH) require that progress reports on project results be submitted with continuation proposals. Most sponsors that support basic research expect project results to also be reported in professional journals. Published progress results always require an acknowledgement of support, and results published in other than professional journals must be accompanied by a disclaimer statement. The National Science Foundation (1978, p. 18) offers the following for an acknowledgement and disclaimer:

> [Acknowledgement:] This material is based upon work supported by the National Science Foundation under Grant _____ .
>
> [Disclaimer:] Any opinions, findings, and conclusions or recommendations expressed in this publication are those of the author(s) and do not necessarily reflect the view of the National Science Foundation.

Required project reports for NSF grants include annual progress reports and final project reports. Project directors are required to submit a technical progress report to their NSF program officer each year in multiple-year grants. The technical progress report summarizes project activities during the past year and describes any significant scientific developments or problems encountered. If available, two reprints of any publications derived from the sponsored project should be sent to NSF.

After the final year of an NSF project, a final project report (NSF Form 98A; Exhibit 37, pages 225–226) is due within ninety days. A summary of about 200 words should be included on Form 98A, and must be in language understandable to the lay public. Other information requested includes related thesis abstracts, publications, scientific collaborators, any potential inventions, pending patent applications, technical summaries of project activities and results, and any deliverables required in the award instrument.

Similar reporting requirements are necessary on NIH grants. Annual NIH continuation grant reports are called summary progress reports, and the report form is included as part of the continuation grant application packet. The final project report, due within ninety days after a project ends, is the terminal progress report. Three copies of the report and pertinent publications are required. The report should include a summary progress statement, results obtained, and a list of resultant publications. The form of this report is left to the project director's discretion; NIH does not supply a printed form.

Cooperative agreements and contracts usually require more frequent results reports, often monthly, and the report form may be specified. They often request a detailed account of the project's status so that the contracting officer and technical officer can closely monitor the results. Report requirements are usually specified in the agreement or contract.

Financial Reports

Financial reports are quite varied in content and frequency. We discussed some of these reports in earlier chapters: suggestions on proposal budgets and revisions in Chapters Eight and Ten, and internal financial reports on project status in Chapter Eleven. In this section we concentrate on financial expenditure reports prepared by recipients and sent to sponsors. Requirements for these reports are usually stated in award notices, or they appear in sponsor manuals and are incorporated into the award by reference. In all cases, it is imperative that reports be prepared accurately and forwarded to the sponsor on time.

After an award is made most recipients need to file a letter of credit and status of funds report, Treasurer Standard Form 183 (Exhibit 38, page 227). The letter of credit may be used when annual funding exceeds $250,000 and allows the recipient organization to withdraw money from its own commercial bank to meet its expenditure of funds. The commercial bank is then reimbursed by the federal reserve bank system. The form shows the name of the federal agency, authorization number, total amount requested, name of bank against which funds will be drawn, status of funds already received, and the sponsored projects for which amounts are requested and their respective amounts. In addition to certifying the amounts as correct, the authorized official must certify that the amounts requested do not exceed current needs.

Financial status reports (Exhibit 39, pages 228–229), or reports of expenditures, are required throughout the project period. Most sponsors require a final report of financial status within ninety days of the end of a project. After the close of a project, a final report of the unobligated funds balance is due, also in ninety days. Interim reports usually require that obligations and expenditures be reported.

The NSF uses a computer-produced quarterly financial report, the federal cash transactions report (SF 272A); see Exhibits 40 and 41, pages 230–231. This report, which is forwarded by the NSF, is the only financial report required, and it serves also as a final unobligated balance report after a project's close. This part of the report shows the federal share of net disbursements and the status of federal cash. The recipients simply fill in the appropriate figures for the quarter and return the report to the NSF within fifteen days.

Other Reports

Other reports may be required, as stated in the award conditions. Special reports and formats may be a condition of the award or the end product of the supported effort. The sponsor's program officer is usually willing to discuss any questions project directors or administrators may have about reporting, and to suggest ways to comply.

Most government-sponsored projects must file an invention statement. Because of the public nature of work supported by government funds, prospective inventions conceived during the project should be promptly reported. Most sponsors require this report to be submitted prior to publication of the project's results. Many continuation support proposals also require a statement of potential inventions or a certification that no inventions were made during the applicable period. Examples of final invention statements are shown in Exhibits 42 and 43, pages 232–234. An invention statement must be signed by the project director or an institutional official authorized by the recipient organization.

Exhibit 44, page 235, proposes general guidelines to help the sponsored projects administrator conform with reporting requirements.

Exhibit 37. NSF Final Project Report.

NATIONAL SCIENCE FOUNDATION Washington, D.C. 20550	FINAL PROJECT REPORT NSF FORM 98A	

PLEASE READ INSTRUCTIONS ON REVERSE BEFORE COMPLETING

PART I—PROJECT IDENTIFICATION INFORMATION

1. Institution and Address	2. NSF Program	3. NSF Award Number
	4. Award Period From To	5. Cumulative Award Amount

6. Project Title

PART II—SUMMARY OF COMPLETED PROJECT *(FOR PUBLIC USE)*

PART III—TECHNICAL INFORMATION *(FOR PROGRAM MANAGEMENT USES)*

1. ITEM *(Check appropriate blocks)*	NONE	ATTACHED	PREVIOUSLY FURNISHED	TO BE FURNISHED SEPARATELY TO PROGRAM	
				Check (√)	Approx. Date
a. Abstracts of Theses					
b. Publication Citations					
c. Data on Scientific Collaborators					
d. Information on Inventions					
e. Technical Description of Project and Results					
f. Other *(specify)*					

2. Principal Investigator/Project Director Name *(Typed)*	3. Principal Investigator/Project Director Signature	4. Date

NSF Form 98A (5-78) Supersedes All Previous Editions   Form Approved OMB No. 99R0013

Exhibit 37 (continued)

INSTRUCTIONS FOR FINAL PROJECT REPORT
(NSF FORM 98A)

This report is due within 90 days after the expiration of the award. It should be submitted in two copies to:

National Science Foundation
Division of Grants and Contracts
Post-Award Projects Branch
1800 G Street, N.W.
Washington, D.C. 20550

INSTRUCTIONS FOR PART I

These identifying data items should be the same as on the award documents.

INSTRUCTIONS FOR PART II

The summary (about 200 words) must be self-contained and intelligible to a scientifically literate reader. Without restating the project title, it should begin with a topic sentence stating the project's major thesis. The summary should include, if pertinent to the project being described, the following items:

- The primary objectives and scope of the project.
- The techniques or approaches used only to the degree necessary for comprehension.
- The findings and implications stated as concisely and informatively as possible.

This summary will be published in an annual NSF report. Authors should also be aware that the summary may be used to answer inquiries by nonscientists as to the nature and significance of the research. Scientific jargon and abbreviations should be avoided.

INSTRUCTIONS FOR PART III

Items in Part III may, but need not, be submitted with this Final Project Report. Place a check mark in the appropriate block next to each item to indicate the status of your submission.

a. Self-explanatory.
b. For publications (published and planned) include title, journal or other reference, date, and authors. Provide two copies of any reprints as they become available.
c. Scientific Collaborators: provide a list of co-investigators, research assistants and others associated with the project. Include title or status, e.g. associate professor, graduate student, etc.
d. Briefly describe any inventions which resulted from the project and the status of pending patent applications, if any.
e. Provide a technical summary of the activities and results. The information supplied in proposals for further support, updated as necessary, may be used to fulfill this requirement.
f. Include any additional material, either specifically required in the award instrument (e.g. special technical reports or products such as films, books, studies) or which you consider would be useful to the Foundation.

Exhibit 38. Letter of Credit and Status of Funds Report.

REQUEST FOR PAYMENT ON LETTER OF CREDIT
AND
STATUS OF FUNDS REPORT

SECTION I—REQUEST FOR PAYMENT

AGENCY STATION SYMBOL	LETTER-OF-CREDIT NUMBER	DOCUMENT NUMBER	AMOUNT REQUESTED $
NAME AND ADDRESS OF U.S. AGENCY	NAME AND ADDRESS OF DRAWER		PAID BY (Treasury Use Only)
NAME AND ADDRESS OF TREASURY DISBURSING OFFICE	MAKE TREASURY CHECK PAYABLE TO:		

VOUCHER APPROVED (Treasury Use Only)

CHECK NUMBER (Treasury Use Only)

SECTION II—STATUS OF FEDERAL FUNDS (Must Be Completed By Drawer)

ITEMS	ESTI-MATED NO. OF DAYS SUPPLY	AMOUNT
1. FEDERAL FUNDS ON HAND (Beginning of Federal Fiscal Year)		$
2. ADD: ADVANCES RECEIVED, FISCAL YEAR TO DATE		
3. ADD: COLLECTIONS, REFUNDS, AND/OR MISCELLANEOUS RECEIPTS		
4. Subtotal		
5. LESS: ACTUAL DISBURSEMENTS, FISCAL YEAR TO DATE		
6. FEDERAL FUNDS ON HAND AT TIME OF THIS REQUEST		
7. ADD: AMOUNT OF THIS REQUEST FOR PAYMENT		
8. ADD: UNPAID REQUESTS FOR PAYMENT PREVIOUSLY SUBMITTED		
9. TOTAL		$
10. OUTSTANDING ADVANCES TO SUB-GRANTEES—NUMBER TOTAL $		Treasury Use Only

SECTION IIA—REMARKS (Drawers Use)

SECTION III—CLASSIFICATION OF THE AMOUNT OF THIS REQUEST (Must Be Completed By Drawer)

PROGRAM, GRANT NO. OR OTHER IDENTIFYING NO.	AMOUNT	PROGRAM, GRANT NO. OR OTHER IDENTIFYING NO.	AMOUNT
	$		$
TOTAL (Must Agree with Amount of this Request for Payment)			$

SECTION IV—CERTIFICATION (Must Be Completed By Drawer)

I certify that this Request for Payment has been drawn in accordance with the terms and conditions of the Letter of Credit cited and that the amount for which drawn is proper for payment to the drawer or for credit to the account of the drawer at the drawer's bank. I also certify that the data reported above is correct and that the amount of the Request for Payment is not in excess of current needs.

DATE	SIGNATURE	TITLE
DATE	COUNTERSIGNATURE	TITLE

Standard Form 183
December 1975
Prescribed By Dept. of Treasury
I T FRM 6-2000

ORIGINAL—Drawer will forward this copy to Treasury Disbursing Office.

183-102

Exhibit 39. Financial Status Report.

FINANCIAL STATUS REPORT
(Follow instructions on the back.)

1. FEDERAL AGENCY AND ORGANIZATIONAL ELEMENT TO WHICH REPORT IS SUBMITTED

2. FEDERAL GRANT OR OTHER IDENTIFYING NUMBER

OMB Approved No. 80-RO180

PAGE ___ OF ___ PAGES

3. RECIPIENT ORGANIZATION *(Name and complete address, including ZIP code)*

4. EMPLOYER IDENTIFICATION NUMBER

5. RECIPIENT ACCOUNT NUMBER OR IDENTIFYING NUMBER

6. FINAL REPORT　☐ YES　☐ NO

7. BASIS　☐ CASH　☐ ACCRUAL

8. PROJECT/GRANT PERIOD *(See instructions)*
FROM *(Month, day, year)*　TO *(Month, day, year)*

9. PERIOD COVERED BY THIS REPORT
FROM *(Month, day, year)*　TO *(Month, day, year)*

10. STATUS OF FUNDS

PROGRAMS/FUNCTIONS/ACTIVITIES ▶	(a)	(b)	(c)	(d)	(e)	(f)	TOTAL (g)
a. Net outlays previously reported	$	$	$	$	$	$	$
b. Total outlays this report period							
c. *Less:* Program income credits							
d. Net outlays this report period *(Line b minus line c)*							
e. Net outlays to date *(Line a plus line d)*							
f. *Less:* Non-Federal share of outlays							
g. Total Federal share of outlays *(Line e minus line f)*							
h. Total unliquidated obligations							
i. *Less:* Non-Federal share of unliquidated obligations shown on line h							
j. Federal share of unliquidated obligations							
k. Total Federal share of outlays and unliquidated obligations							
l. Total cumulative amount of Federal funds authorized							
m. Unobligated balance of Federal funds							

11. INDIRECT EXPENSE	a. TYPE OF RATE *(Place "X" in appropriate box)* ☐ PROVISIONAL ☐ PREDETERMINED ☐ FINAL ☐ FIXED		b. RATE	c. BASE	d. TOTAL AMOUNT	e. FEDERAL SHARE

12. REMARKS: *Attach any explanations deemed necessary or information required by Federal sponsoring agency in compliance with governing legislation.*

13. CERTIFICATION
I certify that to the best of my knowledge and belief that this report is correct and complete and that all outlays and unliquidated obligations are for the purposes set forth in the award documents.

SIGNATURE OF AUTHORIZED CERTIFYING OFFICIAL

DATE REPORT SUBMITTED

TYPED OR PRINTED NAME AND TITLE

TELEPHONE *(Area code, number and extension)*

STANDARD FORM 269 (7-76)
Prescribed by Office of Management and Budget
Cir. No. A-110

269-101

Exhibit 39 (continued)

INSTRUCTIONS

Please type or print legibly. Items 1, 2, 3, 6, 7, 9, 10d, 10e, 10g, 10i, 10l, 11a, and 12 are self-explanatory, specific instructions for other items are as follows:

Item	Entry
4	Enter the employer identification number assigned by the U.S. Internal Revenue Service or FICE (institution) code, if required by the Federal sponsoring agency.
5	This space is reserved for an account number or other identifying numbers that may be assigned by the recipient.
8	Enter the month, day, and year of the beginning and ending of this project period. For formula grants that are not awarded on a project basis, show the grant period.
10	The purpose of vertical columns (a) through (f) is to provide financial data for each program, function, and activity in the budget as approved by the Federal sponsoring agency. If additional columns are needed, use as many additional forms as needed and indicate page number in space provided in upper right; however, the totals of all programs, functions or activities should be shown in column (g) of the first page. For agreements pertaining to several Catalog of Federal Domestic Assistance programs that do not require a further functional or activity classification breakdown, enter under columns (a) through (f) the title of the program. For grants or other assistance agreements containing multiple programs where one or more programs require a further breakdown by function or activity, use a separate form for each program showing the applicable functions or activities in the separate columns. For grants or other assistance agreements containing several functions or activities which are funded from several programs, prepare a separate form for each activity or function when requested by the Federal sponsoring agency.
10a	Enter the net outlay. This amount should be the same as the amount reported in Line 10e of the last report. If there has been an adjustment to the amount shown previously, please attach explanation. Show zero if this is the initial report.
10b	Enter the total gross program outlays (less rebates, refunds, and other discounts) for this report period, including disbursements of cash realized as program income. For reports that are prepared on a cash basis, outlays are the sum of actual cash disbursements for goods and services, the amount of indirect expense charged, the value of in-kind contributions applied, and the amount of cash advances and payments made to contractors and subgrantees. For reports prepared on an accrued expenditure basis, outlays are the sum of actual cash disbursements, the amount of indirect expense incurred, the value of in-kind contributions applied, and the net increase (or decrease) in the amounts owed by the recipient for goods and other property received and for services performed by employees, contractors, subgrantees, and other payees.

Item	Entry
10c	Enter the amount of all program income realized in this period that is required by the terms and conditions of the Federal award to be deducted from total project costs. For reports prepared on a cash basis, enter the amount of cash income received during the reporting period. For reports prepared on an accrual basis, enter the amount of income earned since the beginning of the reporting period. When the terms or conditions allow program income to be added to the total award, explain in remarks, the source, amount and disposition of the income.
10f	Enter amount pertaining to the non-Federal share of program outlays included in the amount on line e.
10h	Enter total amount of unliquidated obligations for this project or program, including unliquidated obligations to subgrantees and contractors. Unliquidated obligations are: Cash basis—obligations incurred but not paid; Accrued expenditure basis—obligations incurred but for which an outlay has not been recorded. Do not include any amounts that have been included on lines a through g. On the final report, line h should have a zero balance.
10j	Enter the Federal share of unliquidated obligations shown on line h. The amount shown on this line should be the difference between the amounts on lines h and i.
10k	Enter the sum of the amounts shown on lines g and j. If the report is final the report should not contain any unliquidated obligations.
10m	Enter the unobligated balance of Federal funds. This amount should be the difference between lines k and l.
11b	Enter rate in effect during the reporting period.
11c	Enter amount of the base to which the rate was applied.
11d	Enter total amount of indirect cost charged during the report period.
11e	Enter amount of the Federal share charged during the report period. If more than one rate was applied during the project period, include a separate schedule showing bases against which the indirect cost rates were applied, the respective indirect rates the month, day, and year the indirect rates were in effect, amounts of indirect expense charged to the project, and the Federal share of indirect expense charged to the project to date.

Exhibit 40. Federal Cash Transactions Report—Federal Share of Net Disbursements.

OMB APPROVAL NO. ZYXW

NATIONAL SCIENCE FOUNDATION
FEDERAL CASH TRANSACTIONS REPORT FOR QUARTER ENDED JULY 30, 1980
SF 272A FEDERAL SHARE OF NET DISBURSEMENTS

UNIVERSITY OF URBANA
1234567890

AWARD NUMBER	EXP DATE	GROSS AMOUNT OF AWARD	FIN. STATUS RPT. UNOBLIG. BALANCE	NET AMOUNT OF AWARD	CUM. NET DISB. THRU PRIOR QTR.	NET DISPURSEMENTS REPORTING QUARTER	RECIPIENT'S ACC'T. NUMBER
7912345	0781	$11,000.00	$ 200.00	$10,800.00	$10,500.00	$ 300.00	54321
8012345	0482	$12,000.00	$	$12,000.00	$ 3,000.00	$ 1,000.00	45678
8112345	0883	$13,000.00	$	$13,000.00	$	$ 200.00	98765
TOTAL		$36,000.00	$ 200.00	$35,800.00	$13,500.00	$ 1,500.00	

Exhibit 41. NSF Federal Cash Transactions Report—Status of Federal Cash.

OMB APPROVAL NO. ZYXW

NATIONAL SCIENCE FOUNDATION
FEDERAL CASH TRANSACTIONS REPORT FOR QUARTER ENDED JULY 30, 1980   UNIVERSITY OF URBANA
SF 272-STATUS OF FEDERAL CASH   1234567890

1. CASH ON HAND BEGINNING OF REPORTING PERIOD	$ 200.00	(COMPLETION OF LINES 17 THRU 21 IS OPTIONAL)
2. LETTER OF CREDIT WITHDRAWALS	$ .00	
3. NON-LETTER OF CREDIT PAYMENTS	$14,800.00	17. TOTAL NET AWARDS (FROM SF 272A) $35,800.00
4. TOTAL RECEIPTS (2 + 3)	$14,800.00	18. CUM. NET. DISB. THRU PRIOR QTR.(FROM SF 272A) $13,500.00
5. TOTAL CASH AVAILABLE (1 + 4)	$15,000.00	19. NET DISB. FOR REPORTING QTR. (FROM SF 272A) $ 1,500.00
6. GROSS DISBURSEMENTS	$ 1,700.00	20. UNEXPENDED BALANCE (17 - 18 - 19) $20,800.00
7. NSF SHARE OF PROJECT INCOME	$ 300.00	21. BALANCE AUTHORIZED (20 - 10) + 10 IF DEFICIT) $ 7,400.00
8. NET DISBURSEMENTS (6 - 7)	$ 1,400.00	
9. ADJUSTMENTS OF PRIOR PERIODS	$ 200.00	22. REMARKS:
10. CASH ON HAND END OF PERIOD (5 - 8 + OR - 9)	$13,400.00	
		LINE 9 REPRESENTS REVISED FINANCIAL STATUS
		REPORT SUBMITTED TO NSF ON 8/15/80 FOR 1234500
11. LAST LETTER OF CREDIT DOCUMENT	N/A	
12. NO. OF LETTER OF CREDIT PAYMENTS RECEIVED	N/A	
13. NO. OF NON-LETTER OF CREDIT PAYMENTS RECEIVED	2	
14. NO. OF DAYS CASH ON HAND REPORTED ON LINE 10	15	
15. INTEREST INCOME	$ .00	
16. ADVANCES TO SUBGRANTEES OR SUBCONTRACTERS	$ .00	

23. CERTIFICATION: I CERTIFY THAT TO THE BEST OF MY KNOWLEDGE AND BELIEF THIS REPORT IS TRUE IN ALL RESPECTS AND THAT ALL
                   DISBURSEMENTS HAVE BEEN MADE FOR THE PURPOSES AND CONDITIONS (INCLUDING COST-SHARING REQUIREMENTS AS
                   STATED IN THE NSF GRANT POLICY MANUAL)

NAME: JOHN DOE   SIGNATURE: TITLE: COMPTROLLER   DATE: 09/22/81   PHONE NO: 202-632-4006

PLEASE MAIL THE COMPLETED ORIGINAL AND COPY 1 TO THE DIVISION OF FINANCIAL AND ADMINISTRATIVE MANAGEMENT, NATIONAL
SCIENCE FOUNDATION, WASHINGTON, DC. 20550 BY NO LATER THAN 15 WORKING DAYS AFTER RECEIPT FROM NSF. INQUIRES
REGARDING THE FEDERAL CASH TRANSACTIONS REPORT (SF272 AND SF272A) SHOULD BE DIRECTED TO THE DIVISION OF
FINANCIAL AND ADMINISTRATIVE MANAGEMENT (202)632-4006. INQUIRES REGARDING THE STATUS OF FINAL REPORTS SHOULD
BE DIRECTED TO THE DIVISION OF GRANTS AND CONTRACTS (202)632-4108.

Exhibit 42. DHHS Final Invention Statement and Certification.

GRANT OR AWARD

DHEW GRANT OR AWARD NUMBER

We hereby certify that, to the best of our knowledge and belief, all inventions are listed below which were conceived and/or first actually reduced to practice during the course of work under the above referenced DHEW grant or award for the period, _____

through _____ .
(DATE OF TERMINATION)   (ORIGINAL EFFECTIVE DATE)

(If no inventions have been made under the grant or award, insert the word "None" under Title of Invention.)

NAME OF INVENTOR	TITLE OF INVENTION	DATE REPORTED TO DHEW

Use Continuation Sheet if Necessary

Signature, in ink, is required in the space provided below, appropriate to the type of grant or award being supported.
SIGNATURE OF INSTITUTIONAL OFFICIAL REQUIRED IN ALL INSTANCES.

TYPE OF GRANT OR AWARD	SIGNATURES
1. FOR A RESEARCH GRANT	(PRINCIPAL INVESTIGATOR OR PROJECT DIRECTOR)
2. FOR A HEALTH SERVICES GRANT	(DIRECTOR)
3. FOR TRAINING GRANT	(PROGRAM DIRECTOR)
4. FOR THE RESEARCH CAREER AWARD PROGRAM	(AWARDEE)
5. FOR A FELLOWSHIP OR DIRECT TRAINEESHIP AWARD _____	(a) (FELLOW OR TRAINEE) (b) (SPONSOR)
6. FOR OTHER TYPES OF GRANTS IDENTIFY TYPE: _____	(RESPONSIBLE PROGRAM OFFICIAL)

APPROVED:	SIGNATURE (INSTITUTION OFFICIAL)	TITLE	DATE
	TYPE NAME		
	NAME OF INSTITUTION	MAILING ADDRESS	

OS FORM 489 (8/68)

Exhibit 43. EPA Final Invention Statement.

Date _____

SUMMARY REPORT OF INVENTIONS AND
SUBAGREEMENTS OR SUBCONTRACTS

The following report must be submitted in *triplicate* as part of the interim or final report as provided for by the patent clause in the grant or contract.

NAME OF CONTRACTOR	ADDRESS
DESCRIPTION OF WORK	
CONTRACTOR'S PRINCIPAL INVESTIGATOR	GOVERNMENT TECHNICAL PROJECT MONITOR

Grant or Contract No.	

(Check appropriate boxes)

1. Type of Report:

☐ Interim ⎰ From _____, 19___
           ⎱ To _____, 19___

☐ Final.

2. Interim Report Data:

   A. Invention made ☐, not made ☐, during interval of *(1)*.

   B. If invention(s) made, provide the following information:
      ☐ Previously fully disclosed in Invention Disclosures. Give dates submitted, and Grantee or Contractor's docket numbers.

      _____ _____ _____ _____

      _____ _____ _____ _____

      _____ _____ _____ _____

      ☐ Invention Disclosures attached herewith. Give Grantee or Contractor's docket numbers.

      _____ _____ _____

      _____ _____ _____

      _____ _____ _____

                                    (1)   (OVER)

EPA Form 3340-4 (Rev. 3-76)   PREVIOUS EDITION MAY BE USED UNTIL SUPPLY IS EXHAUSTED.

Exhibit 43 (continued)

3. Final Report Data:	Date Submitted	Grantee or Contractors Docket Number
A. Invention(s) previously reported—		
B. Invention(s) reported herewith—		

C. Others *(explain)*—

D. No inventions were made under the grant or contract. ☐

4. Patent application(s) filed and contemplated to be filed by the Grantee or Contractor under the terms of the grant or contract:

Application Serial No. . Date of filing . . . . Contractor's Docket No.				

5. Subagreements or Subcontracts containing patent rights clause:

☐ None.   ☐ Listed below are subcontractors.

Name of Subcontractor	Address	Subcontract Number	Date Executed
(1)			
(2)			
(3)			
(4)			

6. Attach a copy of the patent rights clause employed in each subagreement or subcontract set forth in 5.

7. Grantee or Contractor certification.

I certify that this Summary Report of Inventions Subagreements and Subcontracts including any attachments is correct to the best of my knowledge and belief.

Date _____

Signature_____

Title _____

EPA Form 3340-4 (Rev. 3-76) (Reverse)

(2)

Exhibit 44. Guidelines for Filing Reports.

Publishing

- Don't forget to acknowledge support when publishing a sponsored project's results.
- Disclosure statements are needed when publishing in other than professional journals.
- Publish results in journals with wide circulation.
- Don't give up the right to publish in scholarly journals when negotiating sponsored projects.

Reporting

- Don't use abbreviations and acronyms in long reports or where they appear infrequently.
- Report nonprofessional staff activity at least monthly.
- Professional and professorial staff on personnel activity system must be reported at least once an academic term or every six months, whichever is shorter.
- Prepare financial reports accurately and legibly, and send to sponsor on time.
- Don't neglect to notify sponsor promptly of any potential inventions resulting from the sponsored project.
- Letter of credit requests may not exceed current needs.
- Summary reports should be concise and understandable to lay readers.
- Show your appreciation for support received by submitting reports on time.

14

Compliance with Legal and Ethical Requirements

Institutions that receive funds from federal agencies must comply with federal mandates. The nature and scope of such compliance depend largely on the types of research being conducted. If an institution receives a substantial amount of federal sponsorship for research, it is subject to a very regulated system of review procedures and approvals. Compliance topics, generally, are areas of concern that affect certain aspects of research, such as the use and care of animals in research, patent and copyright policies, and the use of human subjects. The special attention given to these areas reflects the concerns of the public, the government, and the research community for the protection of certain rights and privileges. In this chapter we briefly present the major compliance issues emphasized in current federally sponsored research programs.

Care of Laboratory Animals

During World War II the demand accelerated for more and better laboratory animals for use in teaching and research, and the animal

236

colonies at universities grew very rapidly. After the war, a sizable number of university staff members were responsible for overseeing the care of their institutions' laboratory animal populations. These individuals often wrote policies for the care and use of animals in their custody.

From 1945 until 1953, many university animal-care professionals met informally to discuss better ways of breeding and maintaining animals. In 1953, the Animal Care Panel was formally incorporated in Illinois. Since then, the American Association for Accreditation of Laboratory Animal Care (AAALAC), the American Association for Laboratory Animal Science (AALAS), and the Institute of Laboratory Animal Resources (ILAR) have actively undertaken the improvement of animal care. Universities and their staffs contributed to the maintenance of these voluntary associations, which set very high ethical standards for membership and institutional accreditation.

The AAALAC program has achieved wide acceptance. The National Institutes of Health (NIH) recognizes AAALAC accreditation as the best means of demonstrating institutional compliance with NIH policies for the care and use of laboratory animals. The Veterans Administration (VA) also recognizes the AAALAC and has applied for accreditation of all VA centers having laboratory animal research facilities. Many university facilities are accredited by the AAALAC. AAALAC offices are located at 2317 West Jefferson Street, Suite 135, Joliet, Ill. 60435.

In the late 1950s and early 1960s, Congress was besieged by requests from animal owners to pass legislation on "dog-napping." These citizens were concerned about pets' being stolen and then being sold to an organization for scientific experimentation. In 1966, Congress passed the Animal Welfare Act of 1966 (Public Law 89-544) to protect the owners of animals from the theft of their pets, to prevent the sale or use of stolen animals, and to ensure that animals intended for research facilities receive humane care and treatment.

In 1970 and 1976, amendments were passed to further regulate the transportation, purchase, sale, housing, care, handling, and treatment of animals used for research and certain other purposes. These rules are now published in the *Code of Federal Regulations (CFR)*, title 9 (Animals and Animal Products), subchapter A—Animal Welfare, parts 1, 2, and 3. Amendments to the regulations are periodically published in the *Federal Register* under the heading "Department of Agriculture, Animal and Plant Health Inspection Service." Copies of the rules and regulations can be obtained from the Offices of the Deputy Administrator, U.S. Department of Agriculture, Animal and Plant Health Inspection Service, Veterinary Services, Federal Building, 6505 Belcrest Road, Hyattsville, Maryland 20782.

Requirements of the Department of Agriculture

The U.S. Department of Agriculture (USDA) is the federal agency delegated to implement the provisions of the Laboratory Animal Welfare Act. The department's general requirements for universities are as follows (U.S. Department of Agriculture, 1979, section 2.76):

1. Every research facility shall make, keep and maintain systems of records that correctly disclose for dogs and cats purchased:
   a. Name and address of seller
   b. Date of acquisition
   c. USDA tags
   d. Description of animal
   e. Research subject number
   f. Transportation data of transported animals
   g. USDA health certificates for individual animals (VS Form 18-1), multianimals (AVS Forms 18-2), and dogs and cats on hand (VS Form 18-5). These and other records specified in title 9, chapter 1, section 2.77, must accompany each shipment of any live dog or cat sold.
2. University officials shall allow inspection by the veterinary services representative of facilities, property, and animals.
3. Each animal care facility shall provide records for the veterinary services representative's examination.
4. The university shall provide for the humane handling, care, treatment, and transportation of dogs and cats.
5. The university shall follow humane care procedures for rabbits, hamsters, and nonhuman primates.
6. The university shall follow animal health and husbandry standards outlined in the *Code of Federal Regulations.*
7. The university is required to comply with fifty pages of specifications for facilities and reporting requirements found in 9 *CFR* 1–3.

8. Each university research facility is required to submit an annual report, VS Form 18-23, to the USDA (see Exhibit 45, page 270).

The annual report summarizes the number and type of animals used as research subjects and categorizes the state of the animal during experimentation. The staff veterinarian usually prepares the report and in many cases the director of the office of sponsored projects signs as the responsible university official.

Department of Health and Human Services' Policy

Congress decreed that institutions receiving federal funds for research should comply with the Animal Welfare Act and instructed the cognizant government audit agencies to prepare appropriate policies to ensure humane treatment of animals. The Department of Health and Human Services (DHHS) has adopted the policies of its predecessor, the Department of Health, Education and Welfare (HEW). Institutions that use animals in projects or other activities supported by the agency's funds, grants, awards, or contracts must assure the agency in writing that they will evaluate on a continuing basis their animal facilities regarding the care, use, and treatment of such animals. Consistent with the standards established by the Animal Welfare Act, no grant or contract involving the use of animals will be awarded to an institution unless such assurance has been filed (U.S. Department of Health, Education and Welfare, 1978a, 1978b). No grant or contract will be awarded to an individual who is not affiliated with an institution that has accepted responsibility for administration of the funds awarded and has filed an assurance with the agency.

The Animal Welfare Act and subsequent agency policies require reporting by universities. Universities receiving DHHS funds for research using animals must provide assurances to DHHS that they will comply with standards established by the Animal Welfare Act (see Exhibit 46, page 271).

In addition to complying with federal regulations, higher education administrators have the scientific and ethical responsibility to assure the welfare of animals used for research and education. Frequently, the office of sponsored projects is given the responsibility of assuring that the institution's provisions for animal care conform to the regulations and that the organization's procedures promote the project directors' freedom to plan and conduct animal experiments in accord with accepted scientific practices. The office of sponsored projects should establish policies and create an environment that encourages project directors to seek new and better methods for laboratory animal care.

Institutional Policy

Sponsored projects administrators must recognize that each research project has special requirements. The institution's general policy must both assure the welfare of the laboratory animals and allow researchers' *professional judgment* to determine the interpretation of such policy in given cases.

A sponsored projects administrator who has the responsibility for animal care should first find a good veterinarian. Larger universities usually have a staff veterinarian in charge of all animal-care facilities. These professionally trained individuals are in the best position to make informed decisions on general policy and daily operations. Small universities frequently place a consultant veterinarian on retainer. For a relatively modest fee, the consultant veterinarian assists the animal-care technicians in establishing standard operating procedures, performs a periodic examination of facilities, and provides veterinary care for needy animals.

The sponsored projects administrator, with the assistance of the veterinarian consultant, researchers, and animal-care staff, should draft a set of recommended policies that provide for the proper care and humane treatment of animals during their stay on campus.

First, the policy should mandate adequate veterinary care to be provided by either a staff member or consultant who has postdoctoral training in NIH-sponsored training programs, preceptorships, and residencies at various animal-care facilities. The veterinarian should have authority to supervise the animal husbandry programs, to monitor animal experimentation, and to inspect the physical facilities. The staff veterinarian should also be responsible for verifying the health of the animals, providing medical services for ill or injured animals, applying prophylaxis and therapy appropriate for each species, and establishing procedures for disease containment and surveillance.

Second, the policy should authorize the office of sponsored projects to establish an animal-care committee that is representative of the various users, the heads of the various animal facilities, and the staff veterinarian. The chairperson of this committee should probably be someone other than the staff veterinarian, in order to assure accountability for performance of the animal-care providers to individuals who are outside the jurisdiction of the professional staff.

Third, the policy should provide funds for an external evaluation of the campus animal-care facilities and practices. Such evaluation is important to the general morale of researchers and animal-care staff. The American Association for Accreditation of Laboratory Animal Care provides such evaluations at modest fees.

The sponsored projects administrator, in addition to ensuring that appropriate institutional policies and practices are established, may be responsible for managing the regulatory system for the care of animals. Duties in this area include the responsibilities for:

- Monitoring the care and use of animals.
- Making provisions for necessary veterinary care.
- Selecting highly qualified professional staff and well-trained animal-care personnel.
- Instituting training programs for undergraduate, graduate, and postdoctoral students who work with the animals.
- Assuring that professionals with specialized knowledge and skills are present when hazardous agents are used.
- Implementing standard operating procedures associated with experimentation involving hazardous agents.
- Monitoring the animal-care facilities to assure that housing or caging, sanitation, and feeding and watering are adequate, that animal identification and recording systems are appropriate, and that facilities provide quarantine and isolation rooms, and separate rooms by species and source.

Patent Policy

Business Week ("Researcher . . . ," 1981) recently reported that colleges are discovering a profit in patents and that, as traditional research funds decline, universities and nonprofits become more eager to explore patent income as a new source of support. While patenting and licensing are expensive processes, institutions can earn high revenues; MIT obtained $19 million for patents on core memory for computers and $10 million from Bristol-Myers for synthetic penicillin. Columbia University received over $3.5 million for the original laser patents and $2 million for burn ointments. Other universities have similar success stories. Now many universities are, in their negotiations with industries that support their research, insisting that they retain control of any patents that develop from their research or that they share in the revenues generated from industrial licensing and patent royalties ("Education . . .", 1981).

Patents offer organizations a means to obtain a monetary return on their research investment. Therefore, the director of sponsored projects must know the patent system and have a general understanding of the mechanisms necessary to effect the patenting and development process.

The significant practical factors that the office of sponsored projects should consider in drafting a patent policy include:

- The effect of particular patent policies in encouraging research, scholarship, and proposals for sponsored projects
- The state law regarding inventions made by state employees
- The monetary gain, or loss, that the institution can expect in implementing a particular patent policy
- The incentives or disincentives that a particular patent and copyright policy offers faculty
- The equitable disposition of interests in inventions among the project director, the sponsor, and the institution, and the distribution of patent costs
- The relationship of the patent policy to the overall mission of the institution to maximize the dissemination of scientific research findings
- The safeguarding of intellectual property developed by researchers while using institutional resources
- The acceptance of sponsored projects that require all inventions conceived during the grant period to be considered the sponsor's property
- The mechanism by which the institution will determine the significance of innovation for commercial exploitation

- The requirement by sponsors that the results of research leading to commercially exploitable inventions cannot be published until after the sponsor has patented the invention

The patent policy should make some reference to the following topics. First, it should reaffirm the dominance of the institution's missions in all activities over any other motive. Second, it should state that project directors, administrators, students, and other institution employees who, in connection with their work in the institution, make a discovery that has the possibility for commercial exploitation are to disclose the nature and detail of this discovery to the office of sponsored projects. The policy should explain the legitimacy of the institution's claim to an interest in the invention when the invention is rendered into practice in connection with institutional work. Third, the policy should describe both the financial benefits that accrue to project directors and the mechanisms the institution uses to advance research with funds it obtains from inventions. Fourth, the policy should outline the responsibility for administration of the patent policy and procedures, including the names of individuals or corporations with such responsibility. Fifth, the policy should describe the procedures for record keeping; dates and 'acts constituting conception, reduction to practice, and continuance must be corroborated.

Exhibit 47, pages 272–276, serves as an excellent model for a university patent policy. It contains the essential elements that govern the development of a discovery into a public commodity for which the institution can then obtain a financial return.

Administering the Policy

Although a patent policy may provide a thorough explanation of how the policy is to be implemented, the office of sponsored projects will probably be asked to explain the reasons for the adopted conventions. For example, the office may be asked to explain the rationale for the disclosure provisions. In this case, the office should be prepared to state the several general functions served by disclosure: (1) It provides a basis for the technical evaluation of the invention for patent purposes; (2) It may establish a date of invention for patent purposes if prior corroborating materials are deficient; (3) It provides information about the inventor that aids a patent attorney in drafting legal documents; (4) It allows the sponsor's legal officers to review the invention should the institution elect to forward the invention for patenting; (5) It assists the inventor in clarifying the inventive concept and describing it; and (6) It enhances the inventor's chances of obtaining a quality novelty search in the patent office.

There are several reasons that seemingly good inventions will be rejected by the patent committee for inclusion in the joint development process—for example, if the invention is not marketable in the next twenty years, if a novelty search indicates the invention is not novel, or if the invention is an obvious extension of existing know-how. Similarly, if the invention is publicly disclosed by publishing, by submitting an abstract to a conference, by discussing the invention in a conference presentation, or even by the presentation of a student thesis, the inventor may prejudice patent action for many countries, including the United States. Finally, computer software is difficult, if not impossible, to patent, and chemical compounds, especially food and drugs, cannot themselves be patented.

These reasons do not, however, preclude the inventor from pursuing a patent at personal expense if the organization's policy allows the release of patent rights to the inventor.

The Disclosure Statement

The office of sponsored projects is usually delegated to draft a disclosure form or a set of guidelines for preparing a disclosure statement. In this task, thoroughness is more important than format. The disclosure statement is one of the most important documents in the patent development process. Most sponsors require, under terms of their research agreements, a precise disclosure of inventions conceived during supported research. Exhibit 48, pages 277–278, presents a sample disclosure form.

There are professional firms that assist educational institutions in patent administration. Three of these companies, Research Corporation, University Patents, Inc., and Battelle, have a long history in working with colleges and universities. These organizations need a complete and accurate invention disclosure statement to assess the value of the invention and to determine their commitment to carry it forward to patenting and commercial development.

Work with federal sponsors on patent rights is becoming more financially attractive as the agencies conform to the intent of the Patent and Trademark Amendments of 1980 (PL 96-517). The law gives universities and nonprofits a first right of refusal to title in inventions made in performance of federal grants and contracts, subject to some limited exceptions. In creating this right to ownership, the government dramatically changed its previous policy and abolished some twenty-six conflicting statutory and administrative policies. The new provisions for invention disclosure and application procedures for nonprofit organizations require the contractor: (1) to disclose any inventions made under federal sponsorship to the federal agency within six months of disclosure to the contractor; (2) to elect whether or not to retain title to any such invention by notifying the federal agency within twelve months of disclosure to the contractor; (3) to file its initial patent application on an elected invention within two years after election; and (4) to file patent applications in additional countries within either ten months of the corresponding initial patent application, or six months from the date a license is granted by the Commissioner of Patents and Trademarks to file foreign patent applications when such filing is prohibited for security reasons. As there are many exceptions to these general provisions, the sponsored projects officer should consult OMB bulletins for further information on title rights, protection of the government's interest, subcontracts, reporting on utilization of subject inventions, and march-in rights (Office of Management and Budget, 1982).

As of March 1, 1982, OMB circulars take precedence over all previous patent regulations for small firms and nonprofit organizations. These regulations implement landmark patent legislation for universities and nonprofits. Responsibilities and opportunities that previously rested with federal government agencies for holding title to inventions now reside in universities, nonprofit organizations, and small businesses. With this transfer comes the need for the office of sponsored programs to establish and administer an institutional patent program, in a fashion consistent with the intent of Congress, to further technology transfer and initiate a significant increase in the commercialization of inventions.

The special projects administrator must recognize that patent laws change frequently and that the intellectual property rights of research scientists must be protected. The special projects administrator should be working closely with legal counsel to develop policies that govern such new topics as the employer's and employee's rights in cell lines, genetic innovation, microorganism deposition and maintenance, claims to the DNA molecule, and foreign and U.S. patent application disclosure requirements. In the coming decades, the sponsored projects administrator and the patent lawyer will need to design and implement optimum patent protection for genetically engineered microorganisms, cells, and related processes. Biological technology and other new fields open many legal questions that require close collaboration among the researchers, legal counsel, and sponsored projects administrators, who should coordinate these collaborative efforts.

The patenting process is a highly specialized and complex effort that requires technical assistance from a patent attorney. General sources of information include the National Association of College and University Business Officers' booklet *Patents at Colleges and Universities* (1974), Rosenberg's *Patent Law Fundamentals* (1979), and Palmer's *University Research and Patent Policies, Practices and Procedures* (1962). The Society of University Patent Administrators, a voluntary organization of professionals, can provide basic knowledge about patent administration. Sponsored projects administrators are advised to develop a professional patent-counseling source for the institution and to direct the inventors to that service with their questions about a particular invention.

Copyright

A copyright is the right of ownership to an intellectual property. The ownership of the created intellectual product resides exclusively in the creator or the creator's employer. In dealing with copyright questions, the sponsored projects administrator should consult two major sources for guidance: organizational policy and copyright law.

The office of sponsored projects has a responsibility to its organization and to the public to obtain from its activities the greatest organization and public benefit. Sponsored projects result from ideas, and new ideas may yield patents or copyrights. Thus the institution's policy should encourage faculty to generate new ideas and should provide an equitable distribution of credit and responsibility between the creator and sponsor.

Institutional Policy

Many institutions devise policies concerning intellectual property that differentiate between independent and sponsored activities. Activities conducted by staff members on their own time and at their own expense are considered independent activities, and most institutions make no claims or restrictions on any copyrights or discoveries obtained as the result of independent activities. Individual staff members, however, may voluntarily assign all or part of their claims to the results of independent activities to the institution.

Activities conducted by a staff member with the help of the institution, either in the form of a grant or time assigned to an activity, are considered institution-sponsored activities. For such activities, a typical policy stipulates the following:

- If institutional aid does not exceed $3,000 in a fiscal year, or a cumulative total of $5,000, for an individual's research, either in actual funds or in salary for assigned time, or for both together, the institution usually is not considered to have established a right to share in the results.
- If institutional aid exceeds these limits and if results are obtained from research that is part of the regular duties and responsibilities of the staff member, the institution and the researcher usually share equally, unless an agreement in writing specifies otherwise. Individuals who participate in such institution-sponsored programs are considered to have agreed to this principle.
- The institution, or its designated agent, may sometimes assume full responsibility for obtaining a copyright, and for protecting and promoting the property rights inherent in such a copyright, for works arising from institution-sponsored research. Such an arrangement is believed to produce the greatest benefit to the institution and the public.
- Staff members are responsible for reporting to the proper institutional authorities any development coming from institution-sponsored activities that should be protected by copyright.
- When an agreement specifying individual and institutional rights, claims, and responsibilities is to be made, it should be made in writ-

ing before application for a copyright resulting from institution-sponsored activity is submitted to the Register of Copyrights.

• Any controversy or claim arising out of or relating to statements of policy or an agreement between a staff member and the institution delineating individual and institutional rights, claims, and responsibilities, or the breach thereof, should be settled by arbitration in accordance with the rules then obtaining of the American Arbitration Association and judgment upon the award rendered may be entered in the highest court of the forum, state or national, having jurisdiction.

Regarding externally sponsored activities, contracts between the institution and other agencies should state clearly the obligations and rights of the institution and of the sponsoring agency and the procedure to be followed should materials subject to copyright develop from the grant. In each case the institution should be free to negotiate with the sponsoring agency concerning rights to copyright.

Copyright Law

In analyzing any question related to copyright law, the sponsored projects administrator should remember that copyright laws are intended to promote the dissemination of knowledge for the common good and to protect authors who make their knowledge available to the general public.

The basis for modern copyright law is PL 94-553 (1976). This law incorporates a series of complex modifications to previous laws. These changes, needed to meet the technological revolution of the last half of the twentieth century, seriously affect the activities of researchers, musicians, artists, composers, authors, computer programmers, publishers, and broadcasters. Sponsored projects administrators deal with such individuals daily and are expected to understand the relevant laws and to protect these individuals' rights from infringement by government or private sponsors. More than fifty sections of this copyright reform law have either direct or indirect bearing on the administration of sponsored activities.

Although Congress attempted to abolish the differences between the protection given by the common law and federal copyright laws, some voids in the new law are filled by state law. For example, unfixed creative works (improvisations, speeches, lectures, and nonscripted live performances) are unprotected by PL 94-553. Creative artists or researchers who wish to obtain copyright protection for unfixed works must seek such protection under the common law of their state.

Several excellent references provide up-to-date information on changes in the copyright laws and on strategies for managing intellectual property. The *Copyright Law Reporter* (1981), a two-volume looseleaf reporter, is a comprehensive publication designed to serve as a self-contained, comprehensive source for information related to the 1976 revision of the copyright law. Reports on the latest changes and new developments related to copyrights are issued monthly. The core of the *Copyright Law Reporter* consists of topical editorial explanations that summarize and explicate the disparate laws, regulations, cases, and background matters related to copyright law.

Sperber's *Intellectual Property Management* (1980) provides a single, comprehensive source that a sponsored projects administrator can turn to for practical guidance in effectively and successfully dealing with innovation development. Sperber provides considerable insight into the general processes of conception, acceptance, and selection of innovations for commercial success. The recommendations in this book concern patent management as well as copyrights.

A convenient and authoritative guide through the maze of copyright technology and public policy is Henry's *Copyright, Congress and Technology: The Public Record* (1980), a five-volume collection that explores the political brawling associated with the copyright policy and law. Henry makes the point that copyright is one of the least recognized, but most important, public policies of our time, and he argues convincingly that sponsored projects administrators learn more about the formation of policy related to the copyright industry, the biggest business in the United States.

Under the new law, a copyright inheres in creative works the moment the works are recorded, whether or not they are ever published, as long as the works involved are "works of authorship that are fixed in a tangible medium and come within the subject matter of copyright." Works of authorship include the following categories: literary, musical, and dramatic works; pantomimes and choreographic works; pictorial, graphic, and sculptural works; motion pictures and other audiovisual works; and sound recordings.

Copyright protection for an original work does not extend to any idea, procedure, process, system, method of operation, concept, principle, or discovery, regardless of the form in which it is described or embodied. Plans for explaining scientific theories, commercial processes, and accounting systems to laymen cannot be copyrighted since presentation of scientific and systematic information generally can be made only in the way the knowledge mandates. However, the Copyright Office will generally register claims to copyrights with respect to schematic diagrams, mylar sheets, photolithographic masks, and imprinted patterns. Imprinted design patterns of semiconductor chips are tangible representations of the designer's effort that should be protected by copyright.

Authors of original works can be denied copyright ownership when the work is produced under a grant or contract. If a proposal specifies that an author is to create an original work for a federal sponsor, that work can be denied copyright when it is in the public interest to do so.

The sponsored projects administrator should inform the principal investigator that any reference in the proposal or contract to the creation of original works must be excluded if the principal investigator wants to obtain copyright ownership. Principal investigators may secure copyrights for works they have written independently, outside their official duties and beyond the scope of the work described in the proposal, even though the subject matter relates to their sponsored work or professional field.

Copyrights, like patents, are a very specialized field. The sponsored projects administrator should seek legal counsel on the fine points of the law. Only the general provisions of the law are summarized here.

Researchers should first understand the ease of copyrighting an original work. The creator copyrights a work merely by placing a readily visible notice of copyright on the work. The notice of copyright contains three elements:

- The symbol ©, or the word *Copyright*, or the abbreviation *Copr.*
- The year in which the work was completed or presented
- The name of the owner

For example, by placing one of the following on the upper-right corner of the cover page of a paper, John Doe can acquire copyright protection for his manuscript:

Copyright
John Doe   or   © John Doe, 1981
   1981

For placement of copyright notice on other original works, the sponsored projects administrator should see the Register of Copyright publications that suggest specific methods of affixing and positioning the copyright notice on various types of works.

The sponsored projects administrator is often called on to assist the creative artist, researcher, or art group in specifying the terms for ownership of copyright and in completing the recording process for the copyright ownership and transfer. The following general provisions have particular relevance to the management of sponsored activities:

- *Initial ownership:* Copyright in a work vests initially in the author or authors of the work. The authors of a joint work are co-owners of a copyright in the work.
- *Works made for hire:* In the case of a work made for hire, the employer or other person for whom the work was prepared is considered the author and, unless the parties have expressly agreed otherwise in a written instrument signed by them, owns all rights comprised in the copyright.
- *Contribution to collective works:* Copyright in each separate contribution to a collective work is distinct from copyright in the collective work as a whole, and vests initially in the author of the contribution.
- *Transfer of ownership:* The ownership of a copyright may be transferred in whole or in part by any means of conveyance or by operation of law and may be bequeathed by will or pass as personal property.

When sponsored projects administrators become involved in discussion of ownership of copyrights, they should consider the following key points of the law:

- *Ownership of copyright:* Ownership of copyright is distinct from ownership of any material object in which the work is first embodied.
- *Conditions for recordation:* Any transfer of copyright ownership may be recorded in the Copyright Office. Recordation is a prerequisite to the initiation of litigation if it is an infringement action (see Exhibit 49, pages 278–282).

- *Duration of copyright:* In general, copyright subsists from its creation and endures for a term consisting of the life of the author and fifty years after the author's death. Thus institutional recordation of date of first publication, of certificate of transfers, and date of author's death have significant bearing on ownership rights.

The sponsored projects administrator should inform the creator who seeks copyright protection that the owner of a copyright has the exclusive rights to authorize and to do any of the following: (1) to reproduce the copyrighted work in copies or phonorecords; (2) to prepare derivative works based upon the copyrighted work; (3) to distribute copies or phonorecords of the copyrighted work to the public by sale or other transfer of ownership, or by rental, lease, or lending; (4) in the case of literary, musical, dramatic, and choreographic works, pantomimes, and motion pictures and other audiovisual works, to perform the copyrighted work publicly; and (5) in the case of literary, musical, dramatic, and choreographic works, pantomimes, and pictorial, graphic, or sculptural works, including the individual images of a motion picture or other audiovisual work, to display the copyrighted work publicly.

The creator should also be informed that the work is subject to fair use once it is placed before the public. The law defines *fair use* as use of a copyrighted work for purposes such as criticism, comment, news reporting, teaching, scholarship, or research; such use is not an infringement of copyright. In any given case, fair use is determined by considering the purpose and character of the use, including whether such use is of a commercial nature or is for nonprofit educational purposes; the nature of the copyrighted work; the amount and substantiality of the portion used in relation to the copyrighted work as a whole; and the effect of the use on the potential market for or value of the copyrighted work.

Creators are entitled to the protection of law for their original works and to the rewards associated with creative, intellectual, or aesthetic labor. Disputes about the copyrightability of elements of mechanical or scientific devices are frequently taken to court for resolution.

Protection of Human Research Subjects

A comprehensive explanation of the government's role in developing regulations regarding research on human subjects is offered by

McCarthy (1980). The Public Health Service (PHS) played a leading role in formulating a coherent national policy for the protection of human research subjects. In 1953, the National Institutes of Health's (NIH) Clinical Center issued general guidelines for obtaining informed consent from subjects and for organizing competent committees to analyze the risks and benefits of the research to subjects. In 1964, the Helsinki declaration brought international attention to the rights of human research subjects. In 1965, the Center for Law and Medicine at Boston University, after three years of extensive study, released their report on general policies and operational procedures current in the medical and behavioral sciences and recommended improvements in existing provisions. In 1966, Surgeon General Steward issued a memorandum stating more definitive policies for institutions' human subjects review committees. This policy was revised several times, and in the early 1970s, PHS policy was expanded in scope to include *all* research involving human subjects supported by the Department of Health, Education and Welfare. In 1974, the National Research Act (PL 93-348) required that institutions review their human subjects review committees and make appropriate assurances to the PHS when applying for funds. These guidelines, viewed by some institutions project directors as increased government regulation, were reluctantly accepted in the research community.

In January 1981, the Department of Health and Human Services (DHHS) responded to recommendations of the National Commission and the President's Commission for the Study of Ethical Problems in Medicine, and Biomedical and Behavioral Research. DHHS amended its regulations concerning institutional review boards. These amendments reduce the scope of previous regulations by exempting broad categories of research that normally present little or no apparent risk to subjects.

Federal Policies

The cornerstone of federal policy governing research involving human subjects is the regulations contained in the document "Public Health Service Human Research Subjects" (U.S. Department of Health and Human Services, 1981).* This document stipulates that research

---

*Copies of the regulations are available from the Office for Protection from Research Risks, National Institutes of Health, Bethesda, MD 20205.

activities supported by DHHS involving human subjects, unless exempt, must have review and approval by an institutional review board (IRB) approved by DHHS. The review must determine that:

- Risks to subjects are minimized by the use of procedures that are consistent with sound research design and that do not unnecessarily expose subjects to risk; and, whenever appropriate, by the use of procedures already being performed on the subjects for diagnostic or treatment purposes.
- Risks to subjects are reasonable in relation to anticipated benefits, if any, to subjects, and the importance of the knowledge that may reasonably be expected to result.
- Selection of subjects is equitable.
- Informed consent will be sought from each prospective subject or the subject's legally authorized representative, and will be appropriately documented, in accordance with, and as required by, 45 C.F.R. 46.
- When appropriate, the research plan makes adequate provision for monitoring the data collected to ensure the safety of subjects.
- When appropriate, there are adequate provisions to protect the privacy of subjects and to maintain the confidentiality of data.
- If some or all of the subjects are likely to be vulnerable to coercion or undue influence, appropriate additional safeguards are included in the study to protect the rights and welfare of these subjects.

No individuals may receive DHHS funds for research covered by the regulations unless they are affiliated with an institution that assumes responsibility for the research as provided in the regulations or they make other arrangements with DHHS.

The DHHS rules also provide for: requirements for assurances;* IRB membership, functions, and operations; expedited review procedures; cooperative research; general requirements for informed consent and documentation of consent; and additional protections pertaining to

*Samples of assurances (both multiple and single project) that meet the requirements of 45 C.F.R. 46 are available from the Office for Protection from Research Risks, National Institutes of Health, Bethesda, MD 20205.

research involving fetuses, pregnant women, human *in vitro* fertilization, and prisoners.

Exempt Research. The amended regulations of 1981 exempt several classes of research activities involving human subjects from the DHHS regulations. These classes of research generally do not involve risks to subjects or have very minimal risks that do not require the protections provided by the regulations. However, exemption from DHHS regulations does not relieve institutions or investigators from responsibility to meet the requirements of other applicable federal and state laws and regulations, especially with regard to informed consent, or from responsibilities of various professional codes of research ethics.

Broadly speaking, the regulations exempt: (1) Most types of no-risk or low-risk educational research; (2) research on a variety of types of test development when no or low risk is involved and subjects are not identified; (3) interview, survey, or observational research, unless identifiers are used *and* the divulging of the answers of individually identified respondents to questions relating to the subject's own behavior (such as alcohol and drug use, sexual behavior, or other sensitive matters) would adversely affect the subject's employability, financial standing, or legal liability; and (4) research that uses existing data, records, or specimens and that does not involve retaining identifiers.

Determination of whether a class of research is exempt calls for attentive reading of the regulations and careful consideration of all aspects of the proposed research activity. Erroneous claims of exemption on research applications or proposals submitted to DHHS could delay processing and review.

Requirements of the Food and Drug Administration. The Food and Drug Administration's (FDA) requirements for IRB review and informed consent are now virtually identical to those of DHHS, except for small areas in which the FDA's statutory mandate differs from that of DHHS. The FDA is mandated to regulate research—whether or not funded by DHHS—under the Food, Drug and Cosmetic Act. The FDA regulations apply to research designed to test the safety and efficacy of drugs and medical devices that are intended to be marketed.

In enforcing its mandate to assure protection of human research subjects in research under its purview, the FDA relies on an inspection system. Institutions or firms conducting research covered by the FDA regulations are spot-checked to determine if the procedures they employ to protect human subjects are in compliance with FDA rules. Because many institutions, especially universities and affiliated teaching hospitals, carry on a significant amount of research subject to FDA rules, there is some degree of overlap with DHHS regulations. The FDA often relies on the DHHS's assurances, which detail the procedures used to ensure protection of human subjects, in determining whether these institutions are adequately safeguarding the rights and welfare of human subjects. The virtual uniformity of current FDA and DHHS regulations considerably reduces the problems institutions face in compliance. However, the FDA system of ensuring compliance still remains one of retrospective verification of compliance based on inspection of selected single protocols.

Each of five FDA bureaus manages IRB programs: Bureau of Drugs, Bureau of Biologics, Bureau of Medical Devices, Bureau of Radiological Health, and Bureau of Foods. Each bureau is responsible for enforcing the applicable parts of Title XXI of the *Code of Federal Regulations.* The FDA regulations on IRBs and informed consent appear in the *Federal Register,* January 27, 1981, pp. 8942–8980.

Responsibilities of Institutions

Institutions have the primary responsibility for the protection of human research subjects. This responsibility was placed upon institutions by federal and state statutes and by case law. The National Research Act of 1974 mandates that the safeguarding of the rights and welfare of subjects at risk in activities supported under grants and contracts from DHHS is *primarily the responsibility of the institution* that receives or is accountable to DHHS for the funds awarded to support the activity. Further, any nonexempt activity involving human subjects may be undertaken only after IRB review and approval, which must be certified by the institution and submitted to DHHS, in accordance with the requirements of PL 93-348, as implemented by Part 46 of Title 45 of the *Code of Federal Regulations,* as amended.

Usually, the office of sponsored projects has the operational responsibility of assuring compliance with DHHS and FDA regulations and monitoring institutional policy. Specifically, the office of sponsored projects is responsible for developing (1) specific procedures for full IRB review and for expedited IRB review; (2) guidelines stating the basic elements of informed consent, which is a prerequisite for human research subjects; (3) a policy that indicates the circumstances under which an IRB may approve withholding or altering some or all of the elements of informed consent otherwise required; (4) a policy for IRB membership requirements; and (5) procedures by which the institution is to assure compliance with the regulations on the part of all its employees and staff.

Doudera (1980) warns that an institution's failure to restrain a project director's research if such research is unauthorized by the IRB could subject the institution to legal liability to the subjects involved both under the theory of informed consent and under Section 505(i) of Title XXI of the *U.S. Code of Regulations,* which permits investigations with non–FDA-approved drugs only with the consent of the subject, *and* imposes this responsibility for obtaining consent upon the institution.

Doudera suggests that sponsored projects administrators examine their bylaws and policies to assure that they are updated and approved by DHHS in accordance with 45 C.F.R. 46. These policies must recognize and acknowledge the legal authority of the local IRB for final approval of biomedical and behavioral research on human subjects performed within the institution.

DHHS requires that the submission of all research proposals involving human subjects be accompanied by DHHS Form 596, which certifies that the IRB has reviewed and approved the proposal and that the institutional officials concur. Should an institution fail to comply with a review and concurrence, the proposal is considered incomplete and will be returned.

Institutional Assurances. The institution must assure DHHS that it will comply with the DHHS policy for protection of human subjects. The institutional assurance should include three sections.

First, the assurance should contain a statement of principles that govern the institution in the discharge of its responsibilities for protecting the rights and welfare of human subjects of research conducted at or sponsored by the institution, regardless of source of funding. This section may include an appropriate existing code, declaration, or statement of ethical principles, or a statement formulated by the institution itself.

Second, the assurance must designate one or more IRBs established in accordance with the requirements of the regulations and for which provisions are made for meeting space and sufficient staff to support the board's review and recordkeeping duties. Appended to this description should be a list of the IRB members identified by name, earned degrees, representative capacity, indication of experience (such as board certifications and licenses) sufficient to describe each member's chief anticipated contributions to IRB deliberations, and any employment or other relationship between each member and the institution.

Third, the assurance should outline the procedures the IRB will follow in (1) conducting its initial and continuing reviews and reporting its findings and actions to the investigator and the institution; (2) determining which projects require review more often than annually and which projects need verification from sources other than the investigators that no material changes have occurred since previous review; (3) ensuring prompt reporting to the IRB of proposed changes in a research activity; (4) ensuring that changes in approved research may not be initiated without IRB review and approval except when necessary to eliminate apparent immediate hazards to the subject; and (5) ensuring prompt reporting to the IRB and to the Secretary of DHHS of unanticipated problems involving risks to subjects or others.*

The assurance must be executed by an individual authorized to act for the institution and to assume on behalf of the institution the obligations imposed by the regulations.

Sample assurances are available from the NIH Office for Protection from Research Risks (OPRR). One sample is for an institution that conducts or sponsors a relatively large amount of research involving human subjects; a second is for an institution that has only a limited amount of research funded by DHHS. Both samples incorporate all the elements necessary to comply with the new regulations. They are useful aids that can be adapted to meet the organizational structure of a particular institution.

OPRR also provides copies of the complete DHHS regulations for the protection of human subjects and related laws, regulations, and notices, including the regulations concerning additional protections required for research involving human fetuses, pregnant women, and

*Reports should be filed with the Office for Protection from Research Risks, National Institutes of Health, Department of Health and Human Services, Bethesda, MD 20205.

human *in vitro* fertilization as well as for research involving prisoners. OPRR can also provide a list of the categories of expedited review. From time to time, the office sends out notices of clarification or information on matters relating to the protection of human subjects. A revised version of guidelines and commentary on the regulations and related issues should be available from OPRR in the near future.

Institutional Review Boards (IRBs). The prime responsibility of IRBs is to assure the adequate protection of human subjects by review, and when necessary, by requiring modification of particular proposals and of informed-consent procedures. Current DHHS policy (45 C.F.R. 46) specifically requires that:

- An IRB shall review and have authority to approve, require modifications in (to secure approval), or disapprove all research activities covered by the regulations.
- An IRB shall require that information given to subjects as part of informed consent is in accordance with §46.116 of the regulations. The IRB may require that information, in addition to that specifically mentioned in §46.116, be given to the subjects when in the IRB's judgment the information would meaningfully add to the protection of the rights and welfare of subjects.
- An IRB shall require documentation of informed consent or may waive documentation in accordance with §46.117.
- An IRB shall notify investigators and the institution in writing of its decision to approve or disapprove the proposed research activity, or of modifications required to secure IRB approval of the research activity. If the IRB decides to disapprove a research activity, it shall include in its written notification a statement of the reasons for its decision and give the investigator an opportunity to respond in person or in writing.
- An IRB shall conduct continuing review of research covered by the regulations at intervals appropriate to the degree of risk, but not less than once per year, and shall have authority to observe or have a third party observe the consent process and the research.
- An IRB shall be responsible for reporting to the appropriate institutional officials and the OPRR any serious or continuing noncompliance by investigators with the requirements and determinations of the IRB.

An IRB may use an expedited review procedure to review minor changes in previously approved research during the period for which approval is authorized. The only research for which an IRB may use an expedited review procedure is that which involves no more than minimal risk to the subjects *and* in which the *only* involvement of human subjects will be in one or more of the following categories:

- Collection of hair and nail clippings—in a nondisfiguring manner—deciduous teeth, and permanent teeth if patient care indicates a need for extraction.
- Collection of excreta and external secretions including sweat, uncannulated saliva, placenta removed at delivery, and amniotic fluid at the time of rupture of the membrane prior to or during labor.
- Recording of data from subjects eighteen years of age or older using noninvasive procedures routinely employed in clinical practice. This includes the use of physical sensors that are applied either to the surface of the body or at a distance and do not involve input of matter or significant amounts of energy into the subject or an invasion of the subject's privacy. It also includes such procedures as weighing, testing sensory acuity, electrocardiography, electroencephalography, thermography, detection of naturally occurring radioactivity, diagnostic echography, and electroretinography. It does not include exposure to electromagnetic radiation outside the visible range (for example, x-rays, microwaves).
- Collection of blood samples by venipuncture, in amounts not exceeding 450 milliliters in an eight-week period and no more often than two times per week, from subjects eighteen years of age or older and who are in good health and not pregnant.
- Collection of both supra- and subgingival dental plaque and calculus, provided the procedure is not more invasive than routine prophylactic scaling of the teeth and the process is accomplished in accordance with accepted prophylactic techniques.
- Voice recordings made for research purposes such as investigations of speech defects.
- Moderate exercise by healthy volunteers.
- The study of existing data, documents, records, pathological specimens, or diagnostic specimens.
- Research on individual or group behavior or characteristics of indi-

viduals, such as studies of perception, cognition, game theory, or test development, where the research investigator does not manipulate subjects' behavior and the research will not involve stress to subjects.

- Research on drugs or devices for which an investigational new drug exemption or an investigational device exemption is not required.
- Any other category specifically added to this list by DHHS and published in the *Federal Register.*

The expedited review is to be conducted by the IRB chairperson or by one or more of the experienced IRB members designated by the chairperson to conduct the review. A sample of an IRB review form for research involving human subjects and of adult and minor consent forms for participating in an experimental project are presented in Resource E at the back of the book.

Informed Consent. The institution must assure that all persons who will be subjects of research have explained to them in easy-to-understand language the purposes and procedures of the experiment, and what will happen to them as subjects. Informed consent requires the knowing consent of an individual, or his legally authorized representative, so situated as to be able to exercise free power of choice without undue inducement or any element of force, fraud, deceit, duress, or other form of constraint or coercion.

The basic elements of informed consent include:

- A statement that the study involves research, an explanation of the purposes of the research and the expected duration of the subject's participation, a description of the procedures to be followed, and identification of any procedures that are experimental.
- A description of any reasonably foreseeable risks or discomforts to the subject.
- A description of any benefits to the subject or to others which may reasonably be expected from the research.
- A disclosure of appropriate alternative procedures or courses of treatment, if any, that might be advantageous to the subject.
- A statement describing the extent, if any, to which confidentiality of records identifying the subject will be maintained.
- For research involving more than minimal risk, an explanation as to whether any compensation and whether any medical treatments are

available if injury occurs and, if so, what they consist of, or where further information may be obtained.

- An explanation of whom to contact for answers to pertinent questions about the research and research subjects' rights, and whom to contact in the event of a research-related injury to the subject.
- A statement that participation is voluntary, that refusal to participate will involve no penalty or loss of benefits to which the subject is otherwise entitled, and that the subject may discontinue participation at any time without penalty or loss of benefits to which the subject is otherwise entitled.

In addition, other elements of informed consent may be required when appropriate. Generally, the IRB makes this determination based on information furnished by the investigator. The additional elements may include:

- A statement that the particular treatment or procedure may involve risks to the subject (or to the embryo or fetus, if the subject is or may become pregnant) that are currently unforeseeable.
- Anticipated circumstances under which the subject's participation may be terminated by the investigator without regard to the subject's consent.
- Any additional costs to the subject that may result from participation in the research.
- The consequences of a subject's decision to withdraw from the research and procedures for orderly termination of participation by the subject.
- A statement that significant new findings developed during the course of the research which may relate to the subject's willingness to continue participation will be provided to the subject.
- The approximate number of subjects involved in the study.

In certain situations, an IRB may modify or waive the informed consent requirements in DHHS-funded research. One such situation is in the evaluation or demonstration of government benefit or service programs when the research could not be practicably carried out without the modification or waiver of informed consent. Another such situation is in minimal-risk research in which the modification or waiver will not adversely affect the rights and welfare of the subjects and the research could not be practicably carried out without the waiver or alteration.

Obligation to Obtain Informed Consent. An institution is obligated to ensure that researchers obtain legally effective informed consent, unless the IRB waives the requirement in accordance with 45 C.F.R. 46. However, the informed-consent requirements in these regulations do not preempt any applicable federal, state, or local laws that require additional information to be disclosed in order for informed consent to be legally effective. Nor do the regulations limit the authority of a physician to provide emergency medical care, to the extent the physician is permitted to do so under applicable federal, state, or local law. The informed consent, oral or written, may not include any exculpatory language through which the subject is made to waive, or appear to waive, any of his legal rights, including any release of the institution or its agents from liability for negligence.

Documentation of Informed Consent. Informed consent is to be documented by the use of a written consent form approved by the IRB and signed by the subject or the subject's legally authorized representative. Written consent forms may be of two types: (1) a written consent form that embodies the elements of consent as approved by the IRB; or (2) a short form which states that the elements of consent have been presented orally. This oral presentation must be witnessed, and an approved written summary must be signed by the witness and the person obtaining the consent. Copies of the summary and the short form are to be given to the subject or the subject's representative. Either type of consent form must be signed by the subject or the subject's legally authorized representative.

An IRB may, however, waive the requirement for obtaining a signed consent form in certain circumstances. When the principal risk is the harm resulting from a breach of confidentiality, then, if the subject so chooses, the consent form need not be signed. The IRB may waive the requirement for written consent if the research involves only minimal risk and written consent is not normally required outside the research setting.

Compensation of Human Subjects for Physical Injury. Broseghini (1980) points out several problems the office of sponsored projects may encounter in implementing DHHS compensation rules. He specifically mentions the problems of (1) incorporating compensation clauses in informed-consent statements; (2) composing a readable informed-consent statement; (3) paying costs of IRBs and their insurance; and (4) obtaining insurance compensation for human research subjects.

Many university medical research clinics provide free medical care for all control subjects and for those patients whose adverse effects can be shown to be related to the procedures of a research study; these clinics also provide some care if any investigational drug or device is involved. But the procedures developed by various institutions for compensation are strikingly diverse. Current DHHS regulations require, in the case of research that has more than minimal risk, that subjects be informed of the institution's policy concerning medical treatments and compensation for injury. The information must be included in the informed-consent form whenever the IRB determines that the research involves more than minimal risk.

The issue of compensation for research injury has been most recently under study by the President's Commission for the Study of Ethical Problems in Medicine and in Biomedical and Behavior Research. The office of sponsored projects director can remain apprised of new developments by periodically surveying the *Federal Register* and reading specialized reviews such as *IRB A Review of Human Subjects Research* (1979), published by The Hastings Center.

Research Involving Recombinant DNA

Beginning in 1976, the NIH has periodically issued guidelines governing the conduct of research involving recombinant DNA molecules. These guidelines are intended to minimize potential risks by delineating stringent safeguards for the conduct of experiments involving the production of recombinant DNA molecules and their insertion into organisms such as bacteria. Institutions must follow these NIH guidelines and observe state and local regulations. But in large measure the safety of recombinant DNA research depends on how the project directors and their research teams apply these guidelines. Motivation and critical judgment are essential, in addition to particular safety precautions, to secure protection of the research personnel, the public, and the environment.

The NIH guidelines can help the office of sponsored projects and the project director determine the nature of appropriate safeguards, but these guidelines are incomplete because all conceivable experiments with recombinant DNA could not be anticipated at the time of writing. Therefore, they must be supplemented by the project director's knowledgeable and discriminating evaluation. For example, if a project director sees a need to increase containment above levels indicated in the guidelines, he or she has a responsibility to implement such an increase. This type of change may require adjustments in laboratory facilities and procedures, and the office of sponsored projects may become involved. In contrast, the containment conditions called for in the guidelines may not be eased without review and approval by the institution and the NIH.

The discussion of responsibilities and procedures in this section follows the NIH guidelines.

Project Director's Responsibilities

The project director has the primary responsibility for: (1) determining the real and potential biohazards; (2) determining the appropriate level of biological and physical containment; (3) selecting the microbiological practices and laboratory techniques; (4) designing procedures for mitigating accidental spills and overt personnel contamination; (5) determining the applicability of various precautionary medical practices, serological monitoring, and immunization; (6) obtaining approval of the proposed research before beginning work; (7) submitting pertinent information on purported EK2 and EK3 systems to the NIH Recombinant DNA Molecule Program Advisory Committee and on making the strains available to others; (8) informing the institutional biohazards committee and the NIH Office of Recombinant DNA Activities about new information that affects the guidelines, such as technical information relating to hazards and new safety procedures or innovations; (9) applying for approval from the NIH Recombinant DNA Molecule Program Advisory Committee for large-scale experiments with recombinant DNA known to yield harmful products; (10) applying to NIH for approval to lower containment levels when a cloned DNA recombinant derived from a shotgun experiment has been rigorously characterized and there is sufficient evidence that it is free of harmful genes.

Prior to conduct of hazardous research, the project director must supply the program and support staff with copies of those portions of the approved grant application that describe the biohazards and the precautions to be taken, and inform them of the nature and assessment of the real and potential biohazards. The director must also train staff in the practices and techniques required to ensure safety, and in the procedures for dealing with accidentally created biohazards. Finally, the director must inform the staff of the reasons and provisions for any advised or requested precautionary medical practices, vaccinations, or serum collections.

During the conduct of the research, the project director must supervise the safety performance of the staff. The director is to investigate and report to proper authorities any extended illness of a worker; any accident that results in inoculation through cutaneous penetration, ingestion of recombinant DNA materials, or probable inhalation of recombinant DNA materials; and any incident that causes serious exposure to personnel or danger of environmental contamination. The director must ensure the integrity of the physical containment, and must investigate problems pertaining to the operation and implementation of biological and physical containment, safety practices and procedures, or equipment or facility failure. All such events must be reported. The director also must correct any work errors or conditions that may result in the release of recombinant DNA materials.

Institution's Responsibilities

Since almost all NIH grants are made to institutions rather than to individuals, all the preceding responsibilities of the project director are also the responsibilities of the institution. Usually the director of the office of sponsored projects is charged with seeing that these standards are maintained. The institution must also establish a biohazards committee to advise the institution on policies; create and maintain a central reference file and library of catalogues, books, articles, newsletters, and other communiques as a source of advice and reference regarding the potential biohazards associated with certain recombinant DNAs; develop a safety and operations manual for any P4 facility maintained by the institution and used in support of recombinant DNA research; and certify to the NIH that the facilities, procedures, practices, and the training and expertise of the personnel have been reviewed and approved.

Biohazards Committee. The NIH guidelines stress that the biohazards committee must be sufficiently qualified, through the experience, expertise, and the diversity of its membership, to ensure respect for its advice and counsel. Its membership should include individuals from the institution or consultants selected to provide a diversity of professionals competent to assess recombinant DNA technology, biological safety, and engineering. The committee should also possess, or have available to it, the competence to determine the acceptability of its findings in terms of applicable laws, regulations, standards of practice, community attitudes, and health and environmental considerations. Minutes of the committee's meetings should be kept and made available for public inspection. The institution is responsible for reporting the names and professional qualifications of the members of its biohazards committee to the NIH.

Adelberg (1980, p. 177) reports that the Yale Institutional Biosafety Committee (IBC) "consists of 15 members, including the director of the Division of Occupational and Environmental Health Services (DOEHS), University Health Service; the Biological Safety officer; the director of the University Utilities and Engineering Services; and three nonuniversity members: an attorney, a civil engineer, and a microbiologist. The Executive Secretary of the IBC is an assistant to the deputy provost of the university. The Biological Safety officer is a virologist and epidemiologist and the director of the Department of Biological Safety, a unit of the DOEHS. He also holds a senior faculty position in the Section of Comparative Medicine, School of Medicine. His staff includes a full-time technician who assists him in his duties on behalf of the IBC as well as in his other functions in the Department of Biological Safety."

Reporting to NIH. The office of sponsored projects frequently is in charge of maintaining liaison with the administrative staff and study groups of NIH. Usually, this type of communication is conducted through documents such as that shown in Exhibit 50, pages 283–284.

National Institutes of Health's Responsibilities

NIH Study Sections. NIH Study Sections make an independent evaluation of the real and potential biohazards of the proposed research on the basis of the NIH guidelines; determine whether the proposed physical and biological containment safeguards certified by the institutional biohazards committee are appropriate for control of these biohazards; and refer to the NIH Recombinant DNA Molecule Program

Advisory Committee or the NIH Office of Recombinant DNA Activities those problems pertaining to the assessment of biohazards or safeguard determination that they cannot resolve.

NIH Recombinant DNA Molecule Program Advisory Committee. The Recombinant DNA Molecule Program Advisory Committee advises the DHHS and the NIH on the evaluation of potential biological and ecological hazards of recombinant DNAs, on the development of procedures designed to prevent the spread of hazardous DNA molecules within human and other populations, and on guidelines for researchers working with potentially hazardous recombinants.

NIH Staff. NIH staff are responsible for assuring that no NIH grants or contracts are awarded for DNA recombinant research unless they conform to NIH guidelines, have been properly reviewed and recommended for approval, and include a properly executed memorandum of understanding and agreement (Exhibit 50); reviewing and responding to questions, problems, and reports submitted by institutional biohazards committees or project directors, and disseminating findings as appropriate; receiving and reviewing applications for approval to lower containment levels when a cloned DNA recombinant derived from a shotgun experiment has been rigorously characterized and there is sufficient evidence that it is free of harmful genes; referring questions, reports, and applications to the NIH Recombinant DNA Molecule Program Advisory Committee, as deemed necessary; and performing site inspections of all P4 physical containment facilities engaged in DNA recombinant research, and of other facilities as deemed necessary.

Current Sources of Information

The office of sponsored projects staff can stay abreast of the latest development in DNA regulations by reading the NIH *Recombinant DNA Technical Bulletin,* which publishes material in the following areas:

- Scientific information and reports of recent progress in such areas as: (1) isolation, purification, and substrate specificity of restriction endonucleases; (2) development of methods for the construction of recombinant DNA molecules; (3) development and use of effective and safer cloning vehicles and host cells; (4) isolation of specific prokaryotic and eukaryotic genes and expression of such molecules in different host cells; and (5) determination and reduction of potential hazards.

- A periodically updated listing of host-vector systems certified by the NIH.
- Actions taken by NIH and news and comments, including new and revised versions of national guidelines as issued or proposed by the United States and other countries; analysis of legislation affecting recombinant DNA research; and reports of scientific meetings.
- Announcements of training courses in experimental and safety aspects of recombinant DNA research; the availability of contract proposals; future meetings; and NIH policy issuances concerning recombinant DNA research.
- Bibliography of scientific and technical articles, and articles on public policies, laws, and ethics relating to recombinant DNA research.

Exhibit 45. USDA Annual Report Form.

This report is required by law (7 USC 2143). Failure to report according to the regulations can result in an order to cease and desist and to be subject to penalties as provided for in Section 2150.

UNITED STATES DEPARTMENT OF AGRICULTURE ANIMAL AND PLANT HEALTH INSPECTION SERVICE VETERINARY SERVICES **ANNUAL REPORT OF RESEARCH FACILITY** *(Required For Each Reporting Facility Where Animals Are Held And An Attending Veterinarian Has Responsibility)* RCS # 34-VS-56	1. DATE OF REPORT FORM APPROVED OMB NO. 40-R3777 2. HEADQUARTERS RESEARCH FACILITY *(Name & Address, as registered with USDA, include Zip Code)*

INSTRUCTIONS: Reporting Facility complete items 1 through 24 and submit to your Headquarters Facility. Attach additional sheets if necessary.

3. REGISTRATION NO.:

Headquarters Facility complete items 25 through 27 and submit on or before December 1 of each year for the preceding Federal fiscal year (October 1, to September 30) to the Veterinarian in Charge for the State where the research facility headquarters is registered.

4. REPORTING FACILITY *(Name and Address, include Zip Code)*

REPORT OF ANIMALS USED IN ACTUAL RESEARCH, TESTING, OR EXPERIMENTATION - Section 2.28 of Animal Welfare Regulations requires appropriate use of anesthetics, analgesics, and tranquilizing drugs during research, testing, or experimentation. Experiments involving pain or distress without use of these drugs must be reported and a brief statement explaining the research.

ANIMALS COVERED BY ACT A	Number of animals used in research, experiments, or tests involving no pain or distress. B	Number of animals used in research, experiments, or tests where appropriate anesthetic, analgesic, or tranquilizer drugs were administered to avoid pain or distress. C	Number of animals used in research, experiments, or tests involving pain or distress without administration of appropriate anesthetic, analgesic, or tranquilizer drugs. *(Attach brief explanation.)* D	TOTAL E
5. Dogs				
6. Cats				
7. Guinea Pigs				
8. Hamsters				
9. Rabbits				
10. Primates				
Wild Animals *(Specify)* 11.				
12.				
13.				
14.				
15.				

CERTIFICATION BY ATTENDING VETERINARIAN FOR REPORTING FACILITY OR INSTITUTIONAL COMMITTEE - I (We) hereby certify that the type and amount of analgesic, anesthetic, and tranquilizing drugs used on animals during actual research, testing, or experimentation including post-operative and post-procedural care was deemed appropriate to relieve pain and distress for the subject animal.

16. SIGNATURE OF ATTENDING VETERINARIAN	17. TITLE	18. DATE SIGNED
19. SIGNATURE OF COMMITTEE MEMBER	20. TITLE	21. DATE SIGNED
22. SIGNATURE OF COMMITTEE MEMBER	23. TITLE	24. DATE SIGNED

CERTIFICATION BY HEADQUARTERS RESEARCH FACILITY OFFICIAL

I certify that the above is true, correct, and complete and that professionally acceptable standards governing the care, treatment, and use of animals including appropriate use of anesthetic, analgesic, and tranquilizing drugs, during actual research, testing, or experimentation including post-operative and post-procedural care are being followed by the above research facilities or sites (7 U.S.C. Section 2143)

25. SIGNATURE OF RESPONSIBLE OFFICIAL	26. TITLE	27. DATE SIGNED

VS FORM 18-23
(SEP 78)   *Previous editions are obsolete.*

Exhibit 46. DHHS Examples of Acceptable Assurance Statements.

Assurances may take one of several forms depending on circumstances, but should include the information provided by one or more of the examples below, be dated, and be signed by an authorized representative of the institution:

1. This institution uses or intends to use significant numbers of warm-blooded animals in activities supported by DHHS grants, contracts, or awards. We are accredited by the American Association for Accreditation of Laboratory Animal Care—AAALAC. Our director(s) of laboratory animal care, as listed with AAALAC, are as follows: (insert name(s), degree(s), title(s)). Our accreditation applies to the following facilities and components of this institution:

    _____

    _____

    Records of accrediting body determinations will be available for inspection by the Secretary, DHHS, or his authorized representative.

2. This institution uses or intends to use significant numbers of warm-blooded animals in activities supported by DHHS grants, contracts, or awards. We have established a committee of at least three members, at least one of whom is a Doctor of Veterinary Medicine, (insert name), to evaluate the care of all warm-blooded animals held or used for research, teaching, or other activities supported by DHHS grants, contracts, or awards. The committee will be responsible for animals housed at the following facilities and components of this institution:

    _____

    _____

    The evaluation committee will periodically inspect the animal facilities of this institution and report its findings and recommendations to the institution's responsible officials on a schedule the committee determines necessary; but in no case will these reports be issued less than annually. Records will be kept of committee activities and recommendations. These records will be available for inspection by the Secretary, DHHS, or the Secretary's authorized representatives.

Source: Department of Health and Human Services, 1978.

Exhibit 47. Sample Patent and Invention Policy.

I. Preamble

Patentable discoveries or inventions occasionally result from research or educational activities performed at a university. Northwestern University desires to assure that all ideas and discoveries are properly disclosed and utilized for the greatest possible public benefit. The university also desires to protect the patent rights of the Northwestern University faculty, staff, and student body, and to abide by patent regulations of agencies providing funds for sponsored programs. The following paragraphs present to the members of the Northwestern Community the university's policy on patents, inventions, and discoveries.

II. Coverage

The Northwestern University Patent Policy applies to all faculty, administrators, staff, students, or other individuals who receive financial support from the university or who use university facilities or materials in the process of conceiving an idea, invention, or discovery.

All faculty and research staff are required, as a condition of their employment, to sign a patent agreement assigning to the university their right to patents, inventions, and discoveries covered under the above paragraph. Students engaged in research supported by federal or state funds, and students receiving payment by the university while engaged in research, are also required to sign such a patent agreement.

III. Administration

The administration of this Patent Policy will reside in the office of the vice-president for research. The office of the university attorney shall be consulted on all legal matters pertaining to this policy.

IV. Faculty Patents Committee

A Faculty Patents Committee shall be appointed by the president of the university or his designate and will include five to seven faculty members, with the vice-president for research an ex-officio member. A representative of the vice-president for research and one from the office of the university attorney shall serve as nonvoting members of the committee. The committee shall meet periodically upon call of the chairman to review existing patent policy, to recommend any desired changes, and to receive reports on the status of the patent portfolio. The vice-president for research or his designate will present periodic reports on the status of disclosures and patent applications to the committee for its review. When necessary, the committee shall meet with the vice-president for

Exhibit 47 (continued)

research or his representative if an inventor asks the vice-president for a review by the Faculty Patents Committee of decisions relating to, or policies affecting, his invention or discovery. The Faculty Patents Committee shall normally report its decisions to the Board of Trustees through the vice-president for research.

V. Disclosure

All members of the Northwestern community who are covered by this policy shall disclose the nature and detail of their invention or discovery to the vice-president for research or his designated representative.

Within 120 days after such disclosure the vice-president for research or his designate shall notify the inventor in writing whether or not it is the university's intention to retain its interest and to acquire assignment of all ownership rights to the invention or discovery. If such notification cannot be made during that time period, the inventor shall be notified as to the reason for the delay and the additional time necessary to make such determination by the university. The principles to be used in determining ownership rights are given in Section VI.

VI. Ownership Rights

A. Ownership Rights in the University

All inventions or discoveries shall be deemed of proprietary interest to Northwestern University if the inventor was employed or otherwise financially supported by the university or if he used university facilities, materials, or time to conceive and develop the discovery or invention.

If the university decides not to request assignment of ownership rights, and there are no restrictions by the sponsor of the research, the university may release its proprietary interest to the inventor. Notification of such release will normally be made within 120 days of disclosure.

B. No Ownership Rights in the University

The ownership rights to a discovery or invention are considered to be the exclusive property of the inventor if the university has contributed nothing substantial or essential to the conception of development of the discovery or invention in the way of funds, space, materials, or facilities and the discovery or invention was conceived and developed by the inventor on his own time. Members of the Northwestern community must be careful to avoid situations that would be considered conflicts of interest when entering into agreements for consulting or providing of services outside of the university that require the member to assign his ownership rights to the contracting agency. The dean of the inventor's school and the vice-president for research should be notified of any patents or inventions arising from such consulting agreements.

Exhibit 47 (continued)

C. Determination of Ownership Rights

In cases where there is a disagreement between the inventor and the university as to ownership rights or the retention of such rights by the university, the vice-president for research shall ask the Faculty Patents Committee to recommend to him the basis for a possible agreement between the inventor and the university. If such agreement with the inventor cannot be reached, the Faculty Patents Committee shall recommend to the vice-president for research what further action the university shall take.

D. Ownership Rights in Sponsored Programs

In the case of programs sponsored by government agencies or private firms with which the university has negotiated a particular agreement regulating patents, inventions, licensing, etc., the regulations of that agreement will govern. For all federal agencies with which there is no such agreement, the university agrees to provide an irrevocable nonexclusive free license to the government for the use of patents arising from programs that they supported.

VII. Obtaining a Patent

If the rights to an invention or discovery are determined to belong to the university, the vice-president for research or his designate will determine the desirability of acquiring assignment of such rights and filing for domestic (U.S.) or foreign patents. If the university decides to obtain a patent, one of the following alternatives, at the inventor's option, will be pursued:

A. The university will provide the services of its patent attorneys as well as the services of patent development and promotional agencies, at the university's expense.
B. The inventor may, at his own expense, consult with any attorney of his choice or take any other steps he deems advisable toward obtaining and developing a patent. However, the ownership right of the invention and any patent obtained thereupon shall still reside with the university and the division of any proceeds shall be in accord with general university policy on patents.

In the event the university determines that it is not interested in filing for a patent, or if the university decides to terminate the application for a patent after initiating the application process, the inventor shall be notified as is noted in Section V and he may proceed to obtain his own patent, at his own expense.

Exhibit 47 (continued)

VIII. Inventions or Discoveries Arising from Sponsored Programs

The university will review the rules and regulations of potential sponsors of research with regard to ownership rights and licensing of inventions, discoveries, or patents either at the time that a proposal is submitted or prior to accepting an award from the sponsor. The university will perform this review with the following principles in mind:

A. The project director is to have complete freedom to publish the results arising from the sponsored program.
B. Any inventions, discoveries, or patents arising from the program will be used in the public interest.
C. The university shall retain ownership rights in any inventions, discoveries, or patents arising from the sponsored project.
D. All parties involved in the program, including the inventor, the sponsor, and the university shall receive compensation from any proceeds received from a patent or invention.

If, even after negotiation, the regulations of a potential sponsor are contrary to the university's Patent Policy, the vice-president for research will consult with the potential project director and, if the vice-president deems it advisable, with the Faculty Research Committee. After such consultation, the vice-president for research will determine whether or not to accept the sponsorship of the research under those regulations.

IX. Development, Promotion, and Licensing

In administering the patent portfolio of the university, the vice-president for research shall act to bring to the public the inventions and discoveries in which the university has proprietary rights. In doing this, he shall use whatever means seem best for appropriate development, promotion, and licensing of each invention, consistent with the expressed goals of this Patent Policy.

The university is free to enter into agreements with any outside agent which it feels will successfully aid the university in developing inventions or discoveries, in obtaining patents, or in promoting or manufacturing inventions, provided that such agreements are consistent with this Patent Policy. If a particular invention or discovery is to become subject to such an agreement, this shall be made known to the inventor, who will also be notified about any rules governing the relationship among the outside agent, the university, and the inventor due to such agreement.

Exhibit 47 (continued)

The university is free to enter into any licensing agreements that it deems are beneficial to the university, the inventor, and the public in general, provided such agreements are not prohibited by a sponsoring agency's rules or regulations. Any terms governing the relationship among the licensee, the university, or the inventor due to such licensing agreements shall be disclosed to the inventor.

X. Proceeds from Inventions and Discoveries

All income that the university derives from the licensing of inventions and discoveries will be appropriately used for the research and educational functions of the university. Of the net proceeds, 25 percent will be paid to the inventor, personally. If the inventor donates any portion of that 25 percent to the university for use in research by his department, center, or program, the university will add an equal amount into that university research account from its portion of the royalty income; all such funds shall be used for nonrecurring research expenses. All other proceeds will accrue to the university, with research funding as a primary goal for use of these funds.

If the invention or discovery is the result of sponsored research, and the sponsoring agency regulates the distribution of royalty income, such regulations shall apply rather than those in the above paragraph. Also, if such regulations apply because of development, promotion, or licensing agreements with an outside agent, they shall take precedence over those of the above paragraph.

XI. Release of Patent Rights

The university, at its discretion and subject only to the restrictions of a sponsoring agency or a licensing agreement, may release a previously obtained patent to the inventor for promotion and development. In so doing, the university will require that it recover any costs incurred in obtaining the patent or in subsequent promotion.

XII. Applicability of Policy

The policy herein declared may be changed or discontinued at any time by appropriately taken action of the Board of Trustees. Such changes or discontinuance shall not affect the rights accrued prior to the changes or alterations.

Source: Northwestern University, 1974.

Exhibit 48. Sample University Disclosure Statement.

Project Inventor: _____   Research was sponsored by:

Department: _____   _____
                                                    (Agency)
Co-Inventor: _____

Department: _____   Account No.: _____

Explanatory Title (if possible, limit the title to less than ten words that are techni-
     cally accurate and descriptive):

An Abstract of the Invention (limit to 100 words):

Statement of the Background of the Invention (attach necessary documentation):
  1. State discipline or subdiscipline or commercial field to which the invention
     or process belongs. Where does it have its main use or application—that is,
     Medicine, Petrochemical Industry, and so on.

Description of the Prior Act:
  1. Description of the existing devices or processes and their deficiencies that
     will be remedied by the present invention.
  2. Citation of relevant scientific and commercial literature.

Description of the Invention (attach documentation as necessary):
  1. Provide invention design (schematics, blueprints, circuit diagrams, and
     so on).
  2. Provide the operational limitation.
  3. Specify the standards of materials for the construction of the invention, or
     detail the exact sequence of steps in the process, and reference technique
     and materials and technical assistance needed at each step.
  4. Provide illustrations of the working process and state working conditions.
  5. Describe how the invention or process produces a result or results not
     available in the prior art.
  6. List and explain the advantages, such as efficiencies, expanded scope of
     use, cost benefits, and so on, produced by the invention.
  7. Succinctly, describe what new concept has been conceived and reduced to
     practice.

Exhibit 48 (continued)

State the Advantages of the Invention:

List and append all publications in which the invention has been described or meetings in which it was described orally.

Signature of Inventor: _____ Date: _____

Witness: _____ Date: _____

**Exhibit 49. Portion of Copyright Registration Form
for a Nondramatic Literary Work**

Line-by-Line Instructions

Space 1: Title

   Title of This Work: Every work submitted for copyright registration must be given a title to identify that particular work. If the copies or phonorecords of the work bear a title (or an identifying phrase that could serve as a title), transcribe that wording *completely* and *exactly* on the application. Indexing of the registration and future identification of the work will depend on the information you give here.
   Previous or Alternative Titles: Complete this space if there are any additional titles for the work under which someone searching for the registration might be likely to look, or under which a document pertaining to the work might be recorded.
   Publication as a Contribution: If the work being registered is a contribution to a periodical, serial, or collection, give the title of the contribution in the "Title of this Work" space. Then, in the line headed "Publication as a Contribution," give information about the collective work in which the contribution appeared.

Exhibit 49 (continued)

Space 2: Author(s)

General Instructions: After reading these instructions, decide who are the "authors" of this work for copyright purposes. Then, unless the work is a "collective work," give the requested information about every "author" who contributed any appreciable amount of copyrightable matter to this version of the work. If you need further space, request additional Continuation sheets. In the case of a collective work, such as an anthology, collection of essays, or encyclopedia, give information about the author of the collective work as a whole.

Name of Author: The fullest form of the author's name should be given. Unless the work was "made for hire," the individual who actually created the work is its "author." In the case of a work made for hire, the statute provides that "the employer or other person for whom the work was prepared is considered the author."

What is a "Work Made for Hire"? A "work made for hire" is defined as: (1) "a work prepared by an employee within the scope of his or her employment"; or (2) "a work specially ordered or commissioned for use as a contribution to a collective work, as a part of a motion picture or other audiovisual work, as a translation, as a supplementary work, as a compilation, as an instructional text, as a test, as answer material for a test, or as an atlas, if the parties expressly agree in a written instrument signed by them that the work shall be considered a work made for hire." If you have checked "Yes" to indicate that the work was "made for hire," you must give the legal name of the employer (or other person for whom the work was prepared). You may also include the name of the employee along with the name of the employer (for example: "Elster Publishing Co., employer for hire of John Ferguson").

"Anonymous" or "Pseudonymous" Work: An author's contribution to a work is "anonymous" if that author is not identified on the copies or phonorecords of the work. An author's contribution to a work is "pseudonymous" if that author is identified on the copies or phonorecords under a fictitious name. If the work is "anonymous" you may: (1) leave the line blank; (2) state "anonymous" on the line; or (3) reveal the author's identity. If the work is "pseudonymous" you may: (1) leave the line blank; or (2) give the pseudonym and identify it as such (for example: "Huntley Haverstock, pseudonym"); or (3) reveal the author's

Exhibit 49 (continued)

name, making clear which is the real name and which is the pseudonym (for example: "Judith Barton, whose pseudonym is Madeline Elster"). However, the citizenship or domicile of the author **must** be given in all cases.

Dates of Birth and Death: If the author is dead, the statute requires that the year of death be included in the application unless the work is anonymous or pseudonymous. The author's birth date is optional, but is useful as a form of identification. Leave this space blank if the author's contribution was a "work made for hire."

Author's Nationality or Domicile: Give the country of which the author is a citizen, or the country in which the author is domiciled. Nationality or domicile **must** be given in all cases.

Nature of Authorship: After the words "Nature of Authorship" give a brief general statement of the nature of this particular author's contribution to the work. Examples: "Entire text"; "Coauthor of entire text"; "Chapters 11-14"; "Editorial revisions"; "Compilation and English translation"; "New text."

Space 3: Creation and Publication

General Instructions: Do not confuse "creation" with "publication." Every application for copyright registration must state "the year in which creation of the work was completed." Give the date and nation of first publication only if the work has been published.

Creation: Under the statute, a work is "created" when it is fixed in a copy or phonorecorded for the first time. Where a work has been prepared over a period of time, the part of the work existing in fixed form on a particular date constitutes the created work on that date. The date you give here should be the year in which the author completed the particular version for which registration is now being sought, even if other versions exist or if further changes or additions are planned.

Publication: The statute defines "publication" as "the distribution of copies or phonorecords of a work to the public by sale or other transfer of ownership, or by rental, lease, or lending"; a work is also "published" if there has been an "offering to distribute copies or phonorecords to a group of persons for purposes of further distribution, public performance, or public display." Give

Exhibit 49 (continued)

the full date (month, day, year) when, and the country where, publication first occurred. If first publication took place simultaneously in the United States and other countries, it is sufficient to state "U.S.A."

Space 4: Claimant(s)

Name(s) and Address(es) of Copyright Claimant(s): Give the name(s) and address(es) of the copyright claimant(s) in this work even if the claimant is the same as the author. Copyright in a work belongs initially to the author of the work (including, in the case of a work made for hire, the employer or other person for whom the work was prepared). The copyright claimant is either the author of the work or a person or organization to whom the copyright initially belonging to the author has been transferred.

Transfer: The statute provides that, if the copyright claimant is not the author, the application for registration must contain "a brief statement of how the claimant obtained ownership of the copyright." If any copyright claimant named in space 4 is not an author named in space 2, give a brief, general statement summarizing the means by which that claimant obtained ownership of the copyright. Examples: "By written contract"; "Transfer of all rights by author"; "Assignment"; "By will." Do not attach transfer documents or other attachments or riders.

For complete copies of form and for further information about copyright registration, notice, or special questions relating to copyright problems, write: Information and Publications Section, LM-455, Copyright Office, Library of Congress, Washington, DC 20559.

Exhibit 49 (continued)

FORM TX

UNITED STATES COPYRIGHT OFFICE

REGISTRATION NUMBER

            TX   TXU

EFFECTIVE DATE OF REGISTRATION

      Month   Day   Year

DO NOT WRITE ABOVE THIS LINE. IF YOU NEED MORE SPACE, USE A SEPARATE CONTINUATION SHEET.

1

TITLE OF THIS WORK ▼

PREVIOUS OR ALTERNATIVE TITLES ▼

PUBLICATION AS A CONTRIBUTION   If this work was published as a contribution to a periodical, serial, or collection, give information about the collective work in which the contribution appeared.   **Title of Collective Work ▼**

If published in a periodical or serial give: **Volume ▼**   **Number ▼**   **Issue Date ▼**   **On Pages ▼**

2
a

NAME OF AUTHOR ▼

DATES OF BIRTH AND DEATH
Year Born ▼   Year Died ▼

Was this contribution to the work a "work made for hire"?
☐ Yes
☐ No

AUTHOR'S NATIONALITY OR DOMICILE
Name of Country
OR { Citizen of ▶ _____
Domiciled in ▶ _____

WAS THIS AUTHOR'S CONTRIBUTION TO THE WORK
Anonymous? ☐ Yes ☐ No
Pseudonymous? ☐ Yes ☐ No
If the answer to either of these questions is "Yes," see detailed instructions

NATURE OF AUTHORSHIP   Briefly describe nature of the material created by this author in which copyright is claimed. ▼

NOTE

Under the law, the "author" of a "work made for hire" is generally the employer not the employee (see instructions). For any part of this work that was "made for hire" check "Yes" in the space provided, give the employer (or other person for whom the work was prepared) as "Author" of that part, and leave the space for dates of birth and death blank.

b

NAME OF AUTHOR ▼

DATES OF BIRTH AND DEATH
Year Born ▼   Year Died ▼

Was this contribution to the work a "work made for hire"?
☐ Yes
☐ No

AUTHOR'S NATIONALITY OR DOMICILE
Name of country
OR { Citizen of ▶ _____
Domiciled in ▶ _____

WAS THIS AUTHOR'S CONTRIBUTION TO THE WORK
Anonymous? ☐ Yes ☐ No
Pseudonymous? ☐ Yes ☐ No
If the answer to either of these questions is "Yes," see detailed instructions

NATURE OF AUTHORSHIP   Briefly describe nature of the material created by this author in which copyright is claimed. ▼

c

NAME OF AUTHOR ▼

DATES OF BIRTH AND DEATH
Year Born ▼   Year Died ▼

Was this contribution to the work a "work made for hire"?
☐ Yes
☐ No

AUTHOR'S NATIONALITY OR DOMICILE
Name of Country
OR { Citizen of ▶ _____
Domiciled in ▶ _____

WAS THIS AUTHOR'S CONTRIBUTION TO THE WORK
Anonymous? ☐ Yes ☐ No
Pseudonymous? ☐ Yes ☐ No
If the answer to either of these questions is "Yes," see detailed instructions

NATURE OF AUTHORSHIP   Briefly describe nature of the material created by this author in which copyright is claimed. ▼

3

YEAR IN WHICH CREATION OF THIS WORK WAS COMPLETED   This information must be given in all cases.
◀ Year

DATE AND NATION OF FIRST PUBLICATION OF THIS PARTICULAR WORK
Complete this information ONLY if this work has been published.
Month ▶ _____ Day ▶ _____ Year ▶ _____ ◀ Nation

4

COPYRIGHT CLAIMANT(S) Name and address must be given even if the claimant is the same as the author given in space 2.▼

APPLICATION RECEIVED

ONE DEPOSIT RECEIVED

TWO DEPOSITS RECEIVED

REMITTANCE NUMBER AND DATE

See instructions before completing this space.

TRANSFER If the claimant(s) named here in space 4 are different from the author(s) named in space 2, give a brief statement of how the claimant(s) obtained ownership of the copyright.▼

DO NOT WRITE HERE OFFICE USE ONLY

MORE ON BACK ▶   • Complete all applicable spaces (numbers 5-11) on the reverse side of this page.
• See detailed instructions.   • Sign the form at line 10.

DO NOT WRITE HERE

Page 1 of _____ pages

**Exhibit 50. Memorandum of Understanding and Agreement
for Recombinant DNA Research.**

Principal Investigator	Department	Telephone

(Names of other investigators Department   Telephone
in project. Show by * if any
one of these is responsible for
research other than principal
investigator.)

Project Title:

Application/Grant No.   Granting Agency
(if applicable)   (if applicable)

Circle Type of Containment Facility Needed for Project: P1   P2   P3   P4

Description: Briefly explain (1) source(s) of DNA, (2) nature of inserted DNA sequences, and (3) hosts and vectors to be used. Sufficient information about experiment should be included so reference to other documents is not needed. For each performance site list organization name(s), city, and state. Attach additional sheets, if necessary, with investigator's name, project title, and date in upper right-hand corner.

Assessment of Levels of Physical and Biological Containment: Citation of relevant sections of NIH Office of Recombinant DNA Activity guidelines or announcements should be included. Attach additional sheets, if necessary, with investigator's name, project title, and date in upper right-hand corner.

Information on Health Surveillance: Provide information on nature of health surveillance necessary and how planned to be implemented, periodically monitored, and finally reviewed. Attach additional sheets, if necessary, with investigator's name, project title, and date in upper right-hand corner.

I agree to comply with the NIH requirements pertaining to shipment and transfer of recombinant DNA materials and to cooperate with the SIU-C Biological Safety Committee in its supervision of these requirements. I am familiar with

Exhibit 50 (continued)

and agree to abide by the provisions of the current NIH guidelines and other specific NIH instructions pertaining to the proposed project. I am aware that a new MUA must be completed and submitted to the SIU-C Biological Safety Committee if this project is altered after it is begun. The information above is accurate and complete.

_____

Principal Investigator ("per" signature not acceptable)   Date

I certify that the Southern Illinois University–Carbondale Biological Safety Committee has reviewed on (date) _____ this proposed project for recombinant DNA experiments and has found it to be in compliance with the NIH guidelines and other specific NIH instructions pertaining to the proposed project.

and/or

I assure that the Southern Illinois University–Carbondale Biological Safety Committee has reviewed on (date) _____ this proposed project and the plans for facilities proposed or under construction or renovation. Recombinant DNA experimentation will not occur until the complete facilities have been reviewed by the Southern Illinois University–Carbondale Biological Safety Committee and a MUA with certification has been submitted to NIH.

The institution agrees to accept responsibility for the training of all laboratory workers involved in the project. The Southern Illinois University–Carbondale Biological Safety Committee will monitor throughout the duration of the project the facilities, the procedures, and the training and expertise of the personnel involved in the recombinant DNA activity.

_____

SIU-C Biological Safety Chairperson   Date

_____

Applicable Institutional Official   Date

_____

Institutional Official   Date
(additional performance sites, if applicable)

Source: Southern Illinois University at Carbondale, n.d.

15

Administration in Small Organizations

The administration of sponsored projects in small organizations or developing institutions differs from that in large institutions. The former's missions and motives are usually more specific and the resources to support sponsored projects offices are limited. Although the management practices described in this book apply to small institutions, additional topics must be considered. The definition of small organizations and developing institutions is not precise, but organizations receiving less than $1 million annually in sponsored funds or organizations that are initiating a sponsored projects office are considered in this category for the purposes of this chapter. Administrators within units of institutions of higher education and those in small organizations outside of higher education should find this chapter applicable.

Goals, Capabilities, and Motivation

Most small institutions of higher education hold instruction to be their primary mission; research and public service, although valued, do not have as high a priority as teaching. Resources for activities other than teaching are limited, and the reward system for faculty is structured to encourage instructional excellence.

Thus an important part of the responsibilities of the sponsored projects administrator is to motivate faculty to participate in sponsored projects in areas other than teaching.

The size and scope of small institutions do not exclude them from sponsored activities. There are many opportunities for small institutions to receive externally sponsored support for projects; indeed, many small institutions successfully obtain grants and contracts for sponsored activities. The limited mission and resources do, however, require the sponsored projects administrator to work hard and use various methods to motivate and serve the faculty.

The small institution or unit must clearly define its goals and encourage faculty to pursue sponsored activities related to those goals. For example, a college that cites instruction as its major goal and ignores other activities provides few incentives for faculty to seek sponsored support. But a college that establishes teaching as its primary goal and also recognizes scholarly pursuits through research and other projects as important thereby facilitates the work of the sponsored projects administrator. A successful program of sponsored projects requires that the institution's goals recognize some level of sponsored programs as a supporting activity for the basic teaching mission.

Fulfillment of the institution's commitment to sponsored programs depends largely on the capabilities of the faculty. Although the small college has fewer staff, less equipment, and smaller facilities than a large research institution, it has many capable faculty in selected areas. The sponsored projects office should concentrate its services to identify those faculty members with outstanding capabilities and match their skills with specific appropriate programs. The office must provide a collegewide system of communications, but it should target its services for those faculty interested in and capable of attaining outside support. Since administration may be unable to support a full-time position for sponsored projects, the limited efforts must be especially addressed to individuals with the greatest capabilities for obtaining sponsored support.

Organizing and Staffing

The organization of sponsored projects administration in the small institution must be designed to meet specific needs with a limited staff. Some institutions appoint a full-time sponsored projects administrator, but most assign the duties to an assistant to the president, a development officer, an assistant to the dean of faculties, or a faculty member. The administrator assigned responsibility for sponsored projects should be close to the institution's decision-making process.

Another organizational consideration is the financial management of grants and contracts, a responsibility usually performed by the vice-president of business affairs or the treasurer for the institution. If there is no full-time grants and contracts officer, the financial management of sponsored projects may fall to the chief fiscal officer or to the immediate assistant of the fiscal officer. The fiscal management of sponsored projects is critical because small institutions lack continuing experience with sponsors, and because federal regulations related to compliance are complicated and are revised frequently. An officer who works with these regulations only occasionally may not become sufficiently familiar with the requirements. The financial aspects of sponsored programs should be entrusted to a competent person who can understand and satisfy sponsor regulations. This financial officer and the faculty member or staff member managing the sponsored projects function must carefully coordinate their work to serve the faculty.

One last organizational necessity is an effective administrative assistant or secretary. If the sponsored projects administrator is in the office only part time, the flow of communications falls to an assistant or secretary. This person often serves as the first contact and source of information for faculty members seeking assistance with a sponsored program application.

A sample staff for the sponsored projects office at a small institution could thus include three persons with part- or full-time assignments: the sponsored projects administrator, fiscal administrator, and an assistant or secretary. The sponsored projects administrator, reporting to the president or chief academic officer, is responsible for stimulating and assisting all faculty in securing sponsored support for activities. This administrator must be enthusiastic, able to stimulate others, and willing to spend time working with faculty to develop individual projects. He or she must also devote time to learning about the various sources of funding and the process of submitting proposals. Depending on resources, the sponsored projects administrator should attend professional meetings and establish contacts with other sponsored projects administrators who can provide information or assistance. Sponsored projects administration in a small college is often a one-person operation, and the administrator must be committed to learning as much as possible and to serving the faculty.

The institution's chief financial officer, or his or her assistant, can act as financial administrator. This person must help faculty in preparing budgets and managing the fiscal aspects of awards. This assistance is critical in a small institution because many project directors are inexperienced in managing projects.

The sponsored projects administrative assistant or secretary should be an energetic and resourceful person who can support the sponsored projects administrator by providing information and assistance. This person should be available in the office at all times and must be familiar with major funding sources and application procedures.

Assessing Capabilities

The sponsored projects administrator in a small college has to be aware of the campus' resources: the capabilities of the faculty, the present equipment, and the facilities and services available for sponsored activities. The responsibility for stimulating projects may rest with the sponsored projects office to a much greater degree in a small institution than in a large university.

To assess the interests and capabilities of the faculty, so that they can be matched with the appropriate program opportunity when available, the sponsored projects administrator can send out a brief questionnaire and make follow-up visits with individuals. A card file indicating the interests and capabilities of each faculty member should be maintained by the sponsored projects office. The basic information on the card file should be:

- Name
- Department or area
- Major areas of interest for a research project or other sponsored activity
- Research or other projects completed
- Experience on an evaluation or review panel for a sponsored program
- Interest in securing sponsored support to conduct research or other projects

- Other related information (on the back of the card)

The sponsored projects administrator should review the information frequently and visit with those faculty members who indicate an interest in securing outside support. As sponsors' program announcements are received, the administrator should contact the appropriate faculty members and urge them to apply.

An inventory of equipment and other resources available for research and other projects should also be made by the sponsored projects office. An assessment of these resources is a critical element of the institution's capabilities for conducting projects and is essential to the overall effort to stimulate sponsored programs at a small institution.

Communication Systems

Maintaining effective communications is vital to all sponsored projects offices, and small institutions have special needs relating to both external and internal communications. The communications program must be selective and focused on the interests of faculty members; no small institution can otherwise keep up with the continuous flow of information and changes in sponsored programs.

External Communications

The most difficult job for the sponsored projects administrator in the small institution is learning about and keeping abreast of changes in sponsors' programs and federal regulations. The multitude of sponsored support opportunities fills catalogues and directories; indeed, the larger sponsored projects offices employ full-time specialists to maintain and disseminate sponsored program information. Most small institutions are eligible for fewer sponsored programs, and they must design a system to obtain selective information. The heart of such a system is a combination of broad references about all possible programs and selected sources related to the interests and capabilities of the faculty.

There are two basic reference works that all small institutions should have: the *Catalog of Federal Domestic Assistance* and the *Foundation Directory*. These references provide general information about federal and foundation support programs. They function like the card catalogue in a library by providing access to the entire system. The sponsored projects administrator must be familiar with these publications and be able to use them with faculty to identify program opportunities.

The selection of other publications that provide information about sponsored projects should be based on the interests and fields of study of the faculty. For example, the faculty of a liberal arts college who are interested in research support may require information on the programs at the National Endowment for the Humanities, the National Science Foundation, the American Council of Learned Societies, and the Social Science Research Council. The basic guidebooks for these agencies should be a part of the sponsored projects office library. The faculty of a small community college may be more interested in education and training programs. This library should contain programs from the Department of Education, with emphasis on vocational and other training opportunities, as well as state vocational and rehabilitation programs.

In addition to this type of selective information, the library should include a few publications that list only the major programs for faculty by discipline or provide abstracted information from the *Federal Register.* The suggestions in Chapter Seven for a basic library should prove helpful.

Internal Communications

Internal communications at a small institution are facilitated by the small size of the staff. However, the ease of reaching a small group does not necessarily make the communications effective. The sponsored projects administrator has to assess the faculty's capabilities and make a conscious effort to communicate program information to them. As programs are identified that relate to a particular field of interest, the sponsored projects administrator should personally take copies of the information to the appropriate faculty member and discuss the possibility of submitting a proposal for support. Other means of internal communications are presented in the following section.

Stimulating Project Development

The sponsored projects administrator in the small institution should encourage faculty to seek support for projects. If the institution's reward system does not place a premium on research and public service activities, the sponsored projects administrator must serve as a motivating force to stimulate sponsored activity. In many cases he or she has to be the instigator who sees opportunities and structures programs. The job requires an active advocate who can motivate and assist individual faculty members.

The following list of activities indicates the range of actions that the sponsored projects administrator can use to stimulate faculty to develop sponsored programs:

- Review new program announcements and upcoming programs and cross-check them with the faculty profile cards. When there is a match between program and faculty, inform the faculty member of the program opportunity. Direct communication—a personal note or an informal meeting over coffee—is most effective. If the faculty member has questions that are not covered by the materials at hand, call the program office at the agency to obtain the necessary information. Try to include the faculty member in the conversation by using an extension phone.

- Start a regular newsletter or send occasional news briefs to all faculty to keep them informed of opportunities and to publicize successful programs. These communications need not be lengthy nor expensively produced.

- Conduct occasional workshops on topics related to sponsored programs. Sample topics include: the research programs at the National Science Foundation, how to develop and write a proposal, science education programs, program support opportunities from the state, and how to determine a project budget.

- Conduct orientation sessions for new faculty members to acquaint them with the purpose and services of the sponsored projects administration office.

- Meet with each department to answer questions and discuss sponsored funding opportunities for a particular discipline.

- Prepare handout materials on the services of the sponsored projects administration office. These materials can be one-page descriptions of various aspects of obtaining program support. The same information can be put on audiotape and played over the telephone.

- Provide direct assistance to faculty by helping to design programs, outline and edit proposals, and prepare budgets. The degree of assistance will depend on the project, but the sponsored projects administrator should remember that the ideas, the final design, and the writing of the proposal must be completed by the project director.

- Assist faculty members in obtaining the necessary clearances for services and approvals for submission. The sponsored projects administrator should make the preparation and submission process as easy as possible by cutting red tape for faculty.
- Provide assistance such as typing, mailing, and reporting; these services, of course, depend on the staffing level and budget of the office.

Postaward Administration

Compliance with sponsors' regulations is a legal obligation of the institution and influences its future sponsored activities. Small institutions may have difficulty managing the fiscal requirements of an award because of lack of familiarity. Similarly, the completion of final reports may present problems for inexperienced administrators. Thus, it is important that the institution designate an individual as the compliance officer for sponsored awards. This individual, usually an official in the institution's business office, must then become familiar with sponsors' regulations and federal regulations. The compliance officer should pay special attention to the following six areas: accounting for expenditures, equipment control, reporting requirements, indirect-cost calculation— short form, closing out grants and contracts, and auditing requirements.

Contacts with the appropriate grants and contracts officers in agencies and foundations are essential because the institution's compliance officer should know whom to call at an agency or foundation to obtain information. A visit to an institution that has an effective program of serving sponsored projects is advisable.

▱▱ 16 ▱▱

Administration in Nonprofit and University-Connected Organizations

▱▱▱▱▱▱▱▱▱▱▱▱▱▱▱▱▱▱▱

With the growing interest in science and technology after World War II, a new type of research and development organization began to emerge: the nonprofit research organization, a part of which is the university-connected research foundation. Nonprofit research organizations are given their nonprofit status by the state in which they reside. Then, by application to the federal government, some nonprofits can gain favorable tax treatment, as authorized by Section 501(c)(3) of the *Internal Revenue Code*, provided that a substantial amount of the organization's work is made freely available to the public. These organizations perform and administer research (both basic and applied) as well as development and testing for both government and industry. The four major types of nonprofit research organizations are: federally funded research and development centers (FFRDCs), nonprofit institutes, operating foundations, and various endowed institutes.

University-connected research foundations are separately incorporated entities whose major purpose is to provide administrative grant and contract services for their university's research program. Such a foundation often provides a university with more administrative flexibility and freedom than can be obtained by an office of sponsored projects, which is subject to state rules and regulations, some of which affect research funding from sponsors other than state appropriations.

Nonprofit Research Organizations

Nonprofit research organizations are non–degree-granting organizations that devote most of their annual expenditures to the development and transfer of new technology and to research in the natural and social sciences, engineering, humanities, and professions (although expenditures, especially nonfederal expenditures in the latter two areas, are poorly documented). The five principal types of organizations are (Orlans, 1972):

- *Federally financed research and development centers (FFRDCs)* are predominantly financed by a federal agency and operated under contract by universities or nonprofit institutes; examples include the Jet Propulsion Laboratory, the Brookhaven National Laboratory, and Battelle Pacific Northwest Lab.
- *Nonprofit institutes and foundations–independent nonprofit institutes* (such as Southwest Research Institute, SRI International, and the Midwest Research Institute) conduct investigations for industry, government, and other clients. The results, depending on the wishes of the client, may be either confidential or freely publishable. The dependent, university-connected research foundations (such as Texas A&M, SUNY, and Ohio State) provide administrative grant and contract services for their respective institutions.
- *Operating foundations* — such as the Carnegie Institution of Washington, Resources for the Future, and the Institute for Advanced Study — devote more than half of the annual yield from their endowment principal to research by their own staff.
- *Endowed institutes,* such as the Brookings Institution, Wistar Institute, and Sloan-Kettering Institute, derive less than half but more than a tenth of their annual expenditures from their own endowments.
- *Cushioned institutes* receive recurrent income from membership dues;

contributions; publication sales; clinical fees from physicians and hospitals; grants from voluntary health agencies, foundations, state, and local governments; or other sources. For example, the Jackson Laboratory received 42 percent of its $4.0 million revenue in 1970 from the sale of mice and biologicals; philanthropic grants to the Sloan-Kettering Institute from 1960 to 1968 ranged from 24 to 32 percent of its annual operation expenditures of $8.1 to $10.0 million; and the American Institute for Economic Research in 1968 received 77 percent of its $429,000 income from the sale of publications and from the dues of more than 5,000 sustaining members.

These research institutes, unlike university-connected research foundations, have their own professional staffs and research facilities, and perform research and development for a variety of external sponsors.

Unlike the director of the office of sponsored projects or a university-connected research foundation, the director of a nonprofit research organization is instrumental in determining the research and development effort. The director is usually a senior scientist with administrative experience and is influential in determining the direction of the institute. Not unlike a university president, who determines the overall objectives and strategies of the university, the research director of a nonprofit research organization directs and shapes the organization's missions and policies. Unlike a university sponsored projects director, the nonprofit director is a line officer who must decide how to invest scarce resources.

In principle, institutes can often assemble interdisciplinary teams for special projects more rapidly than universities because institute staff do not have teaching obligations, and there are no departmental deliberations. The flexibility of institute staffing is limited only by the capability of the director, prior commitments, budgets, and staff turnover (Orlans, 1972, p. 64).

A major factor in the growth of the nonprofit is the concept of institutional independence. The institute, similar to a university in this case, can examine technical and intellectual questions with a degree of freedom that industry or government agencies are unable to accommodate because of commercial and political interests. Also, the research institute is not hampered by a variety of state constraints, as are many public universities.

One measure of the importance of nonprofit research institutes is

**Table 6. Summary of Federal Funds for Research and
Development and for R&D Plant.**

	Actual 1978	Estimated 1979	1980
		(Dollars in Millions)	
Research and Development			
FFRDCs administered by universities and colleges	1,325.6	1,411.6	1,499.7
Other nonprofit institutions	593.0	646.6	657.1
FFRDCs administered by nonprofit institutions	66.9	88.5	90.3
R&D Plant			
FFRDCs administered by universities and colleges	376.3	418.6	440.7
Other nonprofit institutions	4.4	5.5	5.8
FFRDCs administered by nonprofit institutions	8.3	9.2	8.5
TOTAL	$2,374.5	$2,579.8	$2,702.1

Source: National Science Foundation, 1979, p. 12.

the amount of federal funds awarded these organizations, presented in Table 6. In addition, these organizations often handle large sums of industrial dollars. Southwest Research Institute, for example, derives 70 percent of its revenues from industry.

The National Science Foundation estimates that $4.28 billion in federal funds for research, development, and R&D plant were expended in fiscal 1980 at colleges and universities. As Table 6 shows, the level of support for nonprofit research organizations is approximately two-thirds of the total amount awarded by government agencies to support university research and development. This comparison is another measure of these institutes' major contributions to R&D in this country. Further insight into nonprofit research institutes is provided by Tables 7, 8, and 9. These tables show the three major sub-classes of this type of organization and their respective federal funding.

Recent concerns about declining American productivity, innovations, and patents will spur the growth of nonprofit research institutes, which often specialize in applied research and product development. These organizations greatly assist in technology transfer, having both the

Table 7. Federal Science Obligations to
FFRDCs Administered by Universities and Colleges, FY 1979.

Organization	Total Obligations (Dollars in Thousands)
Ames Laboratory	14,760
Argonne National Laboratory	237,361
Brookhaven National Laboratory	143,090
Center for Naval Analyses	12,747
Cerro Tololo INT-AM Observatory	4,350
Fermi National Accelerator Laboratory	87,765
Jet Propulsion Laboratory	264,278
Kitt Peak National Observatory	10,352
Lawrence Berkeley Laboratory	109,278
Lawrence Livermore Laboratory	364,192
Lincoln Laboratory	112,487
Los Alamos Scientific Laboratory	327,856
National Astronomy & Ionospheric Center	5,121
National Center for Atmospheric Research	35,905
National Radio Astronomical Observatory	23,161
Oak Ridge Institute for Nuclear Standards	9,281
Plasma Physics Laboratory	94,077
Sacramento Peak Observatory	2,725
Stanford Linear Accelerator Center	70,070

Source: National Science Foundation, 1981b, pp. 153–160.

Table 8. Federal Obligations to FFRDCs
Administered by Independent Nonprofit Institutions
for Research, Development and R&D Plant, FY 1979.

Organization	Total Obligations (Dollars in Thousands)
Aerospace Corporation	129,507
Battelle Pacific Northwest Laboratory	77,339
Institute for Defense Analyses	16,027
Mitre Corporation–C3 Division	96,734
Project Air Force	11,200
Solar Energy Research Institute	84,783

Source: National Science Foundation, 1981b, pp. 161–162.

**Table 9. Nonprofit Institutes with FY 1979
Federal Obligations for Research, Development,
and R&D Plant Greater Than $2.0 Million.**

Organization	Total Obligations (Dollars in Thousands)
American Health Foundation, Inc.	3,917
American Institutes for Research	2,124
American Institute of Architects	3,150
Analytic Services, Inc.	8,259
Battelle Memorial Institute	35,746
Beth Israel Hospital	3,637
Bituminous Coal Research, Inc.	9,078
Boston Biomedical Research Institute	3,379
Cedars-Sinai Medical Center	4,825
Central Midwest Regional Education Laboratory	3,055
Child Cancer Research Foundation	15,998
Children's Hospital and Medical Center	11,767
Children's Hospital and Medical Center–Cincinnati	3,486
Children's Hospital of Philadelphia	5,140
City of Hope Medical Center	3,813
Cleveland Clinic Foundation	3,299
Cold Spring Harbor Laboratory	3,916
Consortium International Development	4,201
Draper Laboratories	73,240
E. K. Shriver Center for Mental Retardation	2,164
Environmental Research Institute	7,225
F. Hutchins Cancer Research Institute	10,823
Far West Laboratory for Educational Research & Development	3,356
Forsyth Dental Center	2,425
Franklin Institute	6,993
Gulf Southern Research Institute	2,076
IIT Research Institute	30,196
Institute for Cancer Research	9,328
Institute for Gas Technology	18,466
Institute of Medical Sciences	5,038
International Fertility Development Corporation	2,500
Jackson Laboratory	4,405
Jewish Hospital of St. Louis	2,198
Joslin Diabetes Foundation, Inc.	3,544
Kaiser Foundation Research Institute	2,752
Lovelace Foundation for Medical Education	7,353
Manpower Demonstration Research Corporation	7,504
Massachusetts Eye & Ear Infirmary	2,708
Massachusetts General Hospital	23,007
Mayo Foundation	23,257

Table 9. Nonprofit Institutes with FY 1979
Federal Obligations for Research, Development, and R&D Plant Greater Than $2.0 Million, Cont'd.

McLean Hospital	2,995
Medical Research Foundation of Oregon	5,927
Memorial Hospital–Cancer & Allied Diseases	6,464
Michael Reese Hospital & Medical Center	2,863
Michigan Cancer Foundation	5,781
Midwest Research Institute	6,223
Montana Energy Research & MHD Development Institute	8,893
Montefiore Hospital & Medical Center	5,640
National Academy of Sciences	21,345
National Jewish Hospital–Denver	3,210
New England Medical Center & Hospital	4,279
New York Blood Center	3,736
Northern California Cancer Program	3,601
Northwest Regional Education Laboratory	3,373
Oklahoma Medical Research Foundation	2,779
Operations Research, Inc.	7,670
Palisades Geophysics Institute	2,107
Peter Bent Brigham Hospital	7,975
Radiation Oncology Study Center	3,106
RAND Corporation	27,545
Research for Better Schools, Inc.	2,678
Research Triangle Institute	17,528
Retina Foundation	3,294
Riverside Research Institute	3,963
Robert B. Brigham Hospital	2,458
Roswell Park Memorial Institute	14,068
St. Jude Children's Research Hospital	6,117
Salk Institute for Biological Studies	9,045
Scripps Clinic & Research Foundation	15,455
Sloan-Kettering Institute	28,781
Southern Research Institute	8,370
Southwest Foundation for Research and Education	2,470
Southwest Research Institute	13,860
SRI International	40,579
University Hospital	3,709
University City Science Center	2,015
Urban Institute	5,158
Wistar Institute	9,319
Worcester Foundation for Experimental Biology	5,369
Youthwork, Inc.	2,500

Source: National Science Foundation, 1981b, pp. 153–160.

resources and personnel to bring original basic ideas and concepts into practice. Pondering the future of nonprofit research institutes, Orlans (1972) asks, "Have research institutes found new ways of organizing knowledge, less rigid than those of the college or university, which may give them a leadership position in the future generation of knowledge?" He answers that these institutes *have not* generated a distinctive order of knowledge, but they *have* streamlined the administrative aspects of research: Institutes are better able than university departments to generate knowledge that is reliable and timely, or that requires the coordinated and protracted work of many people. Institutes have found new ways to organize researchers, and the knowledge they produce reflects their respective purposes, organization, and financing.

The organizational structures of independent nonprofit research institutes differ. Here we present the example of one quite successful institute, the Southwest Research Institute based in San Antonio, Texas. In its thirty-third year of operation, its major objectives include: (1) serving industry and government through science and technology, (2) advancing the general welfare of the public, (3) expanding and broadening research and development capabilities, and (4) adding to the nation's high-technology resources. It is an important center of excellence in science and technology. In 1981, its net worth was $35 million; its contract revenue was $95 million; and it had a permanent staff of 2,000. Figure 34 presents the organizational chart of this institute.

The value of nonprofit research institutes to the advancement of science and technology in this country is quite apparent. Because the advancement of the U.S. economy relies heavily on innovations in science, nonprofit institutes that combine basic research with testing and development of new products are essential to this country.

University-Connected Research Foundations

In an effort to gain some of the advantages enjoyed by nonprofit research institutes, some fifty universities have formed separately incorporated, university-connected foundations to administer their sponsored programs. Such foundations either replace or complement the university's office of sponsored projects. In fiscal 1982, these research foundations are expected to administer $500 million in sponsored program funds.

Figure 34. Southwest Research Institute Organization Chart.

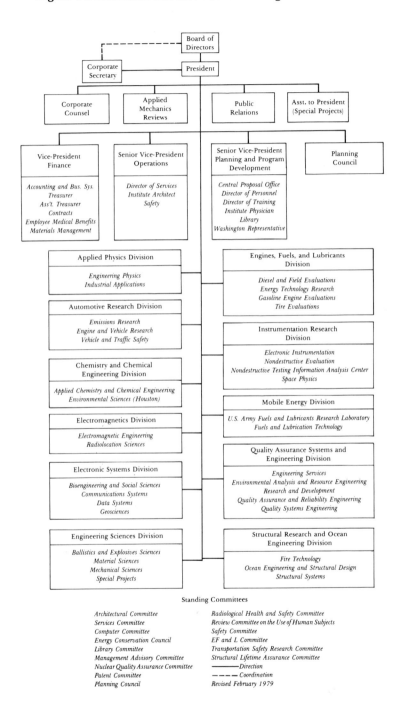

Board of Directors

Corporate Secretary

President

Corporate Counsel

Applied Mechanics Reviews

Public Relations

Asst. to President (Special Projects)

Vice-President Finance

Accounting and Bus. Sys.
Treasurer
Ass't. Treasurer
Contracts
Employee Medical Benefits
Materials Management

Senior Vice-President Operations

Director of Services
Institute Architect
Safety

Senior Vice-President Planning and Program Development

Central Proposal Office
Director of Personnel
Director of Training
Institute Physician
Library
Washington Representative

Planning Council

Applied Physics Division

Engineering Physics
Industrial Applications

Automotive Research Division

Emissions Research
Engine and Vehicle Research
Vehicle and Traffic Safety

Chemistry and Chemical Engineering Division

Applied Chemistry and Chemical Engineering
Environmental Sciences (Houston)

Electromagnetics Division

Electromagnetic Engineering
Radiolocation Sciences

Electronic Systems Division

Bioengineering and Social Sciences
Communications Systems
Data Systems
Geosciences

Engineering Sciences Division

Ballistics and Explosives Sciences
Material Sciences
Mechanical Sciences
Special Projects

Engines, Fuels, and Lubricants Division

Diesel and Field Evaluations
Energy Technology Research
Gasoline Engine Evaluations
Tire Evaluations

Instrumentation Research Division

Electronic Instrumentation
Nondestructive Evaluation
Nondestructive Testing Information Analysis Center
Space Physics

Mobile Energy Division

U.S. Army Fuels and Lubricants Research Laboratory
Fuels and Lubrication Technology

Quality Assurance Systems and Engineering Division

Engineering Services
Environmental Analysis and Resource Engineering
Research and Development
Quality Assurance and Reliability Engineering
Quality Systems Engineering

Structural Research and Ocean Engineering Division

Fire Technology
Ocean Engineering and Structural Design
Structural Systems

Standing Committees

Architectural Committee
Services Committee
Computer Committee
Energy Conservation Council
Library Committee
Management Advisory Committee
Nuclear Quality Assurance Committee
Patent Committee
Planning Council

Radiological Health and Safety Committee
Review Committee on the Use of Human Subjects
Safety Committee
EF and L Committee
Transportation Safety Research Committee
Structural Lifetime Assurance Committee
——— *Direction*
— — — *Coordination*
Revised February 1979

A university-connected research foundation is operationally defined as a separately incorporated [under IRS code 501(c)(3)] organization that serves its parent university (Daniels and others, 1977). It is not a
philanthropic institution, but rather a solicitor or manager of sponsored
funds for its university. It directly employs administrative personnel, but
in most cases the research is performed by university faculty and staff.
The major purpose for creating this type of organization is that it af-
fords the university flexibility in the development and administration of
sponsored programs.

Many public research universities have felt encumbered by legislative and administrative policy controls, procedural formalities, and
arbitrary limitations on management discretion. The separately incorporated university-connected research foundation fulfills research administration needs that cannot legally or conveniently be accomplished
through regular institutional structures. The benefits that may be derived from a separate foundation depend on the extent of the university's autonomy in decision making and in budgetary discretion for
research administration. Daniels and others (1977, p. 70) found that if a
university has a broad range of such powers and exercises them, a separately incorporated foundation will probably not be of significant value.
Specifically, many of the benefits of a foundation result from its exercise
of broad corporate discretion that its host institution may not or cannot
exercise.

Additional benefits that are derived from a separate foundation
depend on the state constitution or specific statute that governs the
public university. If the board of trustees of a university has constitu-
tional authority and exercises broad discretion in the allocation and
expenditure of both state and sponsored funds, the university will probably not need a separate foundation to manage sponsored awards. However, if the university is governed by statute, and if each legislative
session can redefine the university's powers and authority, a university-
connected research foundation may be quite beneficial. In states in
which the indirect-cost funds are not retained on campus but forwarded
to the state treasury, the impetus to develop a more flexible administrative system is strong. Furthermore, some states are now taking steps to
require that university applications to external agencies be reviewed at
the state level prior to submission to sponsors. If this trend toward state
control of sponsored funds continues, new efforts may be made by uni-

versities to establish university-connected research foundations, which will not be subjected to such constraints. Also, some state legislatures, recognizing that often state rules and regulations issued for state agencies simply are not appropriate for state universities, have encouraged their state universities to form research foundations.

In most universities the office of sponsored projects provides preaward services, negotiates awards, establishes accounts, and oversees regulatory committees; and the business office has many postaward responsibilities. In contrast, a university-connected research foundation is often responsible for the entire administration of the sponsored award, which sometimes includes resource identification and proposal development (a full-service foundation), and always includes submitting the application, negotiating the award, and administering the award, including purchasing, accounting, payroll, accounts payable, and financial reports. Daniels and others (1977) distinguish and name five functional models for these foundations: (1) flowthrough, (2) fiscal management, (3) project administration, (4) program development, and (5) full service. The functions associated with each model are shown in Exhibit 51, pages 309–310.

The major differences in the services of a full-service university-connected research foundation and an office of sponsored projects at a university concern postaward responsibilities. University-connected research foundations can develop and implement accounting systems to service the sponsor, project director, and host institution without concern for many of the constraints associated with state-appropriated funds. Many of the better computerized management information systems and accounting systems for sponsored projects are in use at the foundations, for example, at the SUNY Research Foundation, Texas A&M Research Foundation, and Ohio State University Research Foundation.

Purchasing policies of state-regulated universities are often very tedious and cumbersome. Many states now require that sponsored funds abide by all the same purchasing regulations as state funds. Foundations, however, are not subject to state purchasing regulations, which often impede the purchase and delivery of equipment, supplies, and services needed to perform the research. Research foundations can also often prevent nonstate funds for R&D from being subject to state rules and regulations for such funds. Finally, research foundations often house marketing programs, a task some university personnel disdain, but one that is becoming increasingly more important in effecting the necessary linkages with sponsors.

Daniels and his colleagues (1977, p. 235) recommend that universities which are considering establishing a foundation to administer sponsored awards take the following steps:

1. Define research management objectives.
2. Profile the current research administration system.
3. Define new or revised functions for implementation.
4. Define new or revised services for implementation.
5. Analyze foundation organization to deliver services.
6. Analyze foundation procedures, relationships, and budget requirements.
7. Analyze university organization to deliver services.
8. Analyze university procedures, relationships, and budget requirements.

Figure 35 illustrates the organization of Texas A&M Research Foundation, a full-service university-connected research foundation. Although duties and responsibilities of foundation personnel depend on the type of foundation, the following outline of those at the Texas A&M Research Foundation serves as an example.

Office of the President

- Planning and development of policy
- Liaison with Texas A&M University system
- Liaison with sponsors and project directors
- Follow congressional activities and legislation
- Custody and management of corporate assets
- Assist in negotiation of indirect-cost rates and policies
- Liaison with legal counsel
- Information systems analysis and design

Contracts and Grants Division

- Manage negotiations of research contracts and grants
- Liaison with sponsors and researchers
- Manage proposal and budget preparation

Figure 35. Texas A&M Research Foundation Organization Chart.

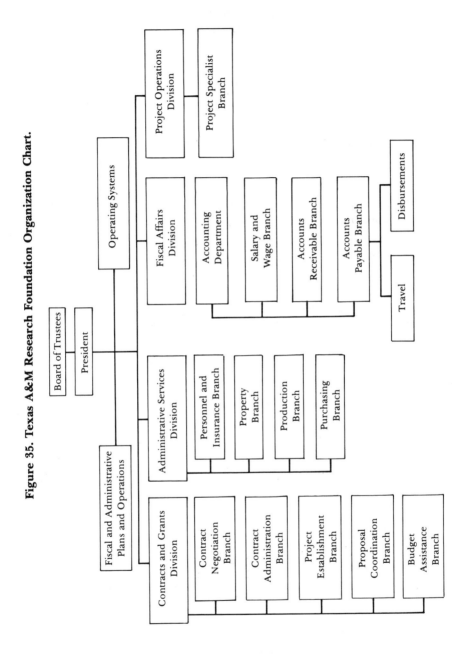

- Establish administrative base for executed contract and grant awards
- Provide contract and grant administration and subcontract assistance

Contract Negotiation Branch

- Negotiate contracts and grants
- Review award documents for execution
- Review and approve final award budgets

Contract Administration Branch

- Liaison with sponsors concerning contract and grant compliance
- Analyze and process requests for contract and grant modifications
- Negotiate, prepare, and coordinate execution of subcontracts
- Monitor compliance of subcontracts

Project Establishment Branch

- Maintain execution and award records
- Prepare and distribute information to establish project
- Provide entry of nonfiscal data to automated information system
- Provide project document processing

Proposal Coordination Branch

- Coordinate timing of research proposal preparation
- Counsel project directors on proposal preparation
- Prepare internal activity reports
- Provide information on requests for proposals

Budget Assistance Branch

- Provide researcher with proposal budget planning and assistance
- Prepare cost-sharing and business management requirements
- Coordinate budget and proposal text
- Counsel project directors on budgeting

Administrative Services Division

- Manage internal administration and corporate activities

- Liaison with researchers and sponsors
- Monitor compliance with statutory security requirements
- Administer patent procedures

Personnel and Insurance Branch

- Supervise employment and insurance programs
- Monitor compliance with affirmative action and statutory requirements
- Administer all administrative and project general insurance
- Brief and debrief employees

Property Branch

- Supervise maintenance of property records
- Identify equipment and conduct inventories
- Acquire excess property and dispose of property

Production Branch

- Supervise proposal production and support services
- Provide printing and reproduction, assembling, binding, and mailing services

Purchasing Branch

- Supervise administrative and research purchasing
- Monitor purchase orders and encumber project budgets
- Monitor processing of bid requests and responses
- Counsel researchers on sources and compliance
- Supervise encumbrance data entry

Fiscal Affairs Division

- Manage administrative financial reports
- Produce project and administrative financial reports
- Manage manual and automated project records and files
- Provide internal audit functions

Accounting Department

- Direct supervision of project and administrative accounting, records, reporting, and internal audit activities

Salary and wage branch

- Review and process payroll encumbrances and billings
- Calculate direct payrolls
- Prepare payroll-related disbursements
- Maintain payroll records and files
- Supervise payroll data entry to automated systems

Accounts receivable branch

- Prepare billings, financial reports, and requests for cash
- Maintain receivables records and files
- Record and report payment of receivables
- Assist preparation of project closeout documentation
- Supervise receipts and receivables data entry

Accounts payable branch

- Process vendor invoices for payment
- Maintain accounts payable records and files
- Process and monitor payables and liquidate encumbrances
- Supervise accounts payable data entry

Travel

- Review and process travel requests, travel advances, and expense accounting

Disbursements

- Review and confirm payables transactions
- Prepare vendor and expense account disbursements
- Supervise disbursements data entry and edit

Projects Operations Division

- Counsel project directors on project administration
- Monitor project budgetary and technical reporting compliance
- Assist project directors with contract and cost compliance
- Coordinate research project closeouts

Exhibit 51. Functional Models of Foundations.

Functions	Flow-through	Fiscal Management	Project Administration	Program Development	Full Service
Planning Process:					
Definition of research mission					
Relationship to mission of institution					
Assessment of research and technology needs				X	X
Institutional planning and investment					
Allocation of institutional resources	X	X	X	X	X
Research trend forecasting				X	X
Research opportunity analysis				X	X
Institutional integration of research					
Institutional incentives and rewards					
Proposal Preparation and Submission Process:					
Interpretation of opportunity				X	X
Assessment of capabilities				X	X
Proposal planning				X	X
Proposal preparation				X	X
Presubmission review				X	X
Proposal submission			X	X	X
Proposal monitoring		X	X		X
Proposal negotiation			X		X

Exhibit 51 (continued)

Functions	Models				
	Flow-through	Fiscal Management	Project Administration	Program Development	Full Service
Research Project Administration:					
Review of grant/contract provisions		X	X		X
Space and special facilities			X		X
Fiscal requirements		X	X		X
Purchasing and property controls			X		X
Project personnel policies and practices			X		X
Appointment procedures and effort reporting			X		X
Technical reporting			X		X
Compliance with special grant and contract provisions		X	X		X
Extension or amendment		X	X		X
Termination		X	X		X
Research Support Services:					
Project accounting		X	X		X
Purchasing			X		X
Editorial and reproduction services				X	X
Continuing Institutional Responsibilities:					
Audit requirements		X	X		X
Patents/copyrights	X			X	X
Technical reports				X	X
Technology transfer			X	X	X
Performance reports				X	X

Source: Daniels and others, 1977, p. 200.

═ 17 ═

Administration in Health Science Organizations

═════════════════════════════════

Each year extensive research and development projects in the health sciences are conducted in schools of medicine, nursing, dentistry, and public health; in independent hospitals; in nonprofit medical institutes; and in the basic medical science departments in universities. The success of such medical research is evident in the improved general health and increasing lifespan of the populace, overall better health care, and the elimination or cure of many diseases. Research and development in the health sciences yields results that may be more immediately appreciated by the individual patient and the general public than do other types of basic research. Research and development is vital to advances in the medical sciences and will continue to be supported as the principal means to the fulfillment of a national priority.

The administration of sponsored programs in the health sciences is similar to that in other organizations conducting sponsored activities, and the principles and practices in this book will help guide sponsored projects administrators in health science organizations. There are, however, special conditions in medical research and development operations that require additional administrative considerations. These special considerations are related to the nature of medical organizations, the personnel conducting the research activities, and the requirements of sponsors supporting health science research.

This chapter discusses such considerations and illustrates the importance of sponsored program administration to the success of efforts to better the nation's health. The effective sponsored projects administrator is a key member of the team that produces new research discoveries and applies the results to cure diseases, relieve pain, and improve individual health.

The Nature of Health Science Organizations

A major consideration in sponsored program administration in the health sciences is the nature of the organization. While the focus of research and development on a university campus may be extremely broad, covering all the disciplines and professional schools, the research program in a medical institution focuses on health-related activities. Basic research in the biomedical sciences and developmental activities to improve health are the principal sponsored project activities in a medical institution.

Medical organizations have a complex structure to fulfill their missions of teaching, patient care, and research. Faculty members are physicians with M.D. degrees and biomedical researchers with Ph.D. degrees. They perform their duties of teaching, patient care and research in the medical school, in teaching hospitals, and in research laboratories. Thus the administration of sponsored projects in a medical organization involves personnel from different backgrounds who perform their major functions in a variety of facilities.

Another factor that complicates sponsored projects management in medical institutions is that projects have multiple sources of income. Research is supported by a variety of sources, both internal and external to the organization—for example, funding may come from state appropriations, medical school tuition, municipal expenditures for hospitals, fees for patient care, permanent endowments, special research funds, and grants and contracts. Research projects that receive multiple support are more difficult to manage and must be closely monitored by the sponsored projects administrator.

Thus, the administration of sponsored programs in a medical organization differs from that of a university or large nonprofit research institute in that the focus of sponsored projects is narrower but the organization to achieve the goal is no less complex. This description applies primarily to medical schools and their teaching hospitals and less so to independent medical research institutes, schools of nursing, public health, and biomedical research in departments on the general campus of a university. However, it is difficult to generalize because there are exceptions, and some of these latter organizations have extensive and complex sponsored project activities.

Another major difference concerns the research personnel who conduct projects. Research and development conducted in industry, nonprofit institutes, and institutions of higher education is performed by individuals trained in a field of science, social science, humanities, arts, or a research program in a professional school. The principal training goal is to teach the scientific method of investigation through prediction and controlled experimentation.

In a health science institution, particularly in a medical school, different sets of individuals carry out research activities than in other research organizations. Researchers include basic biomedical scientists and medical doctors, who conduct research activities along with their teaching and clinical duties. The training and experience of a clinician differ from those of a researcher trained in an academic discipline. While physicians are involved in and appreciate the importance of science as a part of the preclinical, clinical, and internship phases of medical education, physicians are not trained as biomedical researchers. Most physicians refine their scientific research skills through postdoctoral research fellowships or on-the-job learning; and clinicians can learn to perform the same quality of research as scientists who hold Ph.D. degrees. The difference in the quality of researchers in medical organizations, like other organizations, is based primarily on differences in individuals and less on their educational backgrounds.

A factor that does affect physicians' abilities to conduct sponsored projects is the lack of time. Clinicians in medical schools are expected to teach, to carry out research projects, and continue clinical practice with patients. This threefold responsibility severely constrains the amount of time they can direct to research and development activities. Consequently, clinicians often are unable to conduct involved, long-term experimentation, and they usually delegate responsibility to assistants. However, many clinicians pursue empirical studies that depend on the observation of many cases and the effects of variables in different situations. This type of investigation fits their busy schedules because it does not require the long period of investigation needed to control variables, introduce treatments, and monitor results. An empirical study can be conducted in a short time period, using existing or easily gathered data, and it can yield useful normative data. The results can also be presented as an article or delivered at a professional meeting. Again, it is difficult to generalize, and many clinicians are involved in basic biomedical research.

There is also an attitudinal difference between some clinicians and biomedical scientists. Clinicians have to make important decisions regarding a patient's health, and they require a degree of independence in making that decision. Their training, experience, and busy schedule have conditioned them to make relatively quick and independent decisions. This professional style may come into conflict with the bureaucratic requirements associated with the management of a sponsored grant or contract. Basic biomedical scientists, however, have been conditioned to the painstaking pace of conducting research, and years of grantsmanship attune them to federal and other agency requirements.

The sponsored projects administrator in a medical organization must be cognizant of the investigators' backgrounds, responsibilities, time constraints, and attitudes, as well as of the types of research and development activity most feasible within the organization's framework and individual researchers' capabilities. Knowledge of these factors enables the sponsored projects administrator to be more effective in serving the research goals of both the organization and individual investigators.

A third special aspect of sponsored program administration in a health science institution concerns federal requirements related to research and development in medical schools. All research organizations are bound by federal regulations, but, because medical research usually relates directly to human beings, health science centers are subject to more stringent regulation. The sponsored projects administrator must be knowledgeable about the various federal regulations that pertain to the health science fields and capable of directing the appropriate advisory groups and administrative activities to assure compliance with regulations concerning human research subjects, patient care, clinical and pharmaceutical testing, radiation safety, and the care and disposal of radioactive materials.

The responsibilities of program administration in a health science organization are similar to those in any research and development organization. In a study of medical schools, Tally (1977) reports that office names, sponsored projects administrative titles, and degrees earned by sponsored projects administrators showed similar variability to that in other settings. For instance, only 14 percent of the sponsored projects administrators responding reported that they possessed a medical degree, and 40 percent had a doctoral degree. Tally also reports that it is not unusual for the sponsored projects office in a medical school to have other responsibilities as well. For instance, many of these offices serve additional units, and it is not unusual to find the medical school being served entirely by a central university office of sponsored projects. Tally observes that medical schools are primarily administratively oriented. Few staff titles relate to project or program development, and most focus on administrative responsibilities. When medical school sponsored projects administrators were asked which of their activities they considered important, most replied: review proposals for the institution's commitment, review proposals for accuracy of the budget, and review proposals for compliance with agency requirements. Among these administrators, the developmental approach to stimulating research activity was not considered a major concern.

Occasionally a sponsored projects administrator in a medical setting will encounter a situation in which a clinician not formally associated with the medical school becomes involved in a research study. This arrangement obviously presents problems for the institution, most notably liability concerns, and must not be allowed. Some formal arrangement must be completed that officially includes all project staff either on a payroll or on some other official documentation that legally indicates institutional association.

Special Considerations

As stated earlier, the principles and practices presented in this book apply equally as well to health science institutions as to other organizations conducting sponsored programs. But in addition to the regular management conditions, some special considerations pertain to the administration of sponsored activities in a medical organization.

Sources of Funding

The sources of funding for biomedical research are fewer than those for the broad array of programs on a university campus. The major federal agency with the mission of supporting projects in the health sciences is the Public Health Service, whose research arm is the National Institutes of Health. It is imperative for the sponsored projects administrator to become knowledgeable about the programs of the Public Health Service and the various institutes, bureaus, and support divisions. Because the great majority of the sponsored projects in a health science institution are supported by federal programs, the sponsored projects administrator in a medical organization must be familiar with the purposes, programs, application process, review system, award procedures, and regulations associated with federal awards from the Public Health Service.

The Public Health Service prints its own grant application form, PHS-398. The first page requests pertinent information about the project and the applicant's organization. The second page requires an abstract of the research plan, information about the applicant, and a description of any proposed uses of laboratory animals. Page three is the table of contents for the proposal. Pages four and five are for the detailed budget of the direct costs for the first twelve-month period and the entire project period, respectively. The application must include a biographical sketch for each major participant, and the final forms concern other sources of support and information on resources and the environment. The concluding checklist includes such items as assurances and indirect costs. Exhibit 52, pages 320–323, presents the first page, table of contents, first-year budget, and checklist for the application.

A national priority in the health sciences is the training of individuals in various specialties to meet the health needs of the nation. This priority is recognized by Congress through the authorization of programs and the annual appropriation of funds for manpower training programs. Among the training programs sponsored by the Public Health Service are: research and research-related manpower development programs for college, postbaccalaureate, and postdoctorate students (NIH); health administration graduate traineeships; professional nurse traineeships; maternal and child health training; and residency training in general internal medicine. Sponsored projects administrators in health science organizations often have major responsibility for the management of training awards, and they must be familiar with the sources of funding, the applications process, and the regulations for managing and reporting. The volume of training programs available in the health sciences requires a considerable degree of attention.

In addition to funding from the Public Health Service, medical organizations receive research and development support from other sources. Biomedical projects are supported by the National Science Foundation, the National Aeronautics and Space Administration, and some Department of Defense programs, such as the U.S. Army Medical Research and Development Command. However, in comparison to the support received from the Public Health Service, the amount of support from other federal agencies is minimal.

The primary mission of several private foundations is the support of programs in the medical sciences. The sponsored projects administrator should be familiar with such associations and foundations—for example, the American Heart Association, the American Cancer Society, and the Johnson Foundation. Medically related businesses and industries are another source of support for the health sciences. Business and industry support is usually arranged through direct contacts between researchers or administrators in the medical organizations and their counterparts in the company. Competitive proposals are frequently used to secure funding from industry.

Gifts solicited through development activities are another potential source of support for research in a medical institution. Fund-raising campaigns are common, especially in private medical schools, and they raise millions of dollars for hospitals and medical schools. Most development activities focus on raising capital for new buildings, but such campaigns can be organized to raise funds for research laboratories, equipment, and project support. Fund-raising drives are also used to build endowments for an institution, and research can subsequently be supported from the endowment income. The sponsored projects administrator in some medical institutions has the responsibility for directing the fund-raising campaign, and such a development officer's duties resemble those of a regular sponsored projects administrator. If the sponsored projects office does not have direct responsibility for directing fund-raising activities in a medical institution, the office can support the development efforts by providing names of potential donors and by providing data and examples to support the need for funds.

Food and Drug Administration

The nature of research and development in medical fields often involves the development and testing of new drugs. The requirements and regulations of the Food and Drug Administration (FDA) apply to such activities. Knowledge of the FDA regulations and adherence to the requirements is an important aspect of the sponsored projects administrator's responsibilities.

Site Visits

The Public Health Service provides large center contracts and grants that require site visitations. Involvement in site visits to review facilities and other institutional capabilities associated with a sponsored program is often a responsibility of sponsored projects administrators in a health science organization. The dean or director of the particular area has the responsibility for preparation for a site visit by a team from the Public Health Service. The sponsored projects officer assists in planning for the visit by assembling the necessary information related to research and development, arranging for activities during the visit, and organizing the necessary clusters or teams within the institution. The precise duties of the sponsored projects administrator depend on the type of visit, but the office should assume a major role. Site visits are an important part of the sponsored award process and the sponsored projects administrator must be prepared to render whatever services are necessary.

Risk Management

Sponsored research and development in the medical sciences often involves human beings and therefore involves a relatively high degree of risk. To ensure the protection of both subjects and researchers, extensive regulations mandate safeguards in the methods and results of the research. Although these regulations apply to all recipients of sponsored grants and contracts, in a medical organization the number of sponsored awards that require risk-management regulations is very high, and thus risk management occupies a significant portion of sponsored program administration. The sponsored projects administrator is responsible for identifying the risk-management regulations that apply to each project, assembling the proper review teams to assure proper procedures and approvals before a proposal is submitted, and monitoring to ensure that the proper reviews are performed after the award is made. The responsibility of the sponsored projects officer is not to make the decision as to the appropriateness of the risk-management safeguards, but rather to manage the process by which the appropriate officials and committees make these decisions. The areas of major concern in risk management are: protection of human subjects, radiation safety, and the appropriate care and protection of laboratory animals.

IND Clinical Testing

Many health science organizations will participate in Investigational New Drugs (IND) clinical testing programs. In this program a pharmaceutical company contracts with a medical institution or a clinician to test new drugs in a clinically controlled situation. (The FDA requires new drugs to be tested in a controlled situation before they are approved for general distribution.) The IND clinical testing program is an example of an administrative requirement that is a special aspect of sponsored program administration in a medical setting.

IDE Program

Investigational Device Exemptions (IDE) is a similar program. Just as new drugs must be tested, new equipment or medical devices must also be clinically tested before release for general use. In the IDE program the manufacturer of new medical equipment or devices contracts with a health science center to perform tests on its product.

Exhibit 52. PHS Grant Application Form.

FORM APPROVED
O.M.B. NO. 68-R0249

DEPARTMENT OF HEALTH AND HUMAN SERVICES PUBLIC HEALTH SERVICE **GRANT APPLICATION** FOLLOW INSTRUCTIONS CAREFULLY	LEAVE BLANK		
	TYPE	ACTIVITY	NUMBER
	REVIEW GROUP		FORMERLY
	COUNCIL BOARD (Month, year)		DATE RECEIVED

1. TITLE OF APPLICATION (Do not exceed 56 typewriter spaces)

2. RESPONSE TO SPECIFIC PROGRAM ANNOUNCEMENT ☐ NO ☐ YES (If "YES," state RFA number and/or announcement title)

3. PRINCIPAL INVESTIGATOR/PROGRAM DIRECTOR

3a. NAME (Last, first, middle)	3b. SOCIAL SECURITY NUMBER
3c. MAILING ADDRESS (Street, city, state, zip code)	3d. POSITION TITLE
	3e. DEPARTMENT, SERVICE, LABORATORY OR EQUIVALENT
3f. TELEPHONE (Area code, number and extension)	3g. MAJOR SUBDIVISION

4. HUMAN SUBJECTS, DERIVED MATERIALS OR DATA INVOLVED ☐ NO ☐ YES (If "YES," form HHS 596 required)	5. RECOMBINANT DNA RESEARCH SUBJECT TO NIH GUIDELINES ☐ NO ☐ YES

6. DATES OF ENTIRE PROPOSED PROJECT PERIOD (This application) From: Through:	7. TOTAL DIRECT COSTS RE- QUESTED FOR PROJECT PERIOD (from page 5) $	8. DIRECT COSTS REQUESTED FOR FIRST 12-MONTH BUDGET PERIOD (from page 4) $

9. PERFORMANCE SITES (Organizations and addresses)	10. INVENTIONS (Competing continuation application only) Were any inventions conceived or reduced to practice during the course of the project? ☐ NO ☐ YES - Previously reported ☐ YES - Not previously reported
	11. APPLICANT ORGANIZATION (Name, address and congressional district)

12. ORGANIZATIONAL COMPONENT TO RECEIVE CREDIT FOR INSTITUTIONAL GRANT (See instructions) Code ☐ Description	13. ENTITY IDENTIFICATION NUMBER
	14. TYPE OF ORGANIZATION (See instructions) ☐ Private Nonprofit ☐ Public (Specify Federal, State, Local):

15. OFFICIAL IN BUSINESS OFFICE TO BE NOTIFIED IF AN AWARD IS MADE (Name, title, address and telephone number.)	16. OFFICIAL SIGNING FOR APPLICANT ORGANIZATION (Name, title, address and telephone number)

17. PRINCIPAL INVESTIGATOR PROGRAM DIRECTOR ASSURANCE: I agree to accept responsibility for the scientific conduct of the project and to provide the required progress reports if a grant is awarded as a result of this application.	SIGNATURE OF PERSON NAMED IN 3a (In ink. "Per" signature not acceptable)	DATE
18. CERTIFICATION AND ACCEPTANCE: I certify that the statements herein are true and complete to the best of my knowledge, and accept the obligation to comply with Public Health Service terms and conditions if a grant is awarded as the result of this application. A willfully false certification is a criminal offense. (U.S. Code, Title 18, Section 1001.)	SIGNATURE OF PERSON NAMED IN 16 (In ink. "Per" signature not acceptable)	DATE

PHS-398
Rev. 5/80

Exhibit 52 (continued)

PRINCIPAL INVESTIGATOR. PROGRAM DIRECTOR: _____

TABLE OF CONTENTS

Number pages consecutively at the bottom throughout the application. Do not use suffixes such as 5a, 5b. Type the name of the Principal Investigator, Program Director at the top of each printed page and each continuation page.

SECTION 1.   PAGE NUMBERS

    Face Page, Abstract, Table of Contents.. 1-3
    Detailed Budget for First 12 Month Budget Period 4
    Budget Estimates for All Years of Support... 5
    Biographical Sketch-Principal Investigator Program Director *(Not to exceed two pages)*..... _____
    Other Biographical Sketches *(Not to exceed two pages for each)*......................... _____
    Other Support.. _____
    Resources and Environment .... _____

SECTION 2.

    Introduction *(Excess pages; revised and supplemental applications)* .... _____
    Research Plan
        A. Specific Aims *(Not to exceed one page)* .... _____
        B. Significance *(Not to exceed three pages)*...................................... _____
        C. Progress Report/Preliminary Studies *(Not to exceed eight pages)* .... _____
        D. Methods .... _____
        E. Human Subjects, Derived Materials or Data...................................... _____
        F. Laboratory Animals .... _____
        G. Consultants.. _____
        H. Consortium Arrangements or Formalized Collaborative Agreements .... _____
        I. Literature Cited .... _____
    Checklist .... _____

SECTION 3. Appendix *(Six sets)* *(No page numbering necessary for Appendix)*

    Number of publications: _____   Number of manuscripts: _____
    Other items (list):

    Application Receipt Record, form PHS 3830
    Form HHS 596 if Item 4, page 1, is checked

Exhibit 52 (continued)

PRINCIPAL INVESTIGATOR/PROGRAM DIRECTOR: _____

DETAILED BUDGET FOR FIRST 12 MONTH BUDGET PERIOD DIRECT COSTS ONLY		FROM	THROUGH	
		DOLLAR AMOUNT REQUESTED (Omit cents)		

PERSONNEL (Applicant organization only) (See instructions)		TIME/EFFORT		SALARY	FRINGE BENEFITS	TOTALS
NAME	TITLE OF POSITION	%	Hours per Week			
	Principal Investigator					
	SUBTOTALS ⟶					

CONSULTANT COSTS (See instructions)

EQUIPMENT (Itemize)

SUPPLIES (Itemize by category)

TRAVEL	DOMESTIC	
	FOREIGN	
PATIENT CARE COSTS	INPATIENT	
	OUTPATIENT	

ALTERATIONS AND RENOVATIONS (Itemize by category)

CONTRACTUAL OR THIRD PARTY COSTS (See instructions)

OTHER EXPENSES (Itemize by category)

TOTAL DIRECT COSTS (Also enter on page 1, item 8) ⟶ $

PHS-398
Rev. 5/80   PAGE 4

Exhibit 52 (continued)

PRINCIPAL INVESTIGATOR/PROGRAM DIRECTOR:_____

CHECKLIST

This is the required last page of the application.

Check the appropriate boxes and provide the information requested.

TYPE OF APPLICATION:

☐ NEW application *(This application is being submitted to the PHS for the first time.)*

☐ COMPETING CONTINUATION of grant number: _____ .
   (This application is to extend a grant beyond its original project period.)

☐ SUPPLEMENT to grant number: _____ .
   (This application is for additional funds during a funded project period.)

☐ REVISION of application number: _____ .
   (This application replaces a prior version of a new, competing continuation or supplemental application.)

☐ Change of Principal Investigator/Program Director.
   Name of former Principal Investigator/Program Director: _____ .

ASSURANCES IN CONNECTION WITH:

Civil Rights	Handicapped Individuals	Sex Discrimination	Human Subjects General Assurance *(If applicable)*	Laboratory Animals *(If applicable)*
☐ Filed ☐ Not filed	☐ Filed ☐ Not filed	☐ Filed ☐ Not filed	☐ Filed ☐ Not filed	☐ Filed ☐ Not filed

---

INDIRECT COSTS:

Indicate the applicant organization's most recent indirect cost rate established with the appropriate DHHS Regional Office. If the applicant organization is in the process of initially developing or renegotiating a rate, or has established a rate with another Federal agency, it should, immediately upon notification that an award will be made, develop a tentative indirect cost rate proposal based on its most recently completed fiscal year in accordance with the principles set forth in the pertinent *DHHS Guide for Establishing Indirect Cost Rates*, and submit it to the appropriate DHHS Regional Office. Indirect costs will not be paid on foreign grants, construction grants, and grants to individuals, and usually not on grants in support of conferences.

☐ DHHS Agreement Dated: _____
   _____ % Salary and Wages <u>or</u> _____ % Total Direct Costs.

   Is this an off-site or other special rate, or is more than one rate involved? ☐ YES ☐ NO
   Explanation: _____
   _____

☐ DHHS Agreement being negotiated with _____ Regional Office.

☐ No DHHS Agreement, but rate established with _____ Date_____

☐ No Indirect Costs Requested.

▫▫ 18 ▫▫

Emerging Trends and the Future of Sponsored Program Administration

This chapter concerns several developing issues in the field of sponsored programs. At the heart of most of these issues are two very important recurring questions: (1) Should recipient organizations enter into innovative partnerships and use new modes of funding? and (2) What should be the role of the sponsored projects office in developing these partnerships and funding mechanisms?

The conservative view is espoused by Dressel, Johnson, and Marcus (1969), Haaland (1981), and Penman ("Education . . . ," 1981), among others. They argue that sponsored projects and their offices are suspect in the eyes of academicians since they are outside the traditional organizational missions, structures, and funding modes. The conservatives hold that institutions should proceed very cautiously in developing new sponsored activities lest nonacademicians begin to dictate the direction of institutions and influence the appointment of staff, thus limiting academic freedom. An opposing opinion of development, voiced by Hensley (1980), is that the "university research administrator is the architect of the university's future" and that university research administrators should aggressively pursue the formation of new partnerships to improve their institutions and to meet society's changing needs.

The first issue presented in this chapter is the growing trend of new, lasting cooperative projects between industry and universities. This initiative has developed not only from the search for increased funding but also from the needs of industry to stimulate the development of knowledge, and the needs of universities to demonstrate the transfer of technology to the public through industrial applications. Our second topic is the consortium organization, which provides sponsored projects services to several institutions. An example of a successful consortium and potential benefits to participants are presented. Then we discuss how the federal government is seeking to stimulate industrial research and development through university programs, tax initiatives, and associations.

The fourth section of this chapter focuses on the use of sponsored projects to sustain existing programs and to facilitate new ones. The fifth section describes the federal government's change in emphasis from centralized control to decentralized responsibility through the use of block grants. This change demands new operating principles and organizational contacts for sponsored projects administrators.

This chapter concludes with a forecast of the challenges and responsibilities sponsored program administration will have to meet in the coming decade.

Industry-University Cooperation in Sponsored Projects

Many factors have led to an increased cooperation between industries and universities in sponsored projects and programs. The relative decline in federal support for universities' sponsored projects and continued inflation have caused universities to seek new resources for research. Concurrently, industry's major concerns with productivity and innovation have stimulated industry's interest in sponsoring research. The mutual benefits of the transfer of technology from university discoveries to industrial applications have increased both parties' awareness of their cooperative needs. Prager and Omenn (1980, p. 380) summarize the universities' needs:

> There is a growing research interest in solving critical domestic problems and a renewed appreciation for the role of industry in such problem solving. However, the primary motivations are more pragmatic. Academia finds itself being squeezed by its major research sponsor—the federal government. Competition for federal research funds has dramatically increased as inflation has eroded the purchasing power of the research dollar and increasing numbers of young scientists have sought support for their work. At the same time, government regulations related to scientific and financial accountability, human and animal experimentation, biohazards, and affirmative action have reduced the efficiency, flexibility, and independence of the academic scientist. This situation is aggravated by decreasing employment opportunities in academic and government research centers and by a projected decline in student enrollments. For these reasons, university faculty and administrators are beginning to look to industry as a source of research support, as a potential employer of advanced-degree graduates, as a source of part-time faculty, and as a focus for major continuing education programs. Perceived benefits for universities include the potential for long-term research support less entangled in red tape; help from industry in making new knowledge and technology commercially useful; broader educational experience, industrial exposure, dissertation topics, and potential employment opportunities for students; and stimulation of university faculty through interaction with industrial scientists and engineers and through access to specialized industrial equipment.

A report by the National Commission on Research (1980) offers the following conclusions, among others:

- Research relationships between industry and universities can strengthen the innovation process, improve the vigor of research within the universities, and contribute significantly to university research and instructional resources.
- Equitable financial rewards should accrue to industry and to universities from explicit research relationships.
- Hazards to university academic freedom from university-industry research relationships are manageable.

- Universities, in seeking opportunities for cooperative research with industry, must exercise care to avoid subversion of proper university purposes.
- Government can encourage and support the university-industry research relationship by becoming a facilitator rather than an ongoing participant in direction or management.
- The less basic the research, the more difficult becomes the determination of whether the use of public funds for university-industry research relationships is proper.

The commission recommends that research universities and industry explore effective cooperative research relationships in important scientific areas of mutual interest. Effective cooperation requires that the research objectives preserve each partner's purposes and policies and that the individual researchers determine together the specific subjects to be investigated. The research project should provide for financial reward to industry and to the university for assuming the risks of engaging in uncertain scientific and technological programs. Such research relationships can be based on models demonstrated to be effective, for example, the NSF Industrial-University Cooperative Research Project Program.

The commission suggests that companies within a sector of industry review their research needs and explore the possibility of combining their resources for the support of a coordinated program of cooperative research with universities. The federal government should encourage the application of research results to product development by permitting universities to retain title to inventions developed under federally supported research and by providing financial incentives to initiate and maintain closer research ties between industry and universities.

Finally, the commission recommends that universities examine their administrative structures and policies relevant to cooperative research arrangements with industry. Such research arrangements should facilitate cooperation, while protecting the academic research environment. Universities also should examine their patent policies and assign staff to identify and pursue patent opportunities. Universities and industry must act to remove the misunderstanding and mistrust between them and they should inform the public of the rationale for their participation in cooperative research programs. Industry, unlike the federal government, has no program announcements, guidelines, or formal requests for proposals, and its major role is not the support of basic research. Universities that do not have an established industrial affiliations program, such as those at Stanford or MIT, may find it quite difficult to become involved with industry. Also, the integrity of the university must be of prime importance to both partners. Some potential hazards for the university as it strives to improve cooperative research relationships with industry, according to the National Commission on Research (1980), include: (1) restrictions on choice of research direction; (2) emphasis on applied and development programs, rather than basic research; (3) public suspicion that university resources are used for private benefit; and (4) polarization of opinion of special interest groups against universities.

Responsibilities of the Sponsored Projects Administrator

One major role of the office of sponsored projects in cooperative relationships is to perform as the broker between industrial scientists and faculty members. To provide this link, sponsored projects administrators must be knowledgeable about the campus' research capability and transmit that information to potential industrial users. The publication of a directory of faculty capabilities and research interests and its dissemination to business and industrial users is one possible task for the office of sponsored projects. Another is developing contacts with industrial research directors and including those individuals in meetings to discuss industry-university relationships. The major objective of the office in this area is to bring together an industrial scientist and faculty member with the same scientific interests to discuss their research endeavors. Such a meeting may lead to a mutual understanding between them and possible contracts between the industrial firm and the university.

Cooperative relationships may also be initiated at a regional conference or symposium devoted to university-industry cooperation in the university's geographical area. The agenda might include presentations by scientists of their current work; an assessment of the strengths of the university in specific scientific areas; sessions for top management to discuss the importance of industry-university cooperation to corporate productivity; and panels of international, national, or local speakers discussing the needs, barriers, and benefits of cooperation between industry and universities.

In preparing to initiate or expand cooperative relationships, sponsored projects administrators should first focus on improved communication. Next they should gather information on successful cooperative relationships, their structure and purposes. Models for such relationships include: the offering of visiting faculty positions to senior industrial staff, industrial fellowships, consulting relationships, seminars and short courses for scientists to enhance transfer of knowledge, joint research programs, facilities and equipment sharing, and industrial associates programs.

Sponsored projects administrators should also study the common barriers to industry-university cooperation. These include: rights to data and freedom of communication or publication; patent policies and proprietary rights; accountability and timeliness of work; industry's fear that academicians lack hands-on experience; and the different goals and objectives of the organizations. To overcome such barriers, the potential benefits of more effective industry-university relationships should be emphasized on campus. These benefits include: improved research productivity, increased public awareness and interest in research and development, better-prepared graduates, increased support for research with less regulation, sharing of sophisticated experimental equipment and facilities, enhanced professional experience for faculty, enhanced public credibility, and an increased number of innovations.

Consortiums for Sponsored Projects Administration

As noted throughout this book, timely information regarding sources of external funds has become crucial for the overall development of colleges and universities. The major objectives of quality education, research, and community service require sufficient external funding. Yet although the pressure for additional external funding has become acute, funding for sponsored projects offices has been severely constricted as institutions try to control their budgets. Since almost all institutions provide similar information services for their researchers, the establishment of a consortium to provide these services is feasible and cost effective. The consortium can offer a variety of quality services, depending on member institutions' needs, at a reduced cost to each institution. According to Elliott (1973, p. 5), "A consortium of educational institutions usually has two objectives . . . to improve quality and to save money."

A multipurpose service consortium can provide an array of programs that member colleges and universities might not each be able to conduct or be able to conduct as economically. In return, the participating institutions usually provide the consortium with financial support through a basic annual assessment and fees for participation in individual programs. The best-established consortia seem to be those that share two basic characteristics: They have a manageable number of member institutions, and they have understood and agreed-upon goals and functions. Obviously, the central operations and supplementary programs cost each institution less as expenditures are divided among more institutions (Patterson, 1974). A consortium for preaward information for grant and contract activities may well be the most economical and efficient way to provide these services to colleges and universities.

Benefits to participating institutions may include: less duplication of effort, increased awareness of funding sources, improved quality of preaward services, increased extramural funding, greater interinstitutional cooperation, and the receipt of more complete and timely information. The preaward services provided by a consortium may include:

- Faculty profile searches
- Program searches
- Deadline service
- Bulletins of proposed regulations and guidelines for new programs
- Maintenance of a reference library
- Production of a directory of faculty research capability
- Publication of a research newsletter
- Distribution of current guidelines and application forms

Currently, under the aegis of the Association for Higher Education of North Texas, five universities in the Dallas–Fort Worth area belong to a Research Administration Committee (RAC) that provides preaward services to its member universities. The member universities are: North Texas State University, Southern Methodist University, Texas Christian University, University of Texas at Arlington, and University of Texas at Dallas. An evaluation of the program was quite positive, and RAC is now considering serving as the catalyst for developing industry-university relations in the area.

Three-Sector Partnerships to Promote Industrial R&D

For a number of years, dual partnerships—between industry and universities, government and universities, or government and industry—have dominated the relationships among the principals associated with sponsored activities. Since the early 1900s, single industrial corporations have sponsored research in individual universities. Lately, industrial associations (Petroleum Research Fund, Council for Tobacco Research, American Soybean Association Research Foundation) have established support programs to encourage universities to perform basic research in their field. In this instance, the industrial sector joins with the education sector to form a partnership that is mutually beneficial.

Government at all levels has promoted dual partnerships by encouraging its executive agencies to achieve their objectives by establishing programs that solicit mission-related activities from universities. The National Institutes of Health, Department of Energy, and other service agencies have sponsored limited consortia involving several universities, some industrial companies, and some local governments as multiple contractors reporting to the senior partner—a government agency. As an alternative to dual partnerships, the government also establishes its own research and development (R&D) units. But, a comparison of funds allocated to government R&D units and to private R&D shows that the government greatly favors dual partnerships for R&D.

In the late 1970s the federal government began to encourage three-sector partnerships shared by government, industry, and education. Two principal factors account for this interest. First, the federal government believes that technology fuels the nation's economy, that economic prosperity is dependent on research and industrial innovation. Second, the federal government finds that it cannot adequately support many of the services and programs it has initiated. To reduce the federal deficit, the government is seeking new sources of funding for continuing its services. The three-sector partnership allows the federal government to withdraw huge amounts of financial support from certain programs and to relinquish its financial responsibility by sharing it with additional partners. Thus industry and education are being asked to assume more responsibility for these services by joining in three-sector partnerships.

Price (1980), the Joint Economic Committee (1980), and U.S. House of Representatives, Subcommittee on Science, Research and

Technology (1980) all note a great concern about lagging U.S. technological innovation, and they urge the federal government to encourage and facilitate university-industry cooperation in technological development lest U.S. industry lose its economic advantage in world markets. The commentators on three-sector partnerships agree that such relationships must be substantially improved. They suggest that the government (1) change its fiscal policies to encourage industry to utilize university research; (2) increase funding of basic research in targeted industrial areas; (3) provide incentives for universities to develop and pursue relationships with industry; and (4) include provisions in federal research support that emphasize the dissemination of research results.

In the past few years, Congress has directly addressed the lack of a national policy concerning the promotion of three-sector partnerships. The House Committee on Science and Technology initiated hearings regarding the impact of technological innovation on domestic considerations and on the U.S. position in the international marketplace. Similar hearings were held by the Senate, and many studies were conducted by executive agencies. From these hearings a number of bills emerged that were designed to promote three-sector partnerships.

Stevenson-Wydler Technology Innovation Act of 1980. The purpose of the Stevenson-Wydler Technology Innovation Act of 1980 is to improve the economic, environmental, and social well-being of the United States by strengthening three-sector partnerships. Specifically, the act establishes organizations in the executive branch to study and stimulate technology; urges the establishment of centers for industrial technology; and encourages the exchange of scientific and technical personnel among academia, industry, and federal laboratories. The act is intended to stimulate improved utilization of federally funded technological developments by state and local governments and the private sector, and to encourage the development of technology through the recognition of individuals and companies that have made outstanding contributions in technology.

This act promises to strengthen three-sector partnerships such that each sector can contribute to the innovation process in programs of shared responsibilities. The bill authorizes total appropriations of $285 million through fiscal years 1981–1985; actual appropriations, of course, depend on future budgets. It represents direct government encouragement of three-sector partnerships to help develop American industry.

Economic Recovery Tax Act of 1981. The Economic Recovery Tax Act provides tax-credit incentives for research and experimentation. Taxpayers can claim a 25 percent tax credit for certain research and experimental expenditures incurred in a trade or business, to the extent that current-year expenditures exceed the average amount of research expenditures in a base period. Specifically, research expenditures that qualify for the new incremental credit are those in-house expenditures for research wages and supplies and other such charges—up to 65 percent of amounts paid, for example, to a research firm or university for contract research; and 65 percent of corporate grants for basic research to be performed by universities or certain scientific research organizations, or of grants to certain funds organized to make basic research grants to universities. The tax credit applies to research expenditures made after June 30, 1981, and before 1986.

The act also provides for charitable contributions of newly manufactured equipment to universities for research. The act allows a deduction equal to the taxpayer's base plus 50 percent of any appreciation for qualified corporate contributions by the manufacturer of new scientific equipment or apparatus to a college or university for research or experimentation. Thus the act provides indirect assistance to colleges and universities, hard-pressed by soaring equipment prices and shrinking budgets to update their instrumentation capabilities. It is indirect support for basic research that fuels industrial technology.

Other Federal Measures. Other measures, such as the Research Revitalization Act of 1981, were drafted to establish research reserve funds that would allow industrial companies to claim tax credit for amounts paid for research or experimentation performed by any institution of higher education. These funds could be used by industry to support university researchers working on problems directly related to their company. Similar measures were introduced in the Senate to encourage three-sector partnerships in developing basic research useful to American industry.

The National Science Foundation (NSF) has always been acutely aware of the relationships between industrial development, technological innovation, and scientific research. Its industrial science and technological innovation programs were established to provide a focus in this area by consolidating virtually all of NSF's action-oriented programs that involve industry and its cooperation with universities. By encouraging such cooperation, NSF addresses issues of industrial science, technological science, and technological innovation that have been raised frequently by Congress, by the scientific and technological communities, and by industry.

Since the middle seventies, NSF has been encouraging another kind of linkage, Industry-University Cooperative Research Centers. In contrast with the cooperative research projects, the centers involve one university and many companies from one or several industries. Each center focuses on a particular scientific area—for example, polymer processing or computer graphics. A center of this type usually calls on the services of many disciplines within a university, especially those in the business and engineering schools. It also invites participation by the local business and financial communities.

State Programs. Many states are providing direct incentives to universities to help their states develop industry. Milton J. Shapp, governor of Pennsylvania, expresses the feelings shared by most state chief executives: "We must use the findings of science and technology to stimulate new industrial growth in the private sector" (Pennsylvania Office of Science and Technology, 1972). The incentive to promote three-sector partnerships usually comes from the state government in the form of grants to universities to establish technical assistance centers for industry. The following descriptions of four technical assistance centers illustrate some of the forms of partnerships to assist industrial technological development.

The Pennsylvania Technical Assistance Program (PENNTAP) was established in 1965 as the operations control center for a technical information network to help private and public sectors throughout Pennsylvania obtain and apply appropriate scientific and technical information. PENNTAP, a technology transfer system, is designed to produce social and economic benefits by placing the findings of science in the hands of potential users. PENNTAP both responds to service requests and conducts program awareness operations through various media activities. Its advisory council is composed of fifteen members from industry, the professions, and the public sector. With more demands than can be satisfied with current funding levels, PENNTAP's advisory council establishes priorities and develops broad program priority categories, reviews technology dissemination proposals from public and private institutions of higher education and other nonprofit organizations deemed as potential participants, and makes funding recommendations to the director.

Prior to 1969, PENNTAP received continuing financial support from the Pennsylvania legislature through the Department of Commerce. During the past decade, the Pennsylvania legislature has supported PENNTAP with an annual appropriation of at least $100,000 with matching funds, as a provision, from grants and contracts, institutionally provided services and funds, and conference fees and miscellaneous income.

The Ohio Technology Transfer Organization (OTTO) was proposed early in 1978 as a means of assisting small businesses in applying new technologies to improve their position in the marketplace (Bailey, Herdenorf, and Vossler, 1980). OTTO is a statewide network of eleven community and technical colleges working with Ohio State University in a retailer-wholesaler relationship. OTTO provides information, training, and technical assistance to small businesses that usually cannot afford such services. OTTO receives half a million dollars from the Ohio legislature to supplement money from Ohio State University and the OTTO colleges. OTTO is a three-sector venture between state government, education, and industry for the technological advancement of Ohio industry.

The Center for Industrial Services (CIS) is a unit within the Institute for Public Service at the University of Tennessee. CIS has five field offices with one full-time employee each, and eleven full-time people work in the central office. The center's annual budget, approximately $275,000, comes from both the University of Tennessee and the federal government. The services are free (except for training programs), and CIS services about 100 requests each month. CIS provides technology transfer training, marketing, engineering, and field applications to advance Tennessee industry.

The North Carolina Science and Technology Research Center (NC/STRC) is a joint program supported by NASA and the North Carolina Department of Commerce (Business Assistance Division) located in Research Triangle Park. NC/STRC employs thirty-three full-time people in various technical fields, such as computer science, marketing, and the like. NC/STRC has an annual budget in excess of $1 million, of which NASA provides 25 percent. NC/STRC is one of NASA's seven industrial application centers and is the only one not affiliated with a university. NC/STRC, as well as serving North Carolina on a fee-paying basis, serves ten other southeastern states. Currently, NC/STRC handles more than 2,100 searches a year.

The growth of such three-sector partnerships requires sponsored projects administrators to adjust their thinking and systems to coordinate multisector partnerships. They should become actively involved in long-range institutional and regional planning that makes provision for joint ventures with industry, government, labor, and other educational institutions. It appears that the complexity of the interaction among the principals associated with American technological development will increase significantly in the coming decades. The office of sponsored projects will be asked to play a leading development role as emergent ideas are realized in solid agreements. New sets of management systems and new staff positions and responsibilities are being created for sponsored projects by those institutions that are aggressively moving to develop joint ventures with industry and government. PENNTAP and OTTO appear to be prototypes for university-based industrial technological assistance centers that are partially supported by government. Such activities logically fall under the jurisdiction of the sponsored projects office.

Sponsored Projects and Program Development

In this era of shrinking state and federal resources for universities, sponsored projects administrators are becoming very valuable staff members for university presidents, vice-presidents, deans, department heads, individual faculty members, and committees involved in planning and development. It appears they will be increasingly used as higher education searches for better strategies to develop and maintain academic programs.

Most state higher education coordinating boards demand that all planned university developments within the state system be coordinated with state master plans; universities and colleges are required to adopt some form of long-range planning, as presented in the state guides to new and expanded program requests. If universities want to expand or develop new academic programs, they must gain approval from the coordinating boards and obtain legislative appropriations for such development. But many state legislatures are reducing their support to universities and have instructed coordinating boards to eliminate duplicate or unnecessary programs. As a consequence of states' emphasis on program planning and budgeting, universities have devised planning and development mechanisms to gather appropriate information to justify new and expanded program requests and to defend against coordinating board recommendations to cut particular programs.

State colleges and universities that fail to obtain state funding for new or expanded programs should work with their offices of sponsored projects to locate potential outside sponsors. Indeed, university administrators have repeatedly acknowledged the role that sponsored projects administrators have in developing new academic programs. James H. Boggs, vice-president for academic affairs of Oklahoma State University, states, "We became alert to the evolving and developing funding programs at the national level, and some of us even assigned personnel to the scene to keep us advised of new funding possibilities. Our actions were dictated, in large part, by the scarcity of local funding as opposed to a seemingly endless flow of dollars at the national level. We had, also, the very well-intentioned desire to enlarge the intellectual opportunities for our students, particularly at the graduate level. We saw federal funding sources as a means of not only enriching our present graduate programs but of adding new ones, providing stipends for graduate students, professional opportunities for our faculties. . ." (Boggs, 1973, p. 2).

It is generally acknowledged that universities must both reallocate shrinking state resources or private endowments and look to extramural sponsors to fund program development. The director of the office of sponsored projects should be a member of academic planning and development committees, since that office knows the current potential sources of support and can forecast trends in external funding.

Academic officers have for some time relied on the office of sponsored projects to help them plan, develop, manage, and assess sponsored activities; but lately, some institutions have placed greater emphasis on the formal planning functions of these offices. Participation in institutional planning and development is a new role for the sponsored projects administrator, a role that is not assumed by all sponsored activities officers, but one that is a legitimate function which may dominate the future activities of certain individuals in sponsored projects offices. Stauffer (1977), discussing this expanding role, notes that the American Council on Education's Office of Leadership Development urged the

NSF to establish a program for the advancement of research administration and planning. He also lists many ways in which directors of sponsored projects offices are presently assisting institutions in planning.

In some universities, the planning and development functions of the sponsored projects office may be subsumed under the heading of "program development," and those functions are different from the traditional projects administration functions. The purpose of program development is to establish new degree programs, to improve existing ones, and to create organized research units through the use of sponsored activities. Program development requires a proactive rather than reactive approach to development, and it requires particular management techniques. Although there is some opposition from faculty and administrators to the planning and budgeting techniques associated with program development, there is also the growing realization that educational institutions must become involved in long-range program planning and that some institutions cannot afford to rely solely upon the traditional laissez faire approach to development. Some institutions that want to make rapid improvement in programs, to change unit orientation, and to concentrate limited resources have integrated the development of sponsored activities with the development of programs.

Consequently, the sponsored projects administrator should prepare to become an integral part of institutional program planning and development. This role demands a general knowledge of the institution's programs and directions, a precise understanding of the management techniques used to prioritize objectives, and an understanding of the institution's decision-making process. The sponsored projects administrator and the office of sponsored projects are emerging as an important partner in such institutional functions as ranking program objectives, weighing cost alternatives, and applying resources.

Decentralization and Block Grants

One of the major changes in the field of sponsored activities is the recent federal effort to decentralize control of education and service programs and to reduce federal categorical support through the use of block grants. This effort seeks to reverse the spending and control policies that have dominated the federal budget for the past twenty-five years. If this effort is successful, the federal departments will have only the following limited areas of responsibility:

- Allocating monies from departmental appropriations to state applications. (Maximum allocations for each state are fixed by law according to population and authorization by Congress; for example, California probably will be allocated an education block grant of less than $52 million; Illinois' block grant is projected to be about $26 million.)
- Approving the states' comprehensive plans for the block grants.
- Reviewing the states' applications for maintenance of state and local efforts.
- Granting waivers of maintenance-of-effort requirements.
- Reviewing state compliance with federal laws and regulations.

The education block grants will consolidate over twenty funded programs, including: emergency school aid, school libraries and instructional resources, support and innovation, teacher corps, teacher centers, precollege science teacher training, gifted and talented, career education, consumers' education, metric education, cities in schools, PUSH for excellence, ethnic heritage, community education, basic skills, law-related education, biomedical education, and follow through.

Programs that are consolidated and can now be funded at state and local discretion include: preschool partnership, youth employment, environmental education, health education, correction education, dissemination of information, population education, and guidance and counseling.

Once the decentralization plan has taken effect, the office of sponsored projects should continue its contracts with those federal agencies still supporting categorical assistance, but it must also establish contacts with the appropriate state agencies.

At the state level, a state lead agency should have the responsibilities for administering the federal block grant, but these agencies have been caught without adequate plans and money to continue the full range of existing services. It appears that governors will need to form state advisory councils or block-grant boards and that lead agencies will have to prepare for the cognizant federal agencies: (1) a pre-expenditure report for block grants; (2) a comprehensive state plan for the block grants; (3) a report to the legislature about the coordinated planning activities and data-collection efforts of the service agencies; and (4) final budget recommendations regarding the allocation of block grants. These recommendations will then be submitted to the legislature and governor for appropriate action and funding authorization for service agencies' programs.

Office of sponsored projects officers should arrange for institutional constituencies to carefully consider the consequences of block grants for institutional development, and they should impress upon their colleagues the importance of adopting a strategy to respond to the "new federalism." They should also lead in the preparation of a political strategy to assure their institutions' representation in state programs. Although the effects of the cutting of categorical funds on existing grantee administrative systems are unclear, the cuts will have a dramatic impact on sponsored activities.

The state field offices responsible for delivering services are facing serious problems, and several state agencies will be competing for block grant funds. These agencies' network of field and outpost offices often subcontract with grantee organizations to make instructional, research, and service programs generally available throughout the state. But they will probably have to reduce programs, thus reducing the number and size of grants previously made to subcontractors. Therefore, the office of sponsored projects subcontractor must attempt to develop new partnerships with state and local agencies that will direct money to the support of their institutional programs.

Block grants represent a dramatic departure from prior federal categorical programs, and they present new challenges and opportunities for states in determining future directions of their service, training, and research programs. Grantee organizations have an opportunity to take a fresh look at their operating systems and assist in the development of new methods of providing services to those in need. These organizations also have an opportunity to assist in determining the current areas of greatest need, to suggest changes in the service delivery systems and techniques, and to help streamline administrative requirements while assuring public accountability.

The Future of Sponsored Program Administration

Forecasting the future of sponsored program administration requires the prognosticator to extrapolate the future from the present and mix the results with some crystal ball dreaming about forthcoming changes in society. Tomorrow's trends can be discerned from present practices only so far. The future of sponsored program administration, like all other endeavors, will be determined by changes in society as a result of demographic, economic, technological, and political factors. Mindful of the hazards of forecasting, we conclude by conjecturing how sponsored program administration is likely to evolve in the coming decade.

The Need for Sponsored Programs

As the world population continues to increase, the scarcity of land and resources will generate many difficult economic and political problems. To solve some of these problems will require basic research discoveries, applied research, and the development of new products and education programs to increase understanding and better utilize limited resources. Thus the need for sponsored programs to conduct the necessary basic and applied studies will be greater in the 1990s than at present. The effective administration of sponsored programs will also be required to perform the overall management and coordination of sponsored projects within and between institutions.

Humankind's greater reliance on scientific, technological, and educational projects will result in an increased public recognition of their importance and the need to support creative endeavors. As a result, we expect the establishment of a nationwide cooperative system to coordinate research and development among various agencies, institutions, and organizations; and greater emphasis within organizations and institutions on long-term management, prioritizing and planning. The unstructured research and development system of the 1960s and 1970s, in which institutions and organizations conducted projects with little coordination, will be considered too inefficient a means of utilizing limited human and physical resources.

On the national scale, the conduct of research and development will involve matching and coordinating similar activities in order to concentrate resources on the solutions to basic and applied problems. The principal organizations involved in the coordinated approach will be the federal government, government laboratories, state government, foundations, colleges and universities, nonprofit institutes, and profit corporations. New mechanisms, such as a national automated data bank of all research programs, will identify similar research interests, match these interests between organizations, and facilitate a combined approach to research and development activities. These new functions will become the responsibilities of sponsored projects administrators.

Such coordination of research and development activities between sectors may elicit concern from the scientific community. Some may argue that any centralization in the planning of sponsored research will jeopardize the independence of individual scientists and thus restrict their creativity. Obviously, any centralization plan will have to guarantee the independence of the scientific community. Coordination must enhance the creative climate of the primary resource in the discovery process—the genius of the individual investigator.

The increase in sponsored program activity, especially the greater coordination of projects between organizations, will require new institutional policies and decisions. In the 1990s sponsored program administrators are likely to become much more involved in setting institutional policies, plans, and priorities, although the role of sponsored program administrators in top management will depend on the importance of sponsored projects activities within an organization and the nature of its management.

Changing Patterns of Support

In the 1960s and 1970s the nonprofit sector received its primary support to perform research and development from the federal government and foundations, while the profit sector looked to industry. In the 1990s the importance of research and development to the nation's economic and political stability will result in more sources of funding and different distribution patterns.

The federal government will continue to be the major source of support for sponsored programs, but most sponsored projects will be coordinated through a national network. The network will be based on a detailed typology of all areas of research and development, and the identification of crossover links that relate the findings of one area to other areas. Direct fiscal support from the federal government for individual projects will continue to be offered through the appropriate agencies. The mission agencies, such as the Department of Defense research offices, the National Aeronautics and Space Administration, and the Environmental Protection Agency, will continue to address major national concerns as established by Congress. The national laboratories, such as Argonne, Oak Ridge, and Brookhaven, will become more directly involved in cooperative activities. Much the same as the mission agencies, each laboratory will have a defined area of national concern and will conduct or coordinate research and development activities in that area. The laboratories will serve as generic research centers to either conduct the projects on-site or enter into a cooperative agreement with industry, higher education, or nonprofit organizations. The laboratories will provide for greater support for sponsored programs than in the past.

Private foundations have played a key role in supporting important programs and will continue to do so into the 1990s. In the past, foundations often supported areas that were not receiving attention from federal programs. This pattern will continue, but the principle of concentrating resources to solve national problems will lead to more cooperation between private foundations and the other sectors.

State governments will become a source of increasing support for sponsored programs. States will begin to rely more on research and development to solve problems peculiar to their own geographical, economic, and social situation. In most cases, states will provide sponsored support in cooperation with other organizations for a cooperative approach to problem solving.

The largest potential increase in sponsored support, especially for higher education, will come from industry. Industrial growth in new product lines is dependent on the technological innovation brought about by discoveries in the basic sciences. The discovery, development, and application of the transistor and the laser are examples of the impact a basic discovery can have on industrial production. Fostering the symbiotic relationship between basic research and economic growth will be a paramount societal goal in the 1990s. Basic research will be underwritten by industry as a necessary condition for growth, and the patterns of industrial support for basic research will follow the patterns established in the early 1980s. Each industry will encourage research in the scientific areas that appear to yield the best results for its purposes.

Sponsored Projects Administrators' Duties

The most dramatic changes in sponsored program administration in the 1990s will more than likely be in daily office practices. A major portion of a sponsored projects administrator's responsibilities is devoted to communication between project directors, sponsors, and other members of the administration. At present, the sponsored projects administrator spends considerable time locating sources of support, communicating that information to the appropriate research personnel, preparing proposals for submission, interpreting regulations, and reporting. These responsibilities all require the administrator to collect information from various sources and communicate it to others. The future sponsored projects administrator will continue to communicate information, but changes in communications technology will affect daily operations.

Most communications in research and development are likely to use automated systems, telecommunications, and video discs. For example, each sponsored program station might contain a computer console that has access to a national research and development information system. When an investigator has an idea for a project, he or she will use this system to conduct a search for information about the contemplated research or development activity. The investigator will easily identify all potential sources of funding for projects and related research projects recently completed or currently in process through a keyword-in-context system. Once potential funding sources are identified, the investigator or sponsored projects director will be able to access the program guidelines for submitting a proposal; each program will be available on a visual display screen or as hard copy. Reports on related research will be available on video discs. Viewers will see the complete research plan, results, and salient parts of the project; they will also be able to discuss the project with its director over an audiovideo system.

The preparation of proposals will also be automated. Proposal writers will be able to transmit a mini-proposal through telecommunications to potential sponsors. The mini-proposal will be reviewed by an optical scanner and automatically compared with a set of program priorities. The investigator will be advised as to whether the proposal fits program objectives, what changes need to be made before funding consideration is possible, and to what other agencies the proposal might be sent if that sponsor has no funds available for the project. The peer review system, involving experts from all sectors of the research and development field, will be used to set program priorities as well as to evaluate individual proposals.

The primary role of the sponsored projects administrator will be to use such new means of communication to assist research personnel, achieve the goals of the institution, and coordinate in-house programs with other organizations. Computers will provide management information and analysis of activities, and printed words will be replaced by visual displays, automated typesetting, video discs, and video phone communications. Recipients' accounting transactions will be processed electronically to sponsors as they are incurred, thus eliminating local accounting functions for sponsored projects. Video communications between sponsors and recipients will also eliminate most of the current paperwork and enhance the approval process. But although practices will differ, the basic responsibilities will remain virtually the same.

Professional Development

There is a strong possibility that a national association, or federation of existing associations, for sponsored projects administrators will be founded by the 1990s. This association will be formed to represent all practitioners in the field and to set standards of training and performance. The association will contain constituent groups such as government, hospitals, industries, research institutes, and universities to serve the special needs of these sectors. Training programs and admission standards, most likely a special master's program with an internship, will be established and managed by the association.

Future sponsored projects administrators will receive more recognition as professionals as the needs of the world, and especially the needs of the United States, will require their talents to successfully manage research and development activities. The scenario for the future of sponsored program administration is challenging and rewarding, and practitioners will find it exciting to grow with the emerging profession of sponsored program administration.

Resource A
Special Research Program

The Special Research Program is a short-term, project-oriented program of research and project support. Projects can be approved for a period of from one to two years. The primary objective of this program is to provide "seed" support to projects that are likely to develop into more extensive research undertakings eligible for funding from an external source. Other objectives of this program include supporting projects that are: (1) in selected, substantive areas where external funds are usually not available; (2) of a nature requiring a minimum of funds and not warranting the expenditure of time required for the preparation of an external proposal; (3) of a high-risk nature involving radically new concepts which might suffer in comparison with more routine proposals in an external agency review; and (4) in support of projects that may help meet society's immediate needs. Within the above objectives is an overall objective of the Special Research Program: to support those beginning researchers who may not have had the opportunity to prove their abilities.

Proposals prepared for the Special Research Program shall be in accordance with the form "Application for Approval of Research" and shall be submitted to the Office of Research Development and Administration. One signed copy of this form and one signed copy of the budget request will accompany fifteen copies of the narrative proposal submission. Approval signatures of the chairman and dean shall indicate that the proposed project is consistent with the departmental and collegiate objectives and that adequate time is available for the principal investigator(s).

Proposals submitted for the Special Research Program shall be presented to one of three review committees: Research Development and Administration Review Committee for Mathematics and the Natural Sciences; Research Development and Administration Review Committee for Business, Education, and the Social Sciences; and Research Development and Administration Review Committee for the Fine Arts and Humanities. Membership to these committees is by appointment of the Director, Office of Research Development and Administration.

Review committees shall make a recommendation to the Director, Office of Research Development and Administration, on the merits of the proposed project. Committee evaluations and recommendations shall be in the form of a numerical scale according to the following definitions:

4   *Excellent.* Project of high scholarly merit. Principal investigator(s) capable of proposed work, possibly published in area. Project likely to lead to external proposal submission with high probability for success. *High priority for funding.*

3   *Good.* Project of high scholarly merit. Principal investigator(s) capable of proposed work. May result in external proposal submission — likely to result in meritorious publications. Could be project of seed nature or scholarly project not easily supported externally. *Fund if possible.*

2   *Fair.* Project of reasonable scholarly merit. Principal investigator(s) capable of proposed work — worthy publication likely. *Not high priority for funding.*

1   *Poor.* Although approved, project unlikely to produce useful or meaningful results. Probability low for external support — worthy publications doubtful. *Do not fund.*

0   *Rejected.* Project not worthy of approval—should not be resubmitted to committee.

The committee reserves the right to return a proposal to the principal investigator for additional information before making a final decision. In such cases, the Director of Research Development and Administration shall transmit to the proposer the concerns of the committee.

Funding decisions shall be made by the Director, Research Development and Administration, according to recommendations by review committees and the availability of funds, within the overall objectives of the Special Research Program.

The Director, Research Development and Administration, will notify the principal investigator, chairman and dean of the approval of a project and request the establishment of a project account from the General Accounting Office. It is possible that a project be approved and subsequently not funded.

Special Research Projects can be approved for a period of from one to two years. Extension of a project beyond the two-year limitation will be granted by a review committee only in those unusual instances supported by proper justification. Approved projects will be reviewed for progress toward the original objectives on an annual basis. This review will include a budget submission for continuation. Reports will be submitted on the "Special Research Project Progress Report" form and the "Budget Request for Special Research Project" form.

Source: Southern Illinois University, Office of Research Development and Administration, 1981.

SPECIAL RESEARCH APPLICATION

INSTRUCTIONS FOR SUBMISSION:

Submit one copy of this application together with fifteen copies of the narrative portion of the proposal to the Office of Research Development and Administration. It is suggested that the narrative portion of the proposal follow the format on the following page. Certified copies will be returned to the applicant, chairman and dean after they have been acted upon by the committee. The research committees normally meet each month to consider Special Research applications. Each application received in the Office of Research Development and Administration is circulated to members of the appropriate review committee prior to the monthly meeting.

TO THE RESEARCH COMMITTEE:

I hereby request approval for the Special Research Project entitled:

_____

Beginning: _____19 _____ , and ending _____ , 19 _____ .

It is my understanding that committee approval of the project does not necessarily ensure funding of the proposed activity. Financial support of the project is contingent upon the availability of research funds. I also understand that the attached budget sheet is a request and the actual fiscal support for the project will be determined by the Office of Research Development and Administration.

Signature of applicant _____

Date of submission _____

— — — — — — — — — — — — — — — — — — — —

NOTE: This request MUST be submitted through the applicant's *chairman* and *dean* or other supervisors for their signatures and indication of their attitudes toward the proposed research project.

☐ Approval Recommended   ☐ Approval Recommended
☐ Approval Not Recommended   ☐ Approval Not Recommended

Chairman or other supervisor   Date   Dean or other supervisor   Date

---

ACTION OF THE RESEARCH COMMITTEE: ___ Approved ___ Not Approved ___ Returned

Date: _____   Certified by: _____

Office of Research Development and Administration

Date: _____

BUDGET REQUEST FOR SPECIAL RESEARCH PROJECT
RESEARCH GENERAL

Project Title: _____   Project No.: _____

_____   Check:

Researcher _____

New Project   ☐

Department _____

Continuation   ☐

Budget Category	Amount Requested	Office Use Allotment
Salaries: Research Assistant _____ % Time _____ Mos. @ $ _____	_____	_____
Wages: Student Work _____ Hrs./Mo. @ ≈ $3.35	_____	_____
Travel: To _____	_____	_____
Date (if known) _____		
Commodities:	_____	_____
Contractual Services:	_____	_____
Rental of Auto Equipment:	_____	_____

Signed: _____   COMMENTS:
     Researcher   Date

Approved: _____
     Chairman   Date

_____
     Dean   Date

JUSTIFICATION OF BUDGET REQUEST

Salaries: For employment of graduate students as graduate assistants. Tuition and fees may be waived. Dates of pay for half-time appointments are to be consistent, so far as possible, with the rates of pay to teaching assistants in the same department.

Justification:

Wages: For employment of undergraduate students (graduate students may be employed under special circumstances). Tuition and fees are not waived. Students must be employed through the Student Work & Financial Assistance Office. Classification and rate of pay are determined by qualifications and academic standing.

Justification:

Travel: Does not include university cars.

Purpose:

Commodities: Includes supplies, on- or off-campus purchases.

Justification:

Contractual Services: Includes services of on-campus units such as postage, steno services, manuscript typing, and so on.

Justification:

Rental of Auto Equipment: Transit Service passes and rental of university car. Trips must be related to research effort.

Justification:

Resource B

Office of Sponsored Projects Faculty Evaluation Form

Part I. General Information
1. Please indicate your department: _____
2. If you currently direct or manage grants or contracts, please indicate below how many, by source.

    Number   *Source of Funds*
    _____   Federal
    _____   State and local government (nonappropriated)
    _____   Private
    _____   Organized research
    _____   Special line item research

3. Who takes care of most of the routine business tasks for your project account(s)?
    □ I do   □ Graduate student   □ Project secretarial/clerical staff
    □ Departmental secretarial/clerical staff □ Other: _____
4. How would you rate the overall system for the administration and management of grants and contracts at the university?
    □ Excellent   □ Good   □ Adequate   □ Less than adequate
    □ Poor   □ Very poor

352

Part II. Preliminary Evaluation of Service and Support Functions
   Using the following criteria, evaluate each of the grant/contract service and
support functions listed. Keep in mind that you are evaluating a *process* as it
now operates, from the standpoint of *your own* experience as user or provider.

Score	Criteria for Score
0	Those functions you have had no experience with.
1	Those functions you feel currently operate well, the ones you very rarely have trouble with.
2	Those functions you perceive to have minor process deficiencies.
3	Those functions you perceive to have more than a few process deficiencies, the ones you frequently have trouble with.
4	Those functions you perceive to have major process deficiencies, the ones you constantly have trouble with.

Score	Function
_____	1. Preproposal services (sponsor information, opportunities, guidelines, and so on)
_____	2. Proposal development services
_____	3. Proposal routing and submission
_____	4. Negotiation and award document processing
_____	5. Establishing a grant or contract account
_____	6. Personnel appointments
_____	7. Payroll
_____	8. Purchasing major items of equipment
_____	9. Purchasing supplies and minor items of equipment
_____	10. Travel leaves and advances
_____	11. Travel reimbursement
_____	12. Employment and payment of consultants
_____	13. Central computing services
_____	14. Accounting (records, billing, and so on)
_____	15. Rental of university vehicles
_____	16. Budget transfers and extensions
_____	17. Patented and copyright procedures
_____	18. Inventory
_____	19. Setting up workshops and meetings
_____	20. Progress and final reporting
_____	21. Other: _____

Part III. Specific Comments
   The following items solicit your comments regarding specific actions, problems, etc. you have encountered in dealing with the functional processes listed

in Part II. If more space is needed, please use the back of the form or additional sheets.

1. Please list the most common problems you have in managing your grants or contracts, and indicate what you perceive to be the primary causes of each.

    Problems   *Perceived Causes*

2. Do you have any ideas as to how some of the problems could be eliminated? If so, please explain.

3. What do you feel is the greatest barrier to the effective and efficient management of a grant or contract? Why?

4. In general, what do you feel could or should be done to create a more favorable performance environment for your grant or contract activities?

5. Would you be willing to share your experiences, views, and ideas by way of personal interview with a member of the project staff? _____ . If yes, please enter below your name and phone number.

Source: Texas Tech University, Office of Sponsored Projects, 1981.

Resource C

Excerpts from NSF Guidelines for Preparation of Proposals

The Proposal

The proposal should present the (1) objectives and scientific significance of the proposed work; (2) suitability of the methods to be employed; (3) qualifications of the investigator and the grantee institution; and (4) amount of funding required. Since the proposal will compete with others on related topics, it should present the scientific merit of the proposed project clearly and convincingly and should be prepared with the care and thoroughness of a paper submitted for publication. The proposal should be reviewed carefully to ensure that all essential data are included or summarized, unless they are readily available in published literature. Omissions frequently generate additional correspondence and delay processing. A checklist is included . . . .

Checklist for Proposal Submission

Complete proposals help to expedite review and assist the applicant to meet a planned program. To assure that research proposals

355

submitted to the Foundation are complete, an administrative check should be made before mailing.

- ☐ Cover page (use requested format)
- ☐ Appropriate boxes under REMARKS on cover page checked
- ☐ All required signatures
- ☐ Table of contents
- ☐ Project summary (less than 200 words)
- ☐ Summary of progress to date and its relation to proposed work (renewals only)
- ☐ Detailed description of proposed research
- ☐ Bibliography of pertinent literature

What to Submit

Proposals should cover the points discussed in the following paragraphs insofar as they are applicable. To facilitate processing, proposals should be stapled in the upper left-hand corner, but otherwise unbound, single-spaced, with pages numbered at the bottom and a one-inch margin at the top. The original signed copy should be printed only on one side of each sheet. Additional copies may be printed on both sides. . . . Any reprints, appendixes, or other materials to be considered with the proposal must be attached to the individual copies of the proposal. To avoid delay in the review process, the proposal should be complete at the time of submission.*

Since thousands of proposals are received each year, their review is facilitated when the contents are assembled in the following standard sequence: cover page, table of contents, project summary, project description, bibliography, biographical sketches, budget, current and pending support, appendixes. Material on facilities and special considerations affecting the research should be included in appendixes.

Cover Page

The desired format for the cover page is given in Appendix I [Attachment 1 for the purposes of this book].

*Institutions applying for the first time, or which have not received an NSF award within the preceding 2 years, commercial organizations, and nonprofit, nonacademic institutions should refer to the *NSF Grant Policy Manual* for instructions on specific information required.

If there have been prior discussions with a particular NSF program and the proposal is intended for its consideration, complete the box "For Consideration by NSF Organizational Unit."

The title of the proposed research project should be brief, scientifically valid, intelligible to a scientifically literate reader, and suitable for use in the public press. NSF may edit the title of a project before making an award.

The proposed duration for which support is requested should be consistent with the nature and complexity of the proposed research. Research grants may be awarded for periods up to 5 years.

Specification of a desired starting date for the research is important and helpful to NSF staff. However, the institution may not make charges to a grant for costs associated with the project that were incurred before the effective date designated in the grant letter. Should unusual situations, such as long lead time on procurements, create problems regarding the proposed effective date, the investigator should consult the institution's business office for advice and inform the NSF program office to which the proposal has been assigned.

Small businesses should check the small-business box on the cover page. A small business must be organized for profit, independently owned and operated (not a subsidiary of or controlled by a large firm), have no more than 500 employees, and not be dominant in its field . . . The box should be checked also when the proposal involves a cooperative effort between an academic institution and a small business.

Research proposals should be cleared through the institutional officer having responsibility for Federal business relations to ensure conformance with local and Federal administrative procedures. One copy of the proposal must be signed by the principal investigator(s) and an official authorized to commit the institution in business and financial affairs. Proposing institutions may have additional signature requirements. Other copies should record the names and titles of those who have signed the original. Proposals are incomplete if endorsement signatures are omitted.

Table of Contents

The table of contents, which is required, should show the location of each section of the proposal as well as major subdivisions of the project description, such as the summary of previous work, statement of proposed research, and methods and procedures to be used. The major sections are: Table of Contents, Project Summary, Project Description, Bibliography, Biographical Sketches, Budget, Current and Pending Support, and Appendixes.

Project Summary

A 200-word summary of the proposed research, suitable for publication and using the format of Appendix II [Attachment 2], is required. If a grant is awarded, the summary, edited if necessary, will be sent to the Smithsonian Science Information Exchange and made available to the public. The summary should include a statement of the research objectives, scientific methods to be employed, and the significance of the proposed research to the advancement of scientific knowledge. It should be informative to other scientists in the same or related fields and, insofar as possible, understandable by a scientifically literate reader.

Project Description

The main body of the proposal should be a detailed statement of the work to be undertaken and should include: objectives and expected significance; relation to the present state of knowledge in the field, to previous work done on this project, and to related work in progress elsewhere. The statement should outline the general plan of work, including the broad design of experiments to be undertaken and an adequate description of experimental methods and procedures. Any substantial collaboration with individuals not referred to in the budget should be described and documented with a letter from each collaborator.

Proposals for equipment normally compete with proposals for regular research projects. Therefore, each potential major user should describe the research project(s) for which the equipment will be used. The descriptions should be succinct, not necessarily as detailed as in a regular research grant application, and should emphasize the intrinsic scientific merit of the research and the importance of the equipment to it. A briefer summary will suffice for auxiliary users.

Brevity will facilitate effective review. The project description normally should not exceed 15 single-spaced pages. Somewhat greater length may be appropriate for multiple-investigator proposals. Reviewers will be made aware of this norm.

Bibliography

A bibliography of pertinent literature is required.

Biographical Sketches

A short biographical sketch of each senior scientist should be included and a list of each investigator's publications during the past 5 years, including those in press. Equipment proposals should include a brief biographical sketch and a list of publications for each user.

For the personnel categories listed below (see Appendix III for definitions [Attachment 3]), the proposal should include information on exceptional qualifications of these individuals that merit consideration in the evaluation of the proposal.

- Postdoctoral associates
- Other professionals
- Graduate students (research assistants)*
- Secretarial • clerical
- Technical • shop • other

Budget

Unless a particular program brochure provides otherwise, each proposal must contain a budget for each year of support requested and a cumulative budget for the full term of requested NSF support. (The prescribed budget format may be reproduced from Appendix III . . . [Attachment 3]). Contributions to the proposed research from other Federal and non-Federal sources (other than from the submitting institution itself) should be shown under "Remarks." The proposal may

*Note: Research associates and research assistants are not to be designated as "NSF Fellows" or other title of similar import. This designation is reserved for holders of Foundation fellowship awards.

request funds under any of the categories listed so long as the item is considered necessary to perform the research. Normally equipment grants do not provide support for personnel, overhead, installation, or operating costs. If funds for such costs are considered essential to the success of the research to be performed with the requested equipment, the proposal should provide detailed justification. The Foundation requires cost sharing in accordance with policies set forth in the *NSF Grant Policy Manual.*

Source: National Science Foundation, 1978, pp. 1–26.

ATTACHMENT 1

PROPOSAL TO THE NATIONAL SCIENCE FOUNDATION
Cover Page

FOR CONSIDERATION BY NSF ORGANIZATIONAL UNIT
(Indicate the most specific unit known, i.e. program, division, and so on)

IS THIS PROPOSAL BEING SUBMITTED TO ANOTHER FEDERAL AGENCY? Yes _____ No _____ ; IF YES, LIST ACRONYM(S):

PROGRAM ANNOUNCEMENT/SOLICITATION NO.:

CLOSING DATE (IF ANY):

NAME OF SUBMITTING ORGANIZATION TO WHICH AWARD SHOULD BE MADE (INCLUDE BRANCH/CAMPUS/OTHER COMPONENTS)

ADDRESS OF ORGANIZATION (INCLUDE ZIP CODE)

TITLE OF PROPOSED PROJECT

REQUESTED AMOUNT	PROPOSED DURATION	DESIRED STARTING DATE

PI/PD DEPARTMENT	PI/PD ORGANIZATION	PI/PD PHONE NO.

PI/PD NAME	SOCIAL SECURITY NO.*	DATE OF HIGHEST DEGREE ACHIEVED	MALE*	FEMALE*
ADDITIONAL PI/PD				
ADDITIONAL PI/PD				
ADDITIONAL PI/PD				
ADDITIONAL PI/PD				

ATTACHMENT 1, cont'd.

FOR RENEWAL OR CONTINUING AWARD REQUEST, LIST PREVIOUS AWARD NO.:	IF SUBMITTING ORGANIZATION IS A SMALL BUSINESS CONCERN, CHECK HERE ☐ (See CFR Title 13, Part 121 for Definitions)

*Submission of SSN and other personal data is voluntary and will not affect the organization's eligibility for an award. However, they are an integral part of the NSF information system and assist in processing proposals. SSN solicited under NSF Act of 1950, as amended.

CHECK APPROPRIATE BOX(ES) IF THIS PROPOSAL INCLUDES ANY OF THE ITEMS LISTED BELOW:

☐ Animal Welfare

☐ Endangered Species

☐ Historical Sites

☐ Human Subjects

☐ Marine Mammal Protection

☐ Pollution Control

☐ National Environmental Policy Act

☐ Research Involving Recombinant DNA Molecules

☐ Proprietary and Privileged Information

PRINCIPAL INVESTIGATOR/ PROJECT DIRECTOR	AUTHORIZED ORGANIZATIONAL REP.	OTHER ENDORSEMENT (optional)
NAME	NAME	NAME
SIGNATURE	SIGNATURE	SIGNATURE
TITLE	TITLE	TITLE
DATE	DATE	DATE

NOTICE OF RESEARCH PROJECT
SCIENCE INFORMATION EXCHANGE

SMITHSONIAN INSTITUTION
NATIONAL SCIENCE FOUNDATION
PROJECT SUMMARY

ATTACHMENT 2

PROJECT NO. (Do not use this space)

NSF AWARD NO.

1. NAME OF INSTITUTION (INCLUDE BRANCH/CAMPUS AND SCHOOL OR DIVISION)

2. MAILING ADDRESS

3. PRINCIPAL INVESTIGATOR AND FIELD OF SCIENCE/SPECIALTY

4. TITLE OF PROJECT

5. SUMMARY OF PROPOSED WORK (LIMIT TO 22 PICA OR 18 ELITE TYPEWRITTEN LINES)

FOR NSF USE ONLY

DIVISION (OFFICE) AND DIRECTORATE

PROGRAM

SECTION

PROPOSAL NO.

F.Y.

FOR DGC USE ONLY

AMOUNT GRANTED

START AND END DATES

NSF FORM 4 (7-78)
1. Proposal Folder
2. Program Suspense
3. Division of Grants & Contracts
4. Science Information Exchange
5. Principal Investigator
6. Off. of Govt. & Pub. Progs.
7. Assistant Director

ATTACHMENT 3
(SEE INSTRUCTIONS
BEFORE COMPLETING)

SUMMARY PROPOSAL BUDGET

FOR NSF USE ONLY

ORGANIZATION	PROPOSAL NO.	DURATION (MONTHS)
		Proposed Granted
PRINCIPAL INVESTIGATOR/PROJECT DIRECTOR	AWARD NO.	

A. SENIOR PERSONNEL: PI/PD, Co-PI's, Faculty and Other Senior Associates (List each separately with title; A.6. show number in brackets)	NSF FUNDED PERSON-MOS.			FUNDS REQUESTED BY PROPOSER	FUNDS GRANTED BY NSF (IF DIFFERENT)
	CAL.	ACAD	SUMR		
1.				$	$
2.					
3.					
4.					
5. ( ) OTHERS (LIST INDIVIDUALLY ON BUDGET EXPLANATION PAGE)					
6. ( ) TOTAL SENIOR PERSONNEL (1-5)					
B. OTHER PERSONNEL (SHOW NUMBERS IN BRACKETS)					
1. ( ) POST DOCTORAL ASSOCIATES					
2. ( ) OTHER PROFESSIONALS (TECHNICIAN, PROGRAMMER, ETC.)					
3. ( ) GRADUATE STUDENTS					
4. ( ) UNDERGRADUATE STUDENTS					
5. ( ) SECRETARIAL-CLERICAL					
6. ( ) OTHER					
TOTAL SALARIES AND WAGES (A+B)					
C. FRINGE BENEFITS (IF CHARGED AS DIRECT COSTS)					
TOTAL SALARIES, WAGES AND FRINGE BENEFITS (A+B+C)					
D. PERMANENT EQUIPMENT (LIST ITEM AND DOLLAR AMOUNT FOR EACH ITEM EXCEEDING $1,000; ITEMS OVER $10,000 REQUIRE CERTIFICATION)					

TOTAL PERMANENT EQUIPMENT _____

E. TRAVEL 1. DOMESTIC (INCL. CANADA AND U.S. POSSESSIONS) _____

           2. FOREIGN _____

F. PARTICIPANT SUPPORT COSTS

    1. STIPENDS $ _____

    2. TRAVEL _____

    3. SUBSISTENCE _____

    4. OTHER _____

    TOTAL PARTICIPANT COSTS _____

G. OTHER DIRECT COSTS

    1. MATERIALS AND SUPPLIES _____

    2. PUBLICATION COSTS/PAGE CHARGES _____

    3. CONSULTANT SERVICES _____

    4. COMPUTER (ADPE) SERVICES _____

    5. SUBCONTRACTS _____

    6. OTHER _____

    TOTAL OTHER DIRECT COSTS _____

H. TOTAL DIRECT COSTS (A THROUGH G) _____

I. INDIRECT COSTS (SPECIFY) _____

TOTAL INDIRECT COSTS

J. TOTAL DIRECT AND INDIRECT COSTS (H+I)

K. RESIDUAL FUNDS (IF FOR FURTHER SUPPORT OF CURRENT PROJECTS GPM 252 AND 253)

L. AMOUNT OF THIS REQUEST (J) OR (J MINUS K)

$	$

PI/PD TYPED NAME & SIGNATURE*	DATE

INST. REP. TYPED NAME & SIGNATURE*	DATE

NSF FORM 1030 (8-80) SUPERSEDES ALL PREVIOUS EDITIONS

*SIGNATURES REQUIRED ONLY FOR REVISED BUDGET (GPM 233)

Instructions for Use of Summary Proposal Budget (NSF Form 1030)

1. *General*

a. Each grant proposal, including requests for supplemental or incremental funding, must contain a Summary Proposal Budget in this format unless a pertinent guideline specifically provides otherwise.

b. Copies of NSF Form 1030 and instructions should be reproduced locally, as NSF will not supply the form.

c. A separate form should be completed for each year of support requested. An additional form showing the cumulative budget for the full term requested should be completed for proposals requesting more than one year's support. Identify each year's request (e.g., "First year _____," or "Cumulative Budget," etc.) in the remarks section.

d. The summary does not eliminate the need to fully document and justify the amounts requested in each category. Such documentation should be contained, as appropriate, on a budget explanation page immediately following the budget in the proposal. (See below for discussion on various categories).

2. *Budget Line Items*

A full discussion of the budget and the allowability of selected items of cost is contained in *NSF Grants for Scientific Research* (NSF 78-41), *NSF Grant Policy Manual* (NSF 77-47), and other NSF program brochures and guidelines. Following is a brief outline of budget documentation requirements, by line item:

A., B., and C. *Salaries, Wages, and Fringe Benefits* (GPM 511). On the budget explanation page, list individually all senior personnel who were grouped under A5, the requested person-months to be funded, and rates of pay.

D. *Permanent Equipment* (GPM 512 and 204.2). List item and dollar amount for each item exceeding $1,000; items over $10,000 require certification. Fully justify.

E. *Travel* (GPM 514). The type and extent of travel and its relation to the project must be addressed. Travel outside the U.S. and its possessions, Puerto Rico, and Canada must be itemized by destination and cost and justified. Dates of foreign visits or meetings should be included. Fare allowances are limited to round-trip, jet-economy rates. Consultant travel should be included here.

F. *Participant Support Costs* (GPM 518). Normally may only be requested under specific science education programs or for grants supporting conferences or symposia. Consult *Grants for Scientific Research* or specific program guidelines.

G. *Other Direct Costs.*

1. *Materials and Supplies* (GPM 513). Indicate types required and estimate costs.

2. *Publication Costs/Page Charges* (GPM 517). Estimate cost of preparing and publishing project results.

3. *Consultant Services* (GPM 516). Indicate name, daily compensation (limited to $193/day), and estimated days of service, and justify.

4. *Computer Services* (GPM 515). Include justification based on estimated computer service rates at the proposing institution. Computer equipment leasing is included here. Purchase of equipment is included under D.

5. *Subcontracts* (GPM 623). Must be approved in advance. Include a completed budget and justify details.

6. *Other.* Itemize and justify.

I. *Indirect Costs* (GPM 530). Specify current rate and base. Use current rate negotiated with the cognizant Federal negotiating agency. See *GPM* for special policy regarding grants to individuals, travel grants, equipment grants, doctoral dissertation grants, and grants involving participant support costs.

K. *Residual Amounts* (GPM 253). For incremental funding requests on continuing grants, enter the amount in *excess* of 10%. If less than 10%, indicate: none. Residual funds should *not* be reflected in the budget categories A-1. A justification for carryover of funds in excess of 10% is required.

L. Item L will be the same as item J unless the Foundation disapproves of carryover of funds. If disapproved, Item L will equal J minus K.

Resource D
Checklist for Proposal Budget

General

1. Is your budget prepared according to the agency's guidelines?
2. Has enough money in each expense category been requested so the project can be properly executed?
3. Have budget computations been double-checked for accuracy and do all of your budget figures balance?
4. Have you itemized each category of expenditure and are appropriate items described and/or justified in the narrative and/or budget justification page?
5. Have you explained any unusual expenditure (for example, daily use of an airplane for local travel) in the narrative and/or budget justification page?
6. Will the reviewer understand how you arrived at your totals for each category (for example, for salaries, state on budget form or on budget justification page, whichever is appropriate, "principal investigator: 25% of nine-month salary at \$25,000 = \$6,250")?

7. If some items are unusual, and the agency form permits, have you keyed your budget to pages in your narrative? Or, if using a budget justification page, have you keyed it to the budget form and your narrative?

8. Have you itemized each university contribution to the project, both cost-sharing and matching funds? Have these items been approved and allocated by the appropriate administrators?

9. Have you consulted with the Grants and Contracts Office on the most recent indirect-cost figure and fringe-benefit rates for this university? The indirect cost is not a bonus. It is intended to pay for services and facilities that contribute to a project but cannot be identified in line items (for example, heating and air conditioning).

10. Have all the following items been accounted for if relevant: Salaries for principal investigator(s); salaries and tuition for graduate assistants; wages for undergraduate assistants; salaries for secretarial and technical assistance; payments to consultants; travel and per diem costs; building rental costs; equipment rental costs; cost of equipment purchase; cost of expendable supplies; long-distance telephone charges; mail costs; duplication costs; publication costs; cost of specific supplies (for example, magnetic tape, film, batteries); data processing costs; and so on?

11. Has excess "fat" or "padding" been trimmed from the budget while still allowing for normal inflation of items?

12. Has the budget been reviewed by the appropriate personnel in your unit before submitting for final approval, if appropriate, to the Grants and Contracts Office?

Personnel

1. Are salary rates compatible with current salary ranges?

2. If faculty-staff salaries are to be part of the cost-sharing contribution, have they been figured accurately and approval obtained?

3. Does the budget provide for salary increases if the project period extends over more than one university academic year starting August 21?

4. Does the budget include proper support for fringe benefits, that is, retirement, workmen's compensation, life and health insurance?

5. Have the staff positions and the proportion of time being committed to the project by the principal investigator and others been cleared with the appropriate administrators?

Equipment

1. Have you checked with your unit and other units on campus to determine if needed equipment is presently available?
2. Is equipment purchase allowed by the sponsor?
3. Have you considered leasing equipment? Have you compared the costs of leasing vs. purchase of equipment?
4. Have you checked with appropriate sources for information on equipment costs, vendors, procedures for purchase, and so on?
5. Have you included the cost of delivery, installation and auxiliary parts in the purchase price? Have you considered increases in cost if purchase will not be made until sometime in the future?
6. Have you included the cost of maintenance, service agreements and insurance (when appropriate) in the "other direct costs" budget category?
7. Have you included an itemized listing of equipment that includes type of equipment, specific name, model number, price, vendor, and so on, either in the budget form or budget justification page?

Expendable Equipment and Supplies

1. Have you provided for adequate expendable equipment and supplies to complete the project?
2. If substantial funds have been requested in this budget category, has an itemized list and justification been included?
3. Have you allowed for shipping charges (if appropriate) and increases in cost if supplies are to be purchased at a future date?

Travel

1. Have you followed university, agency, or other applicable regulations for allowable rates for travel and per diem expenses?
2. Have you included adequate travel in your budget to complete the project, including possible travel to meetings or conferences?
3. Have you itemized and justified your planned travel, including destination and purpose?
4. Have you allowed for future increases in costs for transportation?
5. Have you included consultant travel in this category (if not included as part of the daily fee)?
6. Have you included all types of travel expenses, that is, transportation, per diem, and local travel?

Other Costs

1. *Publication costs*

   Have you itemized publication costs such as page charges, photography or special layouts, purchase of books, reprints, abstracts, library searches, conference proceedings, and so on?

2. *Computer costs*

   Have you requested the full cost of computer services?

3. *Other direct costs*

   If pertinent, have you itemized expenses for items such as:

   - Space rental at sites other than the university?
   - Shipping of materials?
   - Book/film/data tape rental or purchase?
   - Communications (telephone, long-distance charges, postage, and so on)?
   - Equipment rental, maintenance or service agreements, insurance?
   - Cost of purchase and care of laboratory animals?
   - Payments to human subjects?
   - Non-university personnel hired through the project?
   - Temporary secretarial assistance?
   - Subcontracts?
   - Consultant fees?

Source: University of Illinois, Campus-Wide Research Services Office, 1981.

SAMPLE PROJECT BUDGET FORMAT

☐ 1st Year　　☐ 2nd Year
☐ 3rd Year　　☐ Summary

PROJECT DATES: FROM _____ TO _____

	AMOUNT REQUESTED	UIUC CONTRIB.	TOTAL PROJECT COSTS
I. SALARIES AND WAGES A. Senior Personnel (PI, Co-PI's, Faculty, Other Senior Associates)			
1.			
2.			
3. (　　) Others (List Individually on Budget Jurisdiction Page)			
B. Other Personnel (Show Numbers in Brackets)			
1. (　　) Postdoctoral Associates			
2. (　　) Other Professionals (Technician, Programmer, Etc.)			
3. (　　) Graduate Students			
4. (　　) Undergraduate Students			
5. (　　) Secretarial-Clerical			
6. (　　) Other			
TOTAL SALARIES AND WAGES (A+B)			
II. FRINGE BENEFITS			
A. Retirement (% of Appropriate S&W)			
B. Health and Life Insurance　　(% of Appr. S&W)			
C. Workmen's Compensation　　(% of Appr. S&W)			
TOTAL FRINGE BENEFITS (A+B+C)			
III. PERMANENT EQUIPMENT (List Item and $ Amt. for Each Item)			
A.			
B.			
C.			
TOTAL PERMANENT EQUIPMENT (A+B+C)			
IV. TRAVEL			
A. Domestic			
B. Foreign			
TOTAL TRAVEL (A+B)			

V. MATERIALS AND SUPPLIES (List Item and $ Amt. for Each Item)			
A.			
B.			
C.			
TOTAL MATERIALS & SUPPLIES (A+B+C)			
VI. OTHER DIRECT COSTS			
A. Publication Costs/Page Charges			
B. Xeroxing, Shipping, Communications, Etc.			
C. Computer Charges			
D. Consultants			
E. Subcontracts			
F. Other (Payment to Subjects, Equipment Rental, Etc.)			
TOTAL OTHER DIRECT COSTS (A+B+ . . .+F)			
VII. TOTAL DIRECT COSTS (I. through VI.)			
VIII. INDIRECT COSTS			
A. On Campus: ___ % of ___ (MTDC)			
B. Tuition: ___ % of ___ (I.B.3.)			
TOTAL INDIRECT COSTS (A+B)			
IX. TOTAL DIRECT AND INDIRECT COSTS (VII + VIII)/TOTAL PROJECT COSTS			

Resource E

Sample Human Subjects Review Forms

Source: University of Illinois at the Medical Center, Graduate College, Institutional Review Committee, 1982.

University of Illinois at the Medical Center
Graduate College
Institutional Review Committee

PROCEDURES FOR SUBMITTING PROJECTS INVOLVING HUMANS AS EXPERIMENTAL SUBJECTS

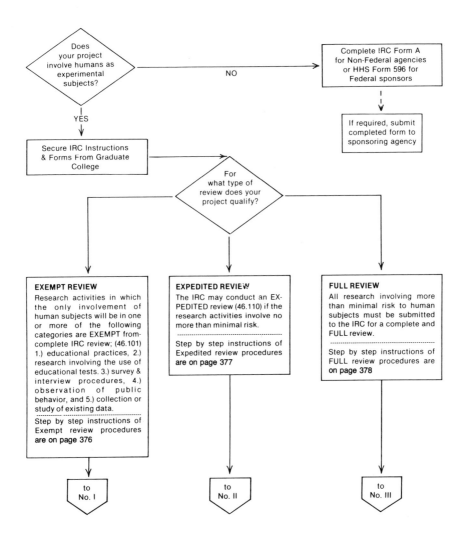

I

EXEMPT

EXEMPT REVIEW: research activities in which the only involvement of human subjects will be in one or more of the following categories are Exempt from IRC review (Federal Register 46.101); 1.) educational practices, 2.) research involving educational tests, 3.) survey and interview procedures, 4.) observation of public behavior, and 5.) collection or study of existing data.

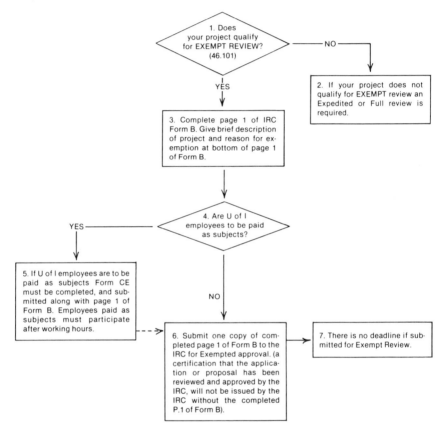

II

EXPEDITED

EXPEDITED REVIEW: The IRC may conduct an Expedited review (Federal Register 46.110) if the research activities involve no more than minimal risk.

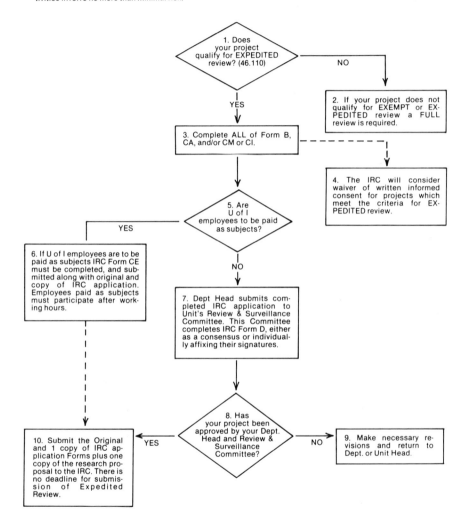

III

FULL REVIEW

FULL REVIEW: All other research involving more than minimal risk to human subjects must be submitted to the IRC for a complete and FULL review.

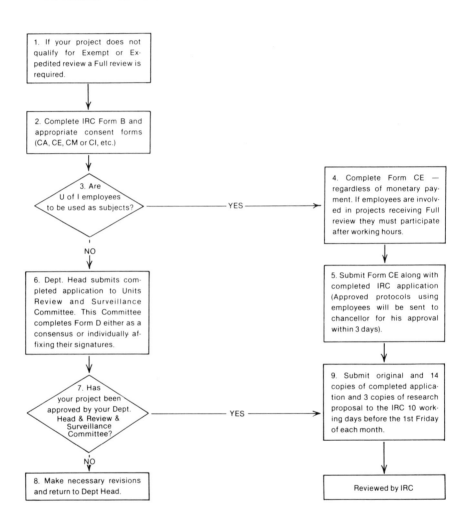

1. If your project does not qualify for Exempt or Expedited review a Full review is required.

2. Complete IRC Form B and appropriate consent forms (CA, CE, CM or CI, etc.)

3. Are U of I employees to be used as subjects?

— YES —

4. Complete Form CE — regardless of monetary payment. If employees are involved in projects receiving Full review they must participate after working hours.

NO

6. Dept. Head submits completed application to Units Review and Surveillance Committee. This Committee completes Form D either as a consensus or individually affixing their signatures.

5. Submit Form CE along with completed IRC application (Approved protocols using employees will be sent to chancellor for his approval within 3 days).

7. Has your project been approved by your Dept. Head & Review & Surveillance Committee?

— YES —

9. Submit original and 14 copies of completed application and 3 copies of research proposal to the IRC 10 working days before the 1st Friday of each month.

NO

8. Make necessary revisions and return to Dept Head.

Reviewed by IRC

IRC NO. _____ DATE OF APPLICATION _____ DATE APPROVED BY IRC _____

University of Illinois at the Medical Center
Institutional Review Committee, Graduate College

REQUEST FOR ETHICAL REVIEW OF AN EXPERIMENTAL PROJECT ON HUMAN SUBJECTS
(Please Type)

1. TYPE OF REVIEW REQUESTED: (See instructions for definitions)
_____ EXEMPT (Complete only page one: Submit original to the IRC Secretary, no deadline for Exempt review)
_____ EXPEDITED (Complete all necessary pages: Submit original and 1 copy to IRC, no deadline for Expedited review)
_____ FULL (Complete all necessary pages: Submit original and 14 copies to the IRC)

2. PROJECT TITLE: (Limit 60 spaces)
3. P.I. NAME: 4. SSN OF PI:
5. COLLEGE/SCHOOL: 6. DEPT/UNIT:
7. MAILING ADDRESS (if different from above):
8. HOSPITAL(S)/FIELD AREA(S) to be used:
9. If Patients facilities and/or Personnel other than your own department/clinic are to be utilized have you received appropriate approval? _____yes; _____no. _____
                                                      Authorizing Signature

10. GIVE IND NUMBER: 11. _____
(If Pertinent)   Name of Supplier of IND
12. NAME OF EXTERNAL SPONSOR SUPPORTING THIS RESEARCH:

_____
(If no external funds provided, write NONE)
13. SPONSOR'S GRANT/CONTRACT NUMBER:
14. TOTAL PROJECT PERIOD: FROM: ___/___/___ TO: ___/___/___
                         M   D   Y   M   D   Y
15. CURRENT YEAR PROJECT BUDGET PERIOD: FROM: ___/___/___ TO: ___/___/___
                                       M D Y   M D Y
16. STATUS OF THIS REQUEST FOR ETHICAL REVIEW (or proposal)
_____ NEW: _____ RENEWAL/CONTINUATION: _____ REVISED/MODIFIED _____ OTHER (Specify)
17. POPULATION AND SAMPLE: (Estimated number of subjects to be used by type)

NUMBER	NUMBER	NUMBER
_____ ADULTS (normal/controls)	_____ ADULTS (employees of UI)	_____ MINORS (other-describe)
_____ ADULTS (experimental)	_____ ADULTS (other-describe)	_____ FETUSES
_____ ADULTS (pregnant women)	_____ MINORS (normal/controls)	_____ ABORTUSES
_____ ADULTS (incompetent)	_____ MINORS (experimental)	_____ OTHER
_____ ADULTS (prisoners)	_____ MINORS (of UI Employees)	

18. DESCRIPTION OF CRITERIA AND PROCEDURES USED FOR SELECTION OF THE SAMPLE(s):

19. For EXEMPT Approval Only — Check one or more for exemption below:
(Submit only page one of Form B for EXEMPT approval).
☐ 1. Research in common educational setting where students are not identified.
☐ 2. Research using educational tests with no identifiers of subjects used.
☐ 3. Research involving surveys or interviews except where respondents are identified.
☐ 4. Research involving observations of public behavior.
☐ 5. Research involving collection, study & use of existing data where subjects are not identified.
      Please refer to the IRC instructions for complete descriptions for EXEMPT approval.

Signature of Principal Investigator: _____

20. STUDY METHOD:
 a . Treatments, procedures or measurements which will be performed on human subject(s);
 (Brief description of experiments on humans or human tissues).

 b . DHHS requires that if the proposed research requires additional costs to the patient (beyond costs for normal diagnostic and treatment purposes) that such cost be stated on the subjects CONSENT FORM. Please state below what these additional research costs are and who will pay them.

21. ETHICAL CONSIDERATION: (Required for *all* research projects at UIMC that utilize humans as subjects).

 a. For projects requesting *EXPEDITED* IRC review subjects must be considered at no or minimal risk and a consent form is not required if they are not directly or indirectly identified with data/information gathered in this project or if the IRC waives the need for a consent form if there is less than minimal risk.

 Each subject is free at all times to withdraw from the study even though a commitment to complete it was made. There will be no coercion by rank, money and or other means. If the study is an interview project a written copy of the interview instrument must be submitted.

 b. For projects requesting a *FULL* IRC review where the subject is placed at more than minimal risk an Adult's and/or Minor's Consent form *must* be completed and filed with this request.

 c. If University of Illinois Employees are to be paid as subjects, a copy of the special consent form (Form CE) must be completed for each employee, *regardless* of the type of review by the IRC. In addition, all projects using employees as subjects that require FULL review must use the Form CE (see IRC instructions for details).

22. KNOWN THEORETICAL OR POTENTIAL RISK(S) TO HUMAN SUBJECT(S):

23. SPECIAL PRECAUTIONS AND SAFEGUARDS TAKEN TO INSURE THE WELFARE OF SUBJECTS (MEDICAL EMERGENCY, CONSULTING COVERAGE, SPECIAL EQUIPMENT, ATTENDANCE. ETC.)

24. SIGNIFICANCE OF INVESTIGATION AND POTENTIAL TO BE DERIVED:

25. INDICATE ANY MONETARY OR OTHER COMPENSATION THAT WILL BE OFFERED TO SUBJECT(S) FOR PARTICIPATION:
(NOTE: If university employees are to be paid as subjects Form CE must be submitted to the IRC and a copy attached to the voucher requesting payment).

26. For EXPEDITED review only. Give brief explanations for reasons why an expedited review is being requested.

THE PRINCIPAL INVESTIGATOR CERTIFIES THAT THE ABOVE INFORMATION IS CORRECT:

_____   _____
Signature of P.I.   Date

_____   _____
Signature of Dept. Head   Date

NOTE: For a *FULL* Review by the IRC the appropriate number of completed Form B must be submitted at least ten (10) working days before the Committee's monthly review date.

University of Illinois at the Medical Center
Institutional Review Committee, Graduate College

MINOR'S CONSENT FOR PARTICIPATION IN AN EXPERIMENTAL PROJECT

1. _____ is _____ years of age and will participate
    (Type or print subject's name)

    in a program of medical research being conducted

    by: _____
        (Physician/Investigator)

2. The purpose of the research is:

3. The experimental procedures are:

4. The personal risks involved are (if none, so state):

5. I understand that I will receive standard medical care, if required, even if I do not participate in this study. Alternative procedures and therapy which might benefit me personally are:

6. I understand and accept the following research related costs (this refers to costs which are beyond those required for my normal diagnostic and treatment purposes). If no additional research costs are to be paid by the patient/subject state NONE.

7. COMPENSATION STATEMENT (Check appropriate statement).

_____a . I understand that in the event of physical injury resulting from this research there is no compensation and/or payment for medical treatment from the University of Illinois at the Medical Center for such injury except as may be required of the University by law.

_____b . I understand that in the event of physical injury resulting from this research, compensation and/or medical treatment may be available from_____
Corporation (who is sponsoring this research). I understand that if I believe that the minor for whom I am responsible is eligible for compensation or medical treatment, I may contact:

_____Name

_____Address

_____Phone of sponsoring company

However, there is no compensation and/or payment for medical treatment from the University of Illinois at the Medical Center for such injury except as may be required of the University by law.

8. PARENTAL CONSENT (a. will apply unless b. is checked).

We, the parents or guardians of the above minor volunteer, agree to his/her participation in the research project outlined above. We have been informed of the need for the research, the benefits to be derived from it, and the risks involved. We have also been informed that the research cannot be conducted with adults because of the nature of the study.

_____a. Being aware of the necessity for the participation of minors in this research project and further being aware that this procedure will not personally benefit the minor here involved personally, we consent to the minor's participation.

_____b . Being aware of the necessity for the participation of minors in this research project and being informed that the procedures will also benefit the above-named minor personally, in the following way:

we consent to the minor's participation.

X _____   _____
Volunteer   (Type Name)   Parent or Guardians   (Type Name)
(Sign & Date)   (Sign & Date)

X _____   _____
Physician/Investigator   (Type Name)   Witness of Explanation   (Type Name)
                                                                    to Volunteer by PI   (Sign & Date)

University of Illinois at the Medical Center
Institutional Review Committee, Graduate College

CONSENT FORM FOR INCOMPETENT ADULT
(Please complete the following statement in the first person and in lay language)

1. I _____ state that I am _____ years of age
     (Type or print subject's name)

   and I wish to participate in a program of medical research being conducted

   by: _____
      (Physician/Investigator)

2. The purpose of the research is:

3. The experimental procedures are:

4. The personal risks involved are (if none, so state):

5. I understand that I will receive standard medical care, if required, even if I do not participate in this study. Alternative procedures and therapy which might benefit me personally are:

6. I understand and accept the following research related costs (this refers to costs which are beyond those required for my normal diagnostic and treatment purposes). If no additional research costs are to be paid by the patient/subject state NONE.

7. COMPENSATION STATEMENT (Check appropriate statement).

_____a . I understand that in the event of physical injury resulting from this research there is no compensation and/or payment for medical treatment from the University of Illinois at the Medical Center for such injury except as may be required of the University by law.

_____b . I understand that in the event of physical injury resulting from this research, compensation and/or medical treatment may be available from_____ Corporation (who is sponsoring this research). I understand that if I believe that the incompetent adult for whom I am responsible is eligible for compensation or medical treatment, I may contact:

_____ Name

_____ Address

_____Phone of sponsoring company

However, there is no compensation and/or payment for medical treatment from the University of Illinois at the Medical Center for such injury except as may be required of the University by law.

8. I the parent, guardian or legal representative for the above incompetent adult volunteer, agree to his/her participation in the research project outlined above. We have been informed of the need for the research, the benefits to be derived from it, and the risks involved.

_____a . Being aware of the necessity for the participation of mentally retarded, handicapped or otherwise incompetent adults in this research project and further being aware that this procedure will not personally benefit the named adult, we consent to this person's participation.

_____b . Being aware of the necessity for participation of mentally retarded, handicapped or otherwise incompetent adults in this research project and being informed that the procedures will also benefit the above named subject personally, in the following way:

we consent to the person's participation.

X _____   _____
Volunteer (Sign & Mark)   (Type Name)   Parent/Guardian/Legal   (Type Name)
                                                  (Sign & Date)

X _____   _____
Physician/Investigator   (Type Name)   Witness of Explanation   (Type Name)
(Sign & Date)   to Volunteer & Legal   (Sign & Date)
                                                 Representative

University of Illinois at the Medical Center
Institutional Review Committee, Graduate College

ADULT'S CONSENT FOR PARTICIPATION IN AN EXPERIMENTAL PROJECT

(Please complete the following statements in the first person and in lay language)

1. I _____ state that I am_____ years of age and I wish to
       (Type or print subject's name)

    participate in a program of medical research being conducted

    by: _____
          (Physician/Investigator)

2. The purpose of the research is:

3. The experimental procedures are:

4. The personal risks involved are (if none, so state):

5. I understand that I will receive standard medical care, if required, even if I do not participate in this study.
    Alternative procedures and therapy which might benefit me personally are:

6. I understand and accept the following research related costs (this refers to costs which are beyond those
    required for my normal diagnostic and treatment purposes). If no additional research costs are to be paid by
    the patient/subject state NONE.

7. COMPENSATION STATEMENT (Check appropriate statement).

_____a . I understand that in the event of physical injury resulting from this research there is no compensation and/or payment for medical treatment from the University of Illinois at the Medical Center for such injury except as may be required of the University by law.

_____b . I understand that in the event of physical injury resulting from this research, compensation and/or medical treatment may be available from_____
Corporation (who is sponsoring this research). I understand that if I believe that I am eligible for compensation or medical treatment, I may contact:

_____ Name

_____ Address

_____ Phone of sponsoring company

However, there is no compensation and/or payment for medical treatment from the University of Illinois at the Medical Center for such injury except as may be required of the University by law.

8. ADULT'S CONSENT (a. will apply unless b. is checked).

_____a . I acknowledge that I have been informed that this procedure is not involved in my treatment and is not intended to benefit my personal health.

_____b . I acknowledge that I have been informed that this procedure is also designed to assist in maintaining or improving my personal health and will benefit me personally in the following way:

I acknowledge that _____has explained to me the risks involved
                    (Physician/investigator)

and the need for the research; has informed me that I may withdraw from participation at any time and has offered to answer any inquiries which I may make concerning the procedures to be followed. I freely and voluntarily consent to my participation in this project.

I understand that I may keep a copy of this consent form for my own information.

X _____   _____
  Volunteer   (Sign & Date)   (Type Name)

X _____   _____
  Physician/Investigator   (Sign & Date)   (Type Name)

X _____   _____
  Witness of Explanation to (Sign & Date)   (Type Name)
  Volunteer by PI

Resource F

Acronyms Used in Sponsored Projects Administration

AAALAC	American Association for Accreditation of Laboratory Animal Care
AAAS	American Association for the Advancement of Science
AAC	Association of American Colleges
AACUO	Association for Affiliated College and University Offices
AASCU	American Association of State Colleges and Universities
AAUP	American Association of University Professors
ACE	American Council on Education
ACHD	Action Cooperative for Human Development
ACLS	American Council of Learned Societies
ACS	American Chemical Society
ADAMHA	Alcohol, Drug Abuse, and Mental Health Administration
ADP	Automated Data Processing
AEC	Atomic Energy Commission (now ERDA)
AID	Agency for International Development
APC	Air Pollution Control

APHIS	Animal and Plant Health Inspection Service
ARO	Army Research Office
ARS	Agricultural Research Service
ASCS	Agricultural Stabilization and Conservation Service
ASEE	American Society for Engineering Education
ASPR	Armed Services Procurement Regulation
BEOG	Basic Education Opportunity Grant
BHE	Bureau of Higher Education
BLM	Bureau of Land Management
BLS	Bureau of Labor Statistics
BOB	Bureau of the Budget (now OMB)
BRSG	Biomedical Research Support Grant
CAB	Civil Aeronautics Board
CAE	Council on Anthropology and Education
CAUSE	Comprehensive Assistance for Undergraduate Science Education
CCH	Commerce Clearing House
CDA	City Demonstration Agency
CDC	Center for Disease Control
CETA	Comprehensive Employment and Training Act
CFDA	Catalog of Federal Domestic Assistance
CFR	Code of Federal Regulations
CHP	Comprehensive Health Planning
CHS	Community Health Service
CLEO	Council on Legal Education Opportunity
CPA	Certified Public Accountant
CPI	Consumer Price Index
CSA	Community Services Administration
CSC	Civil Service Commission
CWS	College Work Study
DEA	Drug Enforcement Administration
DHEW	Department of Health, Education and Welfare (now DHHS)
DHHS	Department of Health and Human Services

DOD	Department of Defense
DOT	Department of Transportation
DRG	Division of Research Grants
DSA	Defense Supply Agency
ED	Department of Education
EEOC	Equal Employment Opportunity Commission
EMI	Exchange of Medical Information
EMS	Emergency Medical Services
EO	Executive Order
EPA	Environmental Protection Agency
ERDA	Energy Research and Development Administration
ESA	Employment Standards Administration
FAA	Federal Aviation Administration
FBI	Federal Bureau of Investigation
FCC	Federal Communications Commission
FDA	Food and Drug Administration
FDAA	Federal Disaster Assistance Administration
FEA	Federal Energy Administration
FHA	Federal Housing Administration
FHWA	Federal Highway Administration
FIA	Federal Insurance Administration
FMC	Federal Management Circular
FMC	Federal Maritime Commission
FMCS	Federal Mediation and Conciliation Service
FPA	Federal Property Assistance
FPR	Federal Procurement Regulation
FR	Federal Register
FRA	Federal Railroad Administration
FSS	Federal Supply Service
FTC	Federal Trade Commission
FY	Fiscal Year
GAO	General Accounting Office
GARP	Global Atmospheric Research Program
GNP	Gross National Product

GPO	Government Printing Office
GSA	General Services Administration
HEA	Higher Education Act
HEGIS	Higher Education General Information System
HMO	Health Maintenance Organization
HRA	Health Resources Administration
HS	Health Services
HSA	Health Services Administration
HUD	Department of Housing and Urban Development
ICC	Interstate Commerce Commission
IHE	Institution of Higher Education
INS	Immigration and Naturalization Service
IPA	Intergovernmental Personnel Act
IPAS	Institutional Prior Approval System
IREX	International Research and Exchanges Board
IRS	Internal Revenue Service
ISEP	Instructional Scientific Equipment Program
JAG	Judge Advocate General
JSIP	Job Service Improvement Program
LEAA	Law Enforcement Assistance Administration
LEAP	Laboratory Evaluation and Accreditation Program
LEEP	Law Enforcement Education Program
LMSA	Labor-Management Services Administration
LSCA	Library Services and Construction Act
MA	Maritime Administration
MARC	Minority Access to Research Careers
MBOC	Minority Business Opportunity Committee
MCA	Model Cities Administration
MDTA	Manpower Development and Training Act
MESA	Mining Enforcement and Safety Administration
MIS	Management Information System
NAB	National Alliance of Businessmen
NACUBO	National Association of College and University Business Officers

NASA	National Aeronautics and Space Administration
NASAPR	National Aeronautics and Space Administration Procurement Regulation
NASULGC	National Association of State Universities and Land-Grant Colleges
NATO	North Atlantic Treaty Organization
NBS	National Bureau of Standards
NCAR	National Center for Atmospheric Research
NCAR	National Conference on the Advancement of Research
NCHEMS	National Commission on Higher Education Management Systems
NCHSRD	National Center for Health Services Research and Development
NCI	National Cancer Institute
NCMA	National Contract Management Association
NCSBCS	National Conference of States on Building Codes and Standards
NCURA	National Council of University Research Administrations
NDEA	National Defense Education Act
NEA	National Education Association
NEA	National Endowment for the Arts
NEH	National Endowment for the Humanities
NEI	National Eye Institute
NEPA	National Environmental Policy Act
NFPCA	National Fire Prevention and Control Administration
NHLBI	National Heart, Lung, and Blood Institute
NHTSA	National Highway Traffic Safety Administration
NIA	National Institute on Aging
NIAID	National Institute of Allergy and Infectious Diseases
NIAMD	National Institute of Arthritis, Metabolism, and Digestive Diseases
NICHD	National Institute of Child Health and Human Development
NIDA	National Institute on Drug Abuse

NIDR	National Institute of Dental Research
NIE	National Institute of Education
NIEHS	National Institute of Environmental Health Sciences
NIGMS	National Institute of General Medical Services
NIH	National Institutes of Health
NIMH	National Institute of Mental Health
NINCDS	National Institute of Neurological and Communicative Disorders and Stroke
NLM	National Library of Medicine
NLRB	National Labor Relations Board
NMFS	National Marine Fisheries Service
NOAA	National Oceanic and Atmospheric Administration
NPS	National Park Service
NRC	Nuclear Regulatory Commission
NRSA	National Research Service Awards
NSC	National Safety Council
NSF	National Science Foundation
NTIS	National Technical Information Service
NWS	National Weather Service
OAWP	Office of Air and Water Programs
OEMA	Office of Educational and Manpower Assistance
OFCCP	Office of Federal Contract Compliance Programs
OGC	Office of General Counsel
OHMO	Office of Health Maintenance Organizations
OIP	Office of International Programs
OJT	On-the-Job Training
OLEP	Office of Law Enforcement Programs
OMB	Office of Management and Budget
OMBE	Office of Minority Business Enterprise
OME	Office of Minerals Exploration
ONR	Office of Naval Research
OPAS	Organizational Prior Approval System
ORAU	Oak Ridge Associated Universities

OSHA	Occupational Safety and Health Administration
OSP	Office of Sponsored Projects
OSS	Office of Science and Society
OWHM	Office of Water and Hazardous Materials
OWRT	Office of Water Research and Technology
PACE	Projects to Advance Creativity in Education
PCPFS	President's Council on Physical Fitness and Sports
PGP	Planning Grant Program
PHA	Public Housing Authority
PHS	Public Health Service
PI	Principal Investigator
PL	Public Law
PPBS	Planning-Programming-Budgeting System
PRM	Planning and Resources Management
PUR	Program of University Research
R & D	Research and Development
RCDA	Research Career Development Awards
RDS	Rural Development Service
REA	Rural Electrification Administration
RFP	Request for Proposals
RFQ	Request for Quotation
RSA	Rehabilitation Services Administration
RSVP	Retired Senior Volunteer Program
SBA	Small Business Administration
SCORE	Service Corps of Retired Executives
SCS	Soil Conservation Service
SEC	Securities and Exchange Commission
SIS	Science Information Services
SMI	Science Manpower Improvement
SRA	Society of Research Administrators
SSA	Social Security Administration
SSIE	Smithsonian Science Information Exchange
SSRC	Social Science Research Council

STPO	Science and Technology Policy Office
SUPA	Society of University Patent Administration
TC	Treasury Circular
TVA	Tennessee Valley Authority
UMTA	Urban Mass Transportation Administration
URP	Undergraduate Research Participation
USAF	United States Air Force
USC	United States Code
USCG	United States Coast Guard
USDA	United States Department of Agriculture
USTES	United States Training and Employment Service
VA	Veterans Administration
VEA	Vocational Education Act
VES	Veterans Employment Services
VISTA	Volunteers in Service to America
WICHE	Western Interstate Commission for Higher Education
WIN	Work Incentives Program
WPI	Wholesale Price Index
WRC	Water Resources Council
YOC	Youth Opportunity Center

Resource G
Federal Regulations Pertaining to Sponsored Projects

This section presents the reference numbers, titles, and short descriptions of federal regulations that govern or pertain to sponsored projects. Copies of most of these laws and circulars can be obtained from the Superintendent of Documents, U.S. Government Printing Office, Washington, DC 20402.

FMC 73-3. Cost Sharing on Federal Research: Presents cost sharing guidelines applicable to all federal agency research grants, contracts, or other research agreements with educational institutions, other not-for-profit or nonprofit organizations, commercial or industrial organizations, or other recipients except other federal agencies.

FMC 73-7. Administration of College and University Research Grants: Provides standard policies and practices for federal agencies in their administration of grants, contracts, and other agreements with educational institutions.

OMB circular A-21. Cost Principles for Educational Institutions: Provides cost accounting principles applicable to research and development, training, and other sponsored work performed by colleges and universities under grants, contracts, and other agreements with the federal government.

OMB circular A-73. Audit of Federal Operations and Programs: Provides for audit follow-up and resolution regarding federal agency systems by setting forth criteria, time limits, and resolution procedures, including periodic evaluation of federal agencies.

OMB circular A-87. Cost Principles for State and Local Governments: Presents uniform rules for determining allowable costs and procedures to recover such costs for grants, contracts, and other agreements with state and local governments, including subgrants and subcontracts. Also, provides for negotiating indirect-cost rates by one federal (cognizant) agency on behalf of all other federal agencies.

OMB circular A-88. Coordinating Indirect-Cost Rates, Audit and Audit Follow-Up at Educational Institutions: Provides policies for establishing indirect-cost rates and auditing such rates at educational institutions.

OMB circular A-95. Evaluation, Review and Coordination of Federal and Federally Assisted Programs and Projects: Presents guidance for federal agencies in cooperating with state and local governments in the evaluation, review, and coordination of federal assistance programs.

OMB circular A-102. Uniform Administrative Requirements for Grants-in-Aid to State and Local Governments: Establishes uniform financial and other administrative requirements for grants to state and local governments and Indian tribal governments including pass-through funds. Topics covered include: cash depositories, bonding and insurance, records retention, program income, matching shares, MIS standards, financial reporting, reporting program performance, grant payment requirements, grant closeout procedures, property management system, procurement standards, and audit standards.

OMB circular A-105. Standard Federal Regions: Discusses the consolidation of seventy-five dispersed federal agencies and bureaus into ten federal regions to decentralize the administration of federal programs and to reduce red tape and processing time.

OMB circular A-110. Grants and Agreements with Institutions of Higher Education, Hospitals, and Other Nonprofit Organizations: Promulgates standards for obtaining consistency and uniformity among federal agencies in the administration of grants to, and other agreements with, public and private institutions of higher education, public and private hospitals, and other quasi-public and nonprofit organizations. Attachments cover such topics as: cash depositories, bonding and insurance, records retention, cost sharing and matching, financial MIS and reporting systems, reporting program performance, payment and closeout procedures, property management, and procurement standards.

OMB circular A-122. Cost Principles for Nonprofit Organizations: Provides cost accounting principles applicable to grants, contracts, and other agreements (including subawards) with nonprofit organizations other than institutions of higher education and hospitals. Also, provides for negotiating indirect-cost rates by one federal (cognizant) agency on behalf of all other federal agencies.

OMB circular A-124. Patents—Small Firms and Nonprofit Organizations: Provides guidelines to inventions made by small business firms and nonprofit organizations, including universities, under funding agreements with federal agencies where the purpose is to perform experimental, developmental, or research work. It provides a standard patent rights clause to be used in funding agreements.

PL 94-553. General Revisions of Copyright Law: Revises the copyright statute first enacted in 1909, and sets forth the definition, scope, rights, limitations, registration, and duration of subject matter copyrighted.

PL 95-224. Federal Grant and Cooperative Agreement Act of 1977: Sets forth the definitions and uses of the three award instruments: grants, cooperative agreements, and contracts.

PL 96-517. The Patent and Trademark Amendments of 1980: Sets forth the regulations for and rights of recipient organizations concerning patents and trademarks developed in the performance of federal grants, agreements, and contracts.

Treasury circular 1075. Withdrawal of Cash from the Treasury of Advances Under Federal Grants and Other Programs: Provides for letter of credit payments from the federal treasury.

Treasury circular 1082. Notification to States of Grant-in-Aid Information: Establishes procedures for federal agency notification to states of the purpose and amounts of grants and assistance awarded to states, local governments, state-affiliated institutions, quasi-public agencies, and nonprofit institutions.

Resource H

Select Bibliography of Information Sources

Sponsored activities officers recommend several hundred periodicals and classic texts for inclusion in a basic library for their offices. Gregory (1972), Beasley (1976), and Hensley (1976) offer listings of information sources for sponsored projects administrators. Beasley also ranks the publications by frequency of use and then rates their usefulness on a three-class scale.

This select bibliography includes Beasley's list (unranked) as well as other texts of general value to sponsored projects administrators. This bibliography is intended as an introduction to information sources for sponsored projects administrators. For more complete listings, see the entries for *R&D Management Bibliography* and *The Register of Publications for Research Administrators.*

Annual Register of Grant Support 1981–1982, for sale by

> Marquis Professional Publications
> 200 East Ohio Street, Room 5641
> Chicago, IL 60611

The *Annual Register* provides details on more than 2,400 current opportunities sponsored by foundations, corporations, government agencies, and professional and educational associations.

Blue Sheet Drug Research Reports, The, published by

> Drug Research Reports, Inc.
> One National Press Building
> Washington, DC 20045

The Blue Sheet provides weekly specialized, in-depth, interpretive coverage of government policies, fundings, and activities in drug and medical research, health, manpower, and health care delivery systems and plans.

Catalog of Federal Domestic Assistance 1981, for sale by

> Superintendent of Documents
> U.S. Government Printing Office
> Washington, DC 20402

Provides comprehensive lists of all federal agencies and their sponsored programs; programs are indexed by popular name, function, and subject.

Chronicle of Higher Education, The, published by

> The Chronicle of Higher Education, Inc.
> 1333 New Hampshire Avenue, N.W.
> Washington, DC 20036

The Chronicle is higher education's newspaper. This weekly publication provides good national coverage of current issues in higher education.

College and University Reporter, published by

> Commerce Clearing House, Inc.
> 4025 W. Peterson Avenue
> Chicago, IL 60646

The *Reporter* furnishes information on federal programs and legislation that affect education.

Commerce Business Daily, The, for sale by

> Superintendent of Documents
> U.S. Government Printing Office
> Washington, DC 20402

This daily publication reports on the federal government's purchases, sales, and contracts; it is also the source of announcements of Requests for Proposals (RFPs).

Complete Grants Sourcebook for Higher Education, The, published by

> The Public Management Institute
> American Council on Education
> One DuPont Circle
> Washington, DC 20036

This paperback edition, published in 1980, contains about 100 pages on how to seek and win grant support, a 300-page directory of funding sources, and three indices.

Federal Notes, published by

> Federal Development Associates
> P.O. Box 986
> Saratoga, CA 95070

Published twenty-two times a year by Federal Development Associates, the *Notes* contain summaries of program information, short notes on upcoming programs, and regulatory notes.

Federal Register, The, for sale by

> Superintendent of Documents
> U.S. Government Printing Office
> Washington, DC 20402

Published daily, the *Register* is an indispensable source of information on federal regulations and legal notices.

Federal Research Report, published by

The Federal Research Group
951 Pershing Drive
Silver Spring, MD 20910

The *Federal Research Report,* published weekly, contains general information on workshops, seminars, agency programs, and results of program evaluations.

Federal Yellow Book, The, published by

The Washington Monitor
499 National Press Building
Washington, DC 20045

This book is designed to give direct and easy access to more than 25,000 high-level administrators in the executive branch of the federal government.

Foundation Directory, The, edited by Marianna O. Lewis and Alexis Gersumky, compiled by

The Foundation Center
888 Seventh Avenue
New York, NY 10106

The Foundation Directory lists over 3,000 foundations and is the standard reference work for information about nongovernmental grants in the United States.

Foundation News, published by

Council on Foundations, Inc.
1828 L Street, N.W.
Washington, DC 20036

The Foundation News, published bimonthly, provides sections for foundation administrators, updates on state activities, special interests, reports on people, book reviews, and a bimonthly foundation grants index.

Government Research Centers Directory, 2nd ed., edited by Anthony T. Kruzas and Kay Gill, published by

> Gale Research Company
> Book Tower
> Detroit, MI 48226

GRC describes about 1,600 research and development facilities operated by the U.S. government, including research centers, bureaus, and institutions; R&D installations; testing and experiment stations; and major research-supporting service units. Name, keyword, agency, and geographical indices are also provided.

Grants Administration, by William Willner and Perry B. Hendricks, published by

> National Graduate University
> 1630 Kalmia Road, N.W.
> Washington, DC 20012

Published in 1972, this book was a good solid reference during the 1970s. It is now considered a classic research administration publication.

Grants Magazine: The Journal of Sponsored Research and Other Programs, published by

> Plenum Press
> 233 Spring Street
> New York, NY 10013

Grants Magazine is a broadly conceived, interdisciplinary, quarterly publication that provides a forum for discussion of the various issues that affect public and private institutions and private philanthropy.

Grants Register, The, published by

> St. Martin's Press, Inc.
> 174 Fifth Avenue
> New York, NY 10010

The Grants Register, published every two years, gives up-to-date information on individual awards available to the researcher and creative artist; it is a good source book for graduate students.

Higher Education Daily, published by

Capitol Publications, Inc.
1300 North 17th
Arlington, VA 22209

Higher Education Daily provides a daily news service for administrators in postsecondary education. It contains six pages of national news, complemented by state reporting and a meetings calendar.

International Research Centers Directory, published by

Gale Research Company
Book Tower
Detroit, MI 48226

The first edition consists of three paperbound issues that cover 1,500 research organizations, arranged by country.

Journal of the Society of Research Administrators, published by

Society of Research Administrators
1505 4th Street, Suite 203
Santa Monica, CA 90401

This excellent quarterly publication usually contains five or six articles by researchers who have studied some aspect of sponsored activities. It also includes book reviews.

Management for Research in U.S. Universities, by Raymond J. Woodrow, published by

National Association of College and University Business Officers
Eleven DuPont Circle, Suite 480
Washington, DC 20036

This excellent volume, published in 1978, deals with modes of management. The general philosophy of the author is administration *for* research. The climate for research, policies and criteria, and development and implementation are the main topics.

Monthly List of GAO Reports, published by

> U.S. General Accounting Office
> Document Handling and Information Services Facility
> Gaithersburg, MD 10760

This GAO publication provides a monthly listing of GAO reports to the Congress.

NIH Guide for Grants and Contracts, The, published by

> National Institutes of Health
> 9000 Rockville Pike
> Bethesda, MD 20205

The *Guide* is published at irregular intervals to announce scientific initiatives and to provide policy and administrative information about opportunities, requirements, and changes in the NIH.

NSF Bulletin, The, published by

> Public Information Branch
> National Science Foundation
> 1800 G Street, N.W.
> Washington, DC 20550

The *NSF Bulletin,* published monthly, contains listings of program guidelines, program information, meetings, and deadlines.

Register of Publications for Research Administrators, The, edited by Oliver D. Hensley, compiled by

> The Clearinghouse for Research Administrators
> Southern Illinois University at Carbondale
> Carbondale, IL 62901

This bibliography provides a monthly listing of new research administration information. The author, title, source, and a brief abstract are provided for each entry. Entries are cross-indexed according to the major subject of the publication.   ·

Reports to the Congress, published by

> U.S. General Accounting Office
> Document Handling and Information Services Facility
> P.O. Box 6015
> Gaithersburg, MD 10760

These reports are the results of GAO investigations into congressional concerns related to sponsored activities. The reports detail deficiencies in systems and recommendations for improvements.

R&D Management Bibliography, by Thomas E. Clarke, published by

> Stargate Consultants
> P.O. Box 995, Station B
> Ottawa, Ontario, Canada K1P 5R1

This extensive bibliography contains over 3,000 references on the management of research and development and related areas. These references are catalogued under more than thirty subject headings.

Research Awards Index, The, published by

> Division of Research Grants
> National Institutes of Health
> 9000 Rockville Pike
> Bethesda, MD 20205

The projects described in *The Index* reflect the broad scope and diversity of research grants and contracts administered by NIH, FDA, and other health agencies. It is helpful in identifying current research activities.

Research Centers Directory, 7th ed., edited by Robert C. Thomas, published by

> Gale Research Company
> Book Tower
> Detroit, MI 48226

This edition contains about 5,000 listings of university-related and other nonprofit research organizations throughout the United States and Canada. For ease of reference, entries are arranged by major subjects and indexed by subjects, institutions, and research centers.

Research Services Directory, published by

> Gale Research Company
> Book Tower
> Detroit, MI 48226

Three periodical issues will cover about 1,200 for-profit organizations that provide research services on a contract or fee-for-service basis to a wide range of clients. The directory emphasizes small R & D firms and individuals specializing in particular areas and industries, including contract laboratories and consulting organizations.

R.F. Illustrated, published by

> Rockefeller Foundation
> 1133 Avenue of the Americas
> New York, NY 10036

This quarterly newsletter reports on projects sponsored by the Rockefeller Foundation and the foundation's plans.

Science, published by

> American Association for the Advancement of Science
> 1515 Massachusetts Avenue, N.W.
> Washington, DC 20005

A weekly journal, *Science* publishes a wide range of scientific information of general interest to scientists and researchers, including articles, news comments, book reviews, and meeting highlights.

Science Trends, published by

> Trends Publishing, Inc.
> National Press Building
> Washington, DC 20045

This brief weekly publication, about a half-dozen pages, provides abstracts of science trends reported in computer information, congressional reports, engineering, and the like. It reports on technical trends and provides sources of information for each.

Sponsored Research in American Universities and Colleges, edited by Stephen Strickland, published by

> American Council on Education
> One DuPont Circle
> Washington, DC 20036

Published in 1968, this anthology presents the work of individuals in different aspects of sponsored activities in the 1960s.

University-Connected Research Foundations, by Raymond D. Daniels, Ralph C. Martin, Lawrence Eisenberg, Jay M. Lewallen, and Ronald A. Wright, published by

> University of Oklahoma Press
> 1005 Asp Avenue
> Norman, OK 73019

This excellent volume characterizes and analyzes university research foundations; it is the definitive work on the subject.

References

Adelberg, E. A. "IBC Procedures: Maximal Compliance with the Guidelines, Minimal Delay of the Research." NIH 80-99. *Recombinant DNA Technical Bulletin,* 1980, *2* (4), 177.

American Council on Education. *The Complete Grants Sourcebook for Higher Education.* Washington, D.C.: American Council on Education, 1980.

Bailey, R. E., Herdenorf, P. B., and Vossler, K. "The Ohio Technology Transfer Organization (OTTO)—An Experiment in Cooperative Assistance." Paper presented at the Ohio Vocational Association Convention, Columbus, Ohio, 1980.

Balderston, J. L. "An Inquiry into Overhead Rates and Distribution Practices." *Journal of the Society of Research Administrators,* 1973, *5* (2), 21–30.

Banus, C. "Mid-West Universities Spending U.S. Millions." *Chicago Tribune,* April 22, 1967, p. 3.

Beasley, K. L. "The Research Administrator as Mediator-Expeditor."

Journal of the Society of Research Administrators, 1970, *2* (1), 1–4.

Beasley, K. L. "Information Sources for Research Administrators." *Journal of the Society of Research Administrators,* 1976, *8* (1), 11.

Boggs, J. H. "Development of Priorities for Extramural Support." In H. Zallen (Ed.), *Transactions.* Stillwater: Oklahoma State University, 1973.

Broseghini, A. L. "Select Comments on Institutional and Government Support of IRB's." In O. D. Hensley (Ed.), *SRA Looks to the 80s.* Los Angeles: Society of Research Administrators, 1980.

Bush, M. V. *Science: The Endless Frontier.* Washington, D.C.: National Science Foundation, 1960.

Cebik, L. B. "Science, Ethics and Research Administration." *Journal of the Society of Research Administrators,* 1980, *11* (3), 5–11.

Copyright Law Reporter. Chicago: Commerce Clearing House, 1981.

Daniels, R. D., and others. *University-Connected Research Foundations.* Norman: University of Oklahoma Press, 1977.

Dingerson, M. R. "Status of Internal Research Programs in Institutions of Higher Education in the United States." *Journal of Higher Education,* 1977, *48* (3), 283–293.

Ditzel, R. D. "A Research Equipment Assistance Program." *Journal of the Society of Research Administrators,* Spring 1976, *7* (4), 26–36.

Doudera, E. A. "The Functions and Authority of Institutional Review Boards." In O. D. Hensley (Ed.), *SRA Looks to the 80s.* Los Angeles: Society of Research Administrators, 1980.

Dressel, P. L., Johnson, B. C., and Marcus, P. M. "The Proliferating Institutes." *Change,* July/August 1969, pp. 21–24.

"Education: A $127 Million Gift Horse." *Newsweek,* October 12, 1981, p. 87.

Elliott, L. H. "An Idea Whose Time Has Come—Trends and Issues in Cooperation." In *American Association of Higher Education Consortium Seminar Proceedings.* Washington, D.C.: American Association of Higher Education, 1973.

Eurich, A. "Reflections on University Research Administration." In S. Strickland (Ed.), *Sponsored Research in American Universities and Colleges.* Washington, D.C.: American Council on Education, 1967.

Food and Drug Administration. "Institutional Review Boards and Informed Consent." *Federal Register,* January 27, 1981, *46* (17), 8942–8980.

Gentry, R. "Institutional Responsibilities and Obligations for Research." Paper presented at Research Development and Administration Colloquium, Carbondale, Ill., April 1980.

Gregory, C. "A Guide to Information Sources for Research Administrators." Nashville, Tenn.: Division for Sponsored Research, Vanderbilt University, 1972. (Mimeographed.)

Haaland, G. "Faculty Consulting Poses 'Thorny' Problem." *Higher Education Daily,* November 12, 1981, p. 4.

Henry, N. *Copyright, Congress and Technology: The Public Record.* Phoenix, Ariz.: Oryx Press, 1980.

Hensley, O. D. "A Model for the Classical Development Process." Unpublished paper, Research Development and Administration Office, Southern Illinois University, 1977.

Hensley, O. D. "Directory of Informational Sources." *The Quarterly Register of Publication for Research Administrators,* 1978, *to* (1), 17–56.

Hensley, O. D. "The University Research Administrator—The Architect of the University's Future." In O. D. Hensley (Ed.), *SRA Looks to the 80s.* Los Angeles: Society of Research Administrators, 1980.

Hess, L. G., and Waters, J. M. "Inventory Control and Stores Management." *Journal of the Society of Research Administrators,* 1975, *6* (3), 39.

Hess, L. G., and Waters, J. M. "User-Oriented Financial Management System." *Journal of the Society of Research Administrators,* 1979, *11* (1), 5–12.

Joint Economic Committee. *Research and Innovation: Developing a Dynamic Economy.* Washington, D.C.: Joint Economic Committee, 1980.

Levine, R. J. (Ed.). *IRB: A Review of Human Subjects Research.* Hastings-on-Hudson, N.Y.: The Hastings Center, 1979.

Lowry, P. S., Bradshaw, L., and Sansone, K. "IRIS: Illinois Researcher Information System." *Journal of the Society of Research Administrators,* 1979, *10* (4), 17.

McCarthy, C. R. "A View from the Center." In O. D. Hensley (Ed.), *SRA Looks to the 80s.* Los Angeles: Society of Research Administrators, 1980.

Machlup, F. *The Production and Distribution of Knowledge in the U.S.* Princeton, N.J.: Princeton University Press, 1962.

Matteson, G. C., and Smiriga, S. R. "Credit Cards for Improved Cost Assignment." *Journal of the Society of Research Administrators,* 1976, *7* (1), 16.

Murdick, R. G., and Ross, J. E. *Information Systems for Modern Management.* Englewood Cliffs, N.J.: Prentice-Hall, 1975.

Murray, J. P., and Biles, B. R. *Survey of Research Administration Practices.* Manhattan: The Graduate School, Kansas State University, 1980.

National Association of College and University Business Officers. *Patents at Colleges and Universities: Guidelines for the Development of Policies Programs.* Washington, D.C.: Committee on Governmental Relations, National Association of College and University Business Officers, 1974.

National Commission on Research. *Industry and the Universities: Developing Cooperative Research Relationships in the National Interest.* Pasadena, Calif.: National Commission on Research, 1980.

National Conference on the Advancement of Research. *Conference Brochure.* Denver, Col.: National Conference on the Advancement of Research, n.d.

National Council of University Research Administrators. "Charter and Bylaws." *1980 Membership Directory.* Washington, D.C.: National Council of University Research Administrators, 1980.

National Institutes of Health. *Guide for the Care and Use of Laboratory Animals.* NIH 80-23. Washington, D.C.: National Institutes of Health, 1980.

National Institutes of Health. "Guidelines for Research Involving Recombinant DNA Molecules." *Federal Register,* July 1, 1981, pp. 34462–34487.

"National Research Act of 1974." *Federal Register,* May 30, 1974, *39* (105), 18914–18920.

National Science Board. *Science and the Challenges Ahead.* Washington, D.C.: National Science Board, 1974.

National Science Foundation. *Grants for Scientific Research.* NSF 78-41A. Washington, D.C.: National Science Foundation, 1978.

National Science Foundation. "Federal Funds for Research and Development Fiscal Years 1978, 1979, 1980." In *Survey of Science Resources Series,* Vol. 28. NSF 79-318. Washington, D.C.: National Science Foundation, 1979.

National Science Foundation. "Federal Support to Universities, Colleges and Selected Nonprofit Institutions, FY 1978." In *Survey of Science Resources Series.* NSF 80-312. Washington, D.C.: National Science Foundation, 1980.

National Science Foundation. *Academic Science Research and Development Expenditures FY 1979.* NSF 81-301. Washington, D.C.: Superintendent of Documents, 1981a.

National Science Foundation. "Federal Support to Universities, Colleges and Selected Nonprofit Institutions, FY 1979." In *Survey of Science Resource Series*. NSF 81-308. Washington, D.C.: National Science Foundation, 1981b.

National Science Foundation. "Summary of Prior Approval Requirements for Direct Charges Against NSF Grant Funds." In *NSF Grant Policy Manual*. NSF 77-47. Washington, D.C.: Superintendent of Documents, 1981c.

News, Notes and Deadlines (Newsletter). Washington, D.C.: Association for Affiliated Colleges and University Offices, November 1981, *11* (2), 3.

Northwestern University. "Patent and Invention Policy." Evanston, Ill.: Board of Trustees, Northwestern University, 1974.

Office of Administrative Management, Public Health Service. *A Guide to Institutional Cost Sharing Agreements for Research Grants Supported by the Department of Health, Education and Welfare*. #05-75-50009. Washington, D.C.: U.S. Department of Health, Education and Welfare, 1975.

Office of Management and Budget. "Property Management Standards." Circular A-110, Attachment N, Section 6. *Federal Register*, July 30, 1976, *41* (48), 32035–32036.

Office of Management and Budget. "Cost Principles for Educational Institutions." Circular A-21. *Federal Register*, March 6, 1979, *44* (45), Part III, 12368–12380.

Office of Management and Budget. *Managing Federal Assistance in the 1980's–A Report to the Congress of the United States Pursuant to the Federal Grant and Cooperative Agreement Act of 1977 (PL 95-224)*. Washington, D.C.: Executive Office of the President, 1980.

Office of Management and Budget. *Patents —Small Firms and Nonprofit Organizations*. Circular A-124. Washington, D.C.: Office of Management and Budget, 1982.

Orlans, H. *The Nonprofit Research Institute*. New York: McGraw-Hill, 1972.

Palmer, A. M. *University Research and Patent Policies, Practices and Procedures*. Washington, D.C.: National Academy of Sciences, National Research Council, 1962.

Patterson, F. *Colleges in Consort: Institutional Cooperation Through Consortia*. San Francisco: Jossey-Bass, 1974.

Pennsylvania Office of Science and Technology. *Action Now Partnerships–Putting Technology to Work*. Resolutions for immediate action advanced by the National Action Conference on Intergovernmental Science and Technology Policy. Harrisburg, Pa.: Pennsylvania Office of Science and Technology, 1972.

Prager, D. J., and Omenn, G. S. "Research, Innovation, and University-Industry Linkages." *Science,* 1980, *207,* 380.

Price, F. O. "Technology Transfer Internationally—Why Governments Are Concerned." In O. D. Hensley (Ed.), *SRA Looks to the 80s.* Los Angeles: Society of Research Administrators, 1980.

Public Law 94-553. "General Revision of the Copyright." *U.S. Statutes at Large,* October 19, 1976, *90,* Part 2, 2541–2602.

Public Law 95-224. "Federal Grant and Cooperative Agreement Act of 1977." Approved by the 95th U.S. Congress, February 3, 1978 [41 U.S.C. 501–509].

Public Law 97-35. "Omnibus Budget Reconciliation Act of 1981." *U.S. Congressional and Administrative News,* August 13, 1981, 7.

Redecke, L. A., and Darling, B. "The Indirect Cost Predicament." *Journal of the Society of Research Administrators,* 1977, *9* (2), 24.

"Researcher: The Colleges Discover a Profit in Patents." *Business Week,* January 12, 1981, pp. 36E–36F.

Rodman, J. A. "A Consortium Approach to Pre-Award Grant/Contract Services." *Journal of the Society of Research Administrators,* 1979, *10* (4), 23.

Rodman, J. A., and Dingerson, M. R. "What Is a University Research Administrator—Current and Future?" *Journal of the Society of Research Administrators,* 1979, *11* (2), 6–9.

Rodman, J. A., and Peters, C. M. "Computerized Management Information and Reporting Systems for Sponsored Projects." *Journal of the Society of Research Administrators,* 1980, *11* (4), 35–36.

Rosenberg, P. *Patent Law Fundamentals.* New York: Clark Boardman, 1979.

"Scientist Says Research is Basic to Best Teaching." *Your University.* Bloomington: Indiana University, March 1967.

Sladek, F. E. [Untitled.] *Foundation News* [San Diego State University Foundation], September/October 1977, pp. 36–37.

Sladek, F. E., and Stein, E. L. *Grant Budgeting and Finance.* New York: Plenum Press, 1981.

Smith, C. W., and Skjei, E. W. *Getting Grants.* New York: Harper & Row, 1980.

Society of Research Administrators. "Bylaws." *1980 Membership Directory.* Los Angeles: Society of Research Administrators, 1980.

Southern Illinois University. "Proposal/Grant Review Checklist." Unpublished form developed by and available from Office of Research Development and Administration, Southern Illinois University, 1980.

Southern Illinois University. "DNA Recombinant Memorandum of Understanding and Agreement." Unpublished form developed by and available from Office of Research Development and Administration, Southern Illinois University, n. d.

Southern Illinois University. "Special Research Program." Unpublished paper developed by and available from Office of Research Development and Administration, Southern Illinois University, n.d.

Sperber, P. *Intellectual Property Management: Law-Business Strategy.* New York: Clark Boardman, 1980.

Stauffer, T. M. *Assessing Sponsored Research Programs.* Washington, D.C.: American Council on Education, 1977.

Steinberg, L. "A Study of University Research Administration: Organization." (Unpublished report.) Ann Arbor: University Microfilms, 1973.

Strickland, S. (Ed.). *Sponsored Research in American Universities and Colleges.* Washington, D.C.: American Council on Education, 1967.

Tally, J. E. "Sponsored Program Administration in U.S. Medical Schools." Unpublished doctoral dissertation, Department of Higher Education, Southern Illinois University, August 1977.

Texas Tech University. "Faculty Evaluation Form." Unpublished form developed by and available from the Office of Sponsored Projects, Texas Tech University, Lubbock, Tex., 1981.

U.S. Department of Agriculture. "Animal Welfare." *U.S. Code of Federal Regulations,* Title 9, January 1979, Parts 1–3, Section 2.76.

U.S. Department of Health, Education and Welfare. *A Guide to Institutional Cost Sharing Agreements for Research Grants Supported by the Department of Health, Education and Welfare.* Washington, D.C.: Department of Health, Education and Welfare, 1975.

U.S. Department of Health, Education and Welfare. *Department Staff Manual—Grants Administration.* Bethesda, Md.: U.S. Department of Health, Education and Welfare, 1978a.

U.S. Department of Health, Education and Welfare. *Guide for the Care and Use of Laboratory Animals.* NIH 78-23. Bethesda, Md.: U.S. Department of Health, Education and Welfare, 1978b.

U.S. Department of Health and Human Services. "Public Health Service Human Research Subjects." *Federal Register,* January 26, 1981, *46* (16), 8366–8392.

U.S. House of Representatives, Subcommittee on Science, Research and Technology. *Government and Innovation: Field Hearings* (September 7–8, 1979). Washington, D.C.: Superintendent of Documents, 1980.

U.S. House of Representatives. "The Economic Recovery Tax Act of 1981." Summary of H.R. 4242. Washington, D.C.: Superintendent of Documents, 1981a.

U.S. House of Representatives. "Research Revitalization Act of 1981." H.R. 1864. Washington, D.C.: Superintendent of Documents, 1981b.

University of California at San Diego. *Grant and Contract Handbook.* San Diego: Office of Contracts and Grants Administration, University of California, 1977.

University of Illinois at the Medical Center. "Request for Ethical Review of and Experimental Projects on Human Subjects." Unpublished form developed by and available from Graduate College, University of Illinois at the Medical Center, Chicago, n.d.

University of Illinois at Urbana. "Proposal Transmittal Form." Unpublished form developed by and available from Grants and Contracts Office, University of Illinois, Urbana, 1976.

University of Illinois at Urbana-Champaign. "Shared Use Equipment Certification Forms." Unpublished forms developed by and available from School of Chemical Sciences, University of Illinois, Urbana-Champaign, 1980.

University of Illinois at Urbana. "Proposal Budget Checklist." Unpublished form developed by and available from Campus-Wide Research Services Office, University of Illinois at Urbana, 1981.

University of Texas at Dallas. "Award and Approval Form." *Grant/Contract Handbook.* Dallas: Office of Sponsored Projects, University of Texas, 1979.

University of Texas at Dallas. "Indirect Cost Negotiated Agreement with the Department of Health and Human Services." Document on record at the Office of Sponsored Projects, University of Texas at Dallas, 1981.

Woodrow, R. J. *Management for Research in U.S. Universities.* Washington, D.C.: National Association of College and University Business Officers, 1978.

Index

A

Academic administrators, communications with, 107

Acceptance of outside support, as policy, 26–27

Accounting office, and sponsored projects office, 57–58

Action Cooperative for Human Development, 388

Adelberg, E. A., 267, 410

Administration of sponsored programs: background of, ix-xi; consortiums for, 329–330; defined, ix, 1–2; development and scope of, 1–11; as emerging field, 14–17; functions and practices in, 37–235; future of, 340–345; in health science organizations, 311–323; introduction to, 1–36; management issues in, 236–323; in nonprofit and university-connected organizations, 293–310; organizing and staffing for, in small organizations, 286–288; purposes of, 2; in small organizations, 285–292; trends in, 324–345

Administration of sponsored projects: acronyms used in, 388–395; central control policy for, 27; defined, 1–2;

institutional commitment to, 29; postaward, in small organizations, 292

Administrators of sponsored projects: analysis of role of, 12–22; assistant or secretary to, 287, 288; in cooperative relationships, 328–239; defined, 12; duties of, 12–14; educational opportunities for, 15–16; ethical issues for, 14; future duties of, 343–345; problems of, 17; professional development of, 345; titles for, 32, 34; voluntary associations of, 17–22

Aerospace Corporation, 297

Agencies. See Sponsoring agencies

Agency for International Development, 388

Agricultural Research Service, 389

Agricultural Stabilization and Conservation Service, 389

Air Pollution Control, 388

Alcohol, Drug Abuse, and Mental Health Administration, 388

Allowable cost, defined, 165

American Association for Accreditation of Laboratory Animal Care (AAALAC), 237, 241, 388

American Association for Laboratory Animal Science (AALAS), 237

American Association for the Advancement of Science, 388

American Association of State Colleges and Universities, 388; Office of Federal Programs of, 100

American Association of University Professors, 388

American Cancer Society, 317

American Chemical Society, 388

American Council of Learned Societies, 290, 388

American Council on Education, x, 28–29, 388, 410; Office of Leadership Development of, 337–338

American Health Foundation, 298

American Heart Association, 317

American Institute for Economic Research, 295

American Institute of Architects, 298

American Institutes for Research, 298

American Society for Engineering Education, 389

American Soybean Association Research Foundation, 331

Ames Laboratory, 297

Analytic Services, 298

Animal and Plant Health Inspection Service, 389

Animal Care Panel (Illinois), 237

Animal welfare. *See* Laboratory animals

Animal Welfare Act of 1966 (PL 89--544), 237, 238, 239

Argonne National Laboratory, 297, 343

Armed Services Procurement Regulations (ASPR), 145, 166, 389

Army Research Office, 9, 389

Arnold, N., xii

Association for Affiliated College and University Offices (AACUO), 388; Grant Information and Search System of, 74, 76, 89

Association for Higher Education of North Texas, 104, 330

Association of American Colleges, 388

Associations, voluntary, of sponsored projects administrators, 17–22

Atomic Energy Commission, 9, 388

Audits, in financial management, 167–168, 181–182

Automated Data Processing, 388

Awards: acceptance of, 151–155; account assignment for, 151–152, 161; budget for, 153, 154–155; checklist for, 154, 162; contracts as, 145–146, 155–156; cooperative agreements as, 143–144; and cost sharing, 138; defined, 141; examination of, 151, 160; grants as, 142–143; negotiations for, 147–150; notification brief for, 152, 153; orientation on, 152; provisional account for, 151, 159; types of, 141–147, 157–158

B

Backlar, B., xii

Bailey, R. E., 335, 410

Balderston, J. L., xiii, 132, 410

Banus, C., 410

Basic Education Opportunity Grant, 389

Battelle, and patents, 244

Battelle Memorial Institute, 298

Battelle Pacific Northwest Lab, 294, 297

Beasley, K. L., 13, 100, 400, 410–411

Bequests, as award type, 146–147

Beth Israel Hospital, 298

Biles, B. R., 53, 54, 56, 412

Biohazards committee, for recombinant DNA, 266–267

Biologically hazardous materials, compliance with regulations on, 122

Biomedical Research Support Grant, 389

Bituminous Coal Research, 298

Block grants, impact of, 338–340

Boggs, J. H., 337, 411

Boston Biomedical Research Institute, 298

Boston University, Center for Law and Medicine at, 253

Bradshaw, L., 75, 412

Bristol-Myers, and patents, 242

Brookhaven National Laboratory, 294, 297, 343

Brookings Institution, 294
Broseghini, A. L., 263–264, 411
Budget, and expenditure control, in financial management, 169–176
Budget specialist, responsibilities of, 65
Buildings, as facilities, 188–189
Bureau of Higher Education, 389
Bureau of Labor Statistics, 389
Bureau of Land Management, 389
Bureau of the Budget, 10, 389; and cost sharing, 134
Bush, M. V., 5, 8, 411
Business office, communication with, 108–109

C

California, block grants to, 339
California, University of, 131
California, University of, at Berkeley, facilities administration at, 193
California, University of, at San Diego, 417; awards at, 147, 159, 161; handbook of, 58
Capabilities, assessing, in small organizations, 288–289
Carnegie Foundation, 10
Carnegie Institution of Washington, 294
Catalog of Federal Domestic Assistance, 389, 401
Cebik, L. B., 14, 411
Cedars-Sinai Medical Center, 298
Center for Disease Control, 389
Center for Industrial Services (CIS), 335
Center for Naval Analyses, 297
Central Midwest Regional Education Laboratory, 298
Cerro Toledo INT-AM Observatory, 297
Certified Public Accountant, 389
Chicago, University of, 131
Child Cancer Research Foundation, 298
Children's Hospital and Medical Center, 298
Children's Hospital and Medical Center—Cincinnati, 298

Children's Hospital of Philadelphia, 298
City Demonstration Agency, 389
City of Hope Medical Center, 298
Civil Aeronautics Board, 389
Civil Service Commission, 389
Clarke, T. E., 407
Cleveland Clinic Foundation, 298
Code of Federal Regulations, 389
Cold Spring Harbor Laboratory, 298
College Work Study, 389
Colorado State University, 131
Columbia University: indirect costs at, 131; patents of, 242
Commerce Clearing House, 389
Commitment statement, as policy, 26
Communications: with academic administrators, 107; with agency representatives, 98; analysis of, 96–110; external, 97–100, 289–290; with faculty, 105–107; future of, 344; information sources for, 100–104; internal, 105–109, 290; network for, 97, 110; in small organizations, 289–290; with staff, 109
Community Action Agencies, 6
Community colleges, sponsored programs in, 24
Community Health Service, 389
Community Services Administration, 389
Comprehensive Assistance for Undergraduate Science Education, 389
Comprehensive Employment and Training Act, 389
Comprehensive Health Planning, 389
Computers, as facilities, 191–192
COMSEARCH, 74, 104
Consortium International Development, 298
Consortiums, trends in, 329–330
Consumer Price Index, 389
Contracts: as award type, 145–146, 155–156; handbook on, 58; types of, 145
Cook, T., xiii
Cooperative agreements: as award type, 142, 143–144; types of, 144
Copying and printing, facilities for, 116–117, 190

l

Copyrights: institutional policy for, 247–248; law on, 248–252; legal and ethical requirements for, 246–252; notice of, 250–251; ownership of, 251–252, 278–282; references on, 249

Cornell University: indirect costs at, 131; management information system at, 86

Cost Accounting Standards Board Regulations, 166

Cost sharing: and administration of institutional agreements, 138–139; and amendments to agreements, 138; analysis of, 134–139; and applications, 138; and awards, 138; and documentation, 138–139; and expenditure report, 138; and level of contributions, 135; and methods of providing contributions, 135–136; and negotiation of institutional plans, 137–138; project-by-project, 139

Costs: allowable, 164–168; and award limitations, 165; consistent treatment of, 165; direct, 132; OMB regulations on, 165–166, 177–180, 396–399; and sponsor regulations, 166–167. *See also* Indirect costs

Council for the Advancement and Support of Education, 20

Council for Tobacco Research, 331

Council on Anthropology and Education, 389

Council on Legal Education Opportunity, 389

D

Daniels, R. D., 302, 303, 304, 309–310, 409, 411

Darling, B., 131, 415

Dean, proposal role of, 118

Decentralization, impact of, 338–340

Defense Acquisition Regulations, 166

Defense Supply Agency, 390

Demonstration programs, as nonresearch activities, 6–7

Department, governmental. *See* U. S.

Department of . . .

Departments: and chairperson's role in proposals, 117–118; and priorities, 43–44

Dingerson, M. R., 46, 59, 411, 415

Direct costs, bases of, 132

Director, project: and negotiations for awards, 148–149; recombinant DNA responsibilities of, 265–266; responsibilities of, 64–65

Ditzel, R. D., 206, 411

Division of Research Grants, 390

DNA. *See* Recombinant DNA

Doudera, E. A., 257, 411

Draper Laboratories, 298

Dressel, P. L., 324, 411

Drug Enforcement Administration, 389

E

Economic Recovery Tax Act of 1981, 333

Education, through nonresearch activities, 6. *See also* Higher education

Eisenberg, L., 409

E. K. Shriver Center for Mental Retardation, 298

Elliott, L. H., 329, 411

Emergency Medical Services, 390

Employment Standards Administration, 390

Energy Research and Development Administration, 390

Environmental Protection Agency (EPA), 9, 342, 390; invention statement for, 233–234

Environmental Research Institute, 298

Equal Employment Opportunity Commission, 390

Equipment: administration of, 205–209; annual inventory of, 209, 218; automated inventory system for, 208–209; defined, 205; inventory management for, 207–208; inventory of shared-use, 209, 217; inventory report for, 208–209, 216; for project group, 209; shared use of, 205–207, 212–215

Ethical issues: and compliance, 236–284; and copyrights, 246–252; and human research subjects, 252–264; and laboratory animals, 236–241; and patents, 241–246; and recombinant DNA, 264–269; for sponsored projects administrators, 14

Eurich, A., 13–14, 411

Evaluation: as nonresearch activity, 7; of special projects office, 67–68, 352–354

Exchange of Medical Information, 390

F

Facilities: administration of, 187–205; automated inventory and billing system for, 193–205; buildings as, 188–189; computers as, 191–192; for copying and printing, 190; defined, 187; shops as, 190–191; for specialized services, 192–193; stores as, 189–190

Faculty: communication with, 105–107; profile of information on, 70, 71–73, 87–88

Faculty Evaluation Form, 352–354

Far West Laboratory for Educational Research and Development, 298

Federal Assistance Programs Retrieval System (FAPRS), 73–74, 104

Federal Aviation Administration, 390

Federal Bureau of Investigation, 390

Federal Communications Commission, 390

Federal Disaster Assistance Administration, 390

Federal Energy Administration, 390

Federal government: compliance with regulations of, 121–122, 236–284; in cooperation with industry and institutions, 331–334; history of support by, 7–10; and indirect costs, 128–129; and nonprofit research organizations, 296, 298–300

Federal Grant and Cooperative Agreement Act of 1977 (PL 95-224), 142, 143–144, 145, 398, 415

Federal Highway Administration, 390

Federal Housing Administration, 390

Federal Insurance Administration, 390

Federal Management Circular, 390, 396

Federal Maritime Commission, 390

Federal Mediation and Conciliation Service, 390

Federal Procurement Regulations, 145, 390

Federal Property Assistance, 390

Federal Railroad Administration, 390

Federal Register, 390, 402

Federal Supply Service, 390

Federal Trade Commission, 330

Fellowships, as award type, 146

Fermi National Accelerator Laboratory, 297

F. Hutchins Cancer Research Institute, 298

Financial management: account description for, 171; and allowability of costs, 164–168; analysis of, 163–186; audits in, 167–168, 181–182; budget and expenditure control in, 169–176, budget summary for, 171, 173; consolidated summary for, 176, 185–186; expenditure section for, 175–176; notes section for, 171, 173; obligations section for, 173–175; and prior approval system, 168–169, 183; and reports to sponsor, 222-223, 227–231; in small organizations, 287, 288; and statement of account, 171–176; summary statement of account for, 176, 184; user-oriented system for, 170–176

Florida State University, 131

Food, Drug and Cosmetic Act, 255

Food and Drug Administration (FDA), 390, 411; and health science organizations, 318, 319; and human research subjects, 255–256

Ford Foundation, 10

Forsyth Dental Center, 298

Foundation Center, 403; COM-SEARCH of, 74, 104

Foundation Grants Index, 104

Foundations, history of support by, 10.

Foundations *(continued)*
See also University-connected re-
search foundations
Franklin Institute, 298

G

General Accounting Office, 390, 406
General Services Administration, 391;
and indirect costs, 128
Gentry, R. E., 132, 412
George Washington University, 131
Georgia Tech, 131
Gersumky, A., 403
Gifts, as award type, 146–147
Gill, K., 404
Global Atmospheric Research Pro-
gram, 390
Goals, of sponsored programs, 23–26
Government Printing Office, 391
Grants: as award type, 142–143; block,
impact of, 338–340; handbook on,
58; seed, 147; types of, 143
Gregory, C., 400
Gross National Product, 390
Gulf Southern Research Institute, 298

H

Haaland, G., 324, 412
Hall, M., 101, 113
Hartman, R. D., xiii
Hatch Act of 1887, 7
Health Maintenance Organization,
391
Health Resources Administration, 391
Health science organizations: administration of, 311–323; clinical
testing programs of, 319; and federal requirements, 314–318; income
sources of, 312–313, 316–318, 320–
323; nature of, 312–315; research
personnel in, 313–314; and risk
management, 315, 318–319; site
visits for, 318; and special considerations, 315–319; and sponsored
programs, 3
Health Services, 391
Health Services Administration, 391
Hendricks, P. B., 404

Henry, N., 249, 412
Hensley, O. D., 49–51, 325, 400, 406,
412
Herdenorf, P. B., 335, 410
Hess, L. G., 170, 412
Higher education: administrative locations in, 31–36; in cooperation with
government, 8–9; goals of, and
sponsored programs, 3; institutional
mission in, 23–25; and research
projects, 4–6. *See also* Institutions
Higher Education Act, 391
Higher Education General Information System, 391
Hillman, H., 101
Human research subjects: compensation of, for physical injury, 263–264;
compliance with regulations on, 122;
and exempt research, 255; federal
policies on, 253–256; and informed
consent, 261–263; and institutional
assurances, 257–258; institutional
responsibilities for, 256–264; institutional review board (IRB) for, 254,
256, 257, 258, 259–261, 262, 263,
264, 274–287; legal and ethical requirements on, 252–264

I

IIT Research Institute, 298
Illinois, block grant to, 339
Illinois, University of: indirect costs at,
131; proposal budget checklist of,
368–373
Illinois, University of, at the Medical
Center, 417; handbook of, 58;
human subjects review form of,
374–387; newsletter of, 106
Illinois, University of, at Urbana, 417;
facilities and equipment administration at, 193–205, 206–209, 212–215;
management information system at,
76, 89–90, 104; newsletter of, 106;
proposal transmittal form of, 126
Illinois Research Information System
(IRIS), 74–75, 89–90, 104
Immigration and Naturalization Service, 391
Indirect costs: and agency-fixed rates,

129; allowable, 129–130, 140; analysis of, 127–132, 134; defined, 127–128; determining, 130–134; by geographical regions, 131; and institution-negotiated rates, 129; obligation of, 174–175. *See also* Costs

Individualized Grant Information and Search System, 104

Industry: in cooperation with institutions, 325–329; government and institutional cooperation with, 331–336

Information: automated, 104; basic library for, 101, 103–104; bibliography of sources of, 400–409; periodicals for, 101–102; services for, 102–103; sources of, 100–104; on state and local support, 104. *See also* Management information systems

Information specialist, responsibilities of, 66

Informed consent: documentation of, 263; elements in, 261–262; of human research subjects, 261–263; obligation to obtain, 263

Institute for Advanced Study, 294

Institute for Cancer Research, 298

Institute for Defense Analyses, 297

Institute for Gas Technology, 298

Institute of Laboratory Animal Resources (ILAR), 237

Institute of Medical Sciences, 298

Institution of Higher Education, 391

Institutional Prior Approval System, 391

Institutional program conformance, as policy, 27

Institutions: cooperation of government and industry with, 325–329, 331–336; missions of, 23–25; small, goals and capabilities in, 285–286. *See also* Higher education

Instruction, research and, 5–6

Instructional Scientific Equipment Program, 391

Intergovernmental Personnel Act, 391

Internal allocations, as award type, 147

Internal research program, for developing capacity, 46, 346–351

Internal Revenue Act, 10

Internal Revenue Service, 391

International Fertility Development Corporation, 298

International Research and Exchanges Board, 391

Interstate Commerce Commission, 391

Investigational Device Exemptions (IDE) program, 319

Investigational New Drugs (IND) program, 319

Iowa State University, shared use of equipment at, 206

J

Jackson Laboratory, 295, 298

Jet Propulsion Laboratory, 294, 297

Jewish Hospital of St. Louis, 298

Job Corps Centers, 6

Job Service Improvement Program, 391

Johnson, B. C., 324, 411

Johnson Foundation, 317

Joint Economic Committee, 331, 412

Joslin Diabetes Foundation, 298

Judge Advocate General, 391

K

Kaiser Foundation Research Institute, 298

Kitt Peak National Observatory, 297

Knowledge, extension of, through research, 5

Krebs, R. E., xii

Kruzas, A. T., 404

L

Labor-Management Services Administration, 391

Laboratory animals: care of, legal and ethnical requirements for, 236–241; compliance with regulations on, 122; federal regulations on, 238–240, 270, 271; institutional policy on, 240–241

Laboratory Evaluation and Accreditation Program, 391

Lasker, L., xii
Law Enforcement Assistance Administration, 9, 391
Law Enforcement Education Program, 391
Lawrence Berkeley Laboratory, 297
Lawrence Livermore Laboratory, 297
Legal requirements: compliance with, 236–284; on copyrights, 246–252; on human research subjects, 252–264; on laboratory animals, 236–241; on patents, 241–246; on recombinant DNA, 264–269
Letter of inquiry, contents of, 49
Levine, R. J., 412
Lewallen, J. M., xii, 409
Lewis, M. O., 403
Liberal arts college, sponsored programs in, 24
Library Services and Construction Act, 391
Licensing Executives Society (LES), 22
Lincoln Laboratory, 297
Los Alamos Scientific Laboratory, 297
Louisiana State University, 131
Lovelace Foundation for Medical Education, 298
Lowry, P. S., 75, 412

M

McCarthy, C. R., xiii, 253, 412
Machlup, F., 6, 412
MacKay, C. R., xii
McLean Hospital, 299
Management. *See* Financial management
Management information and reporting system (MIRS), 71, 77–86
Management information systems (MIS): analysis of, 69–95; defined, 69–70; and faculty profile system, 70, 71–73, 87–88; hardware configuration for, 78–79; and implementation, 78; input formats for, 79–86, 93–95; and management information and reporting system, 71, 77–86; and program information system, 71, 73–77; trends in, 86–87; types of, 70–86

Manpower Demonstration Research Corporation, 298
Manpower Development and Training Act, 391
Mansfield amendment of 1970, 9
Marcus, P. M., 324, 411
Maritime Administration, 391
Martin, R. C., 409
Maryland, University of, 131
Massachusetts Eye and Ear Infirmary, 298
Massachusetts General Hospital, 298
Massachusetts Institute of Technology (MIT): indirect costs at, 131; and industrial affiliation, 328; management information system at, 86; patents of, 242
Matching award funds, for developing capacity, 48
Matteson, G. C., 193, 412
Mayo Foundation, 298
Medical Research Foundation of Oregon, 299
Medina, V., xiii
Memorial Hospital—Cancer and All Allied Diseases, 299
Merritt, A., xiii
Michael Reese Hospital and Medical Center, 299
Michigan, University of, management information system at, 72
Michigan Cancer Foundation, 299
Midwest Research Institute, 294, 299
Mini-sabbaticals, for developing capacity, 47
Mining Enforcement and Safety Administration, 391
Minority Access to Research Careers, 391
Minority Business Opportunity Committee, 391
Mission agencies, history of, 9
Mitre Corporation—C3 Division, 297
Model Cities Administration, 391
Montana Energy Research and MHD Development Institute, 299
Montefiore Hospital and Medical Center, 299
Morrill Act of 1862, 7
Murdick, R. G., 70, 412

Murphy, C. A., xiii
Murray, J. P., 53, 54, 56, 412

N

National Academy of Sciences, 299
National Aeronautics and Space Administration, 9, 317, 335, 342, 392
National Aeronautics and Space Administration Procurement Regulation, 392
National Alliance of Businessmen, 391
National Assistance Management Association (NAMA), 22
National Association of College and University Business Officers (NACUBO), 20, 246, 391, 412–413; Council on Governmental Relations of, 22
National Association of Scientific Materials Managers (NASMM), 22
National Association of State Universities and Land-Grant Colleges, 392
National Astronomy and Ionospheric Center, 297
National Bureau of Standards, 392
National Cancer Institute, 392
National Center for Atmospheric Research, 297, 392
National Center for Health Services Research and Development, 392
National Commission on Higher Education Management Systems, 392
National Commission on Research, 326–327, 328
National Conference of States on Building Codes and Standards, 392
National Conference on the Advancement of Research (NCAR), 18, 392, 413
National Contract Management Association (NCMA), 22, 392
National Council of University Research Administrators (NCURA), 392, 413; as professional organization, 15, 16, 19–20, 98, 114
National Defense Education Act, 392
National Education Association, 392
National Endowment for the Arts, 392
National Endownment for the Humanities, 290, 392

National Environmental Policy Act, 392
National Eye Institute, 392
National Fire Prevention and Control Administration, 392
National Heart, Lung, and Blood Institute, 392
National Highway Traffic Safety Administration, 392
National Institute of Allergy and Infectious Diseases, 392
National Institute of Arthritis, Metabolism, and Digestive Diseases, 392
National Institute of Child Health and Human Development, 392
National Institute of Dental Research, 393
National Institute of Education, 393
National Institute of Environmental Health Sciences, 393
National Institute of General Medical Services, 393
National Institute of Mental Health, 393
National Institute of Neurological and Communicative Disorders and Stroke, 393
National Institute on Aging, 392
National Institute on Drug Abuse, 392
National Institutes of Health (NIH), 393, 406, 413; and compliance with regulations, 122; and contracts, 145; and facilities administration, 192; and financial management, 166–167, 169; founding of, 8; and health science organizations, 316, 317; and legal and ethical requirements, 237, 240, 253, 264, 265, 266, 267–268, 283–284; Office for Protection from Research Risks (OPRR) of, 258–259; Office of Recombinant DNA Activities of, 265, 268; and partnerships, 331; Recombinant DNA Molecule Program Advisory Committee of, 265, 267–268; reporting to, 221, 222; Study Sections of, 267–268
National Jewish Hospital—Denver, 299

National Labor Relations Board, 393
National Library of Medicine, 393
National Marine Fisheries Service, 393
National Oceanic and Atmospheric Administration, 393
National Park Service, 393
National Radio Astronomical Observatory, 297
National Research Act of 1974 (PL 93-348), 253, 256
National Research Service Awards, 393
National Safety Council, 393
National Science Board, 413
National Science Foundation (NSF), 25, 290, 296, 297–299, 338, 393, 406, 413–414; and facilities administration, 192; and financial management, 166–167, 169, 183; founding of, 8; and health science organizations, 317; Industrial-University Cooperative Research Project Program of, 327, 334; and proposal preparation, 115, 355–367; reporting to, 221–222, 223, 225–226, 230–231; Research Management Improvement Program of, xiii; and research partnerships, 327, 333–334
National Technical Information Service, 393
National Weather Service, 393
Negotiations: for awards, 147–150; strategy for, 149–150; techniques and principles for, 150
Nevada, University of, 131
New England Medical Center and Hospital, 299
New York Blood Center, 299
New York University, management information system at, 72
Nonacademic organizations, administrative structures in, 30–31
Nonprofit research organizations: administration of, 294–301; concept of, 293, 294; federal funds for, 296, 297–299; future of 300; sponsored programs in, 3–4; types of, 294–295
Nonresearch activities, purposes of, 6–7

Norris, J. T., xiii
North Atlantic Treaty Organization, 392
North Carolina, research partnership in, 335–336
North Carolina, University of, indirect costs at, 131
North Carolina Science and Technology Research Center (NC/STRC), 335–336
North Texas State University, in consortium, 330
Northern California Cancer Program, 299
Northwest Regional Education Laboratory, 299
Northwestern University, Patent and Invention Policy of, 272–276, 414
Nuclear Regulatory Commission, 393

O

Oak Ridge Associated Universities, 393
Oak Ridge Institute for Nuclear Standards, 297, 343
Occupational Safety and Health Administration, 394
Office of Administrative Management, Public Health Service, and cost sharing, 137, 414
Office of Air and Water Programs, 393
Office of Educational and Manpower Assistance, 393
Office of Federal Contract Compliance Programs, 393
Office of General Counsel, 393
Office of Health Maintenance Organizations, 393
Office of International Programs, 393
Office of Law Enforcement Programs, 393
Office of Management and Budget (OMB), 142, 393, 397–398, 414; and costs, 165–166, 177–180, 396–399; and facilities and equipment administration, 188, 205, 207; and indirect costs, 128, 130, 132–133; and legal and ethical requirements, 245; regulation by, 10; and reporting, 220–221

Office of Minerals Exploration, 393
Office of Minority Business Enterprise, 393
Office of Naval Research, 9, 393
Office of Science and Society, 394
Office of Scientific Research and Development, 7
Office of sponsored projects (OSP), 394; and accounting office, 57–58; activities of, 2; analysis of, 52–68; characteristics of, 54; division of responsibilities in, 62–67; evaluation of, 67–68, 352–354; legal and ethical responsibilities of, 241, 243–244, 247–248, 256–264, 266–267; negotiation role of, 147–148; organizational models for, 60–62; organizational structures for, 52–55; parallel, 32–33; proposal role of, 118–119, 123–126; regulatory responsibilities of, 121–122; roles of, 96; scope and functions of, 55–58; staffing for, 58–60; word processing equipment for, 117
Office of Water and Hazardous Materials, 394
Office of Water Research and Technology, 394
Ohio, research partnership in, 335
Ohio State University Research Foundation, 294, 303
Ohio Technology Transfer Organization (OTTO), 335, 336
Oklahoma Medical Research Foundation, 300
Omenn, G. S., 326, 415
On-the-Job Training, 393
Oregon, University of, 131
Organizational Prior Approval System, 393
Orlans, H., 294, 295, 300, 414

P

Palisades Geophysics Institute, 299
Palmer, A. M., 246, 414
Patent and Trademark Amendments of 1980 (PL 96-517), 245, 399
Patents: administering policy on, 243–244; disclosure statement for, 244–246, 277–278; legal and ethical requirements for, 241–246; policy for, 242–243, 272–276
Patterson, F., 330, 414
Peace Corps Training Centers, 6
Pennsylvania, research partnership in, 334–335
Pennsylvania, University of, management information system at, 72, 86
Pennsylvania Office of Science and Technology, 334, 414
Pennsylvania State University, 18
Pennsylvania Technical Assistance Program (PENNTAP), 334–335, 336
Peter Bent Brigham Hospital, 299
Peters, C. M., 70, 415
Petroleum Research Fund, 331
Pittsburgh, University of, management information system at, 72, 73
Planning and Resources Management, 394
Planning Grant Program, 394
Planning-Programming-Budgeting System, 394
Plasma Physics Laboratory, 297
Policies: auxiliary, 28; basic, 26–28; defined, 26; in sponsored programs, 26–29; for sponsored research, 28–29
Postaward services officer, responsibilities of, 67
Prager, D. J., 326, 415
Preaward grants specialist, responsibilities of, 66
President and vice-presidents, communication with, 107–108
President's Commission for the Study of Ethical Problems in Medicine and in Biomedical and Behavioral Research, 253, 264
President's Council on Physical Fitness and Sports, 394
Price, F. O., 331, 415
Printing and copying, facilities for, 116–117, 190
Prizes, as award type, 146
Profession, criteria for, 16
Program information, and management information system, 71, 73–77

Program of University Research, 394
Project Air Force, 297
Project Head Start, 6
Projects to Advance Creativity in Education, 394
Proposal development officer, responsibilities of, 65–66
Proposals: abstract of, 114; analysis of preparation and processing of, 111–126; approvals policy for, 28; automated preparation of, 344; budget development for, 115–116, 368–373; deadlines for, 121; evaluation and dissemination section of, 115; introduction of, 114; methods section of, 115; objectives in, 114–115; parts of, 113–115; preparation services for, 112–117, 355–367; processing and coordination of, 117–121; regulatory responsibilities of, 121–122; reviews of, 119–120; sponsor information for, 116; statement of problem for, 114; typing and duplication of, 116–117; writing workshops for, 44–46
Prospectus, guidelines for, 50–51
Public Health Service (PHS), 394; and cost sharing, 135, 137, 414; and health science organizations, 316–318, 320–323; and human research subjects, 253
Public Housing Authority, 394
Public Law 89–544, 237, 238, 239
Public Law 93–348, 53, 256
Public Law 94–553, 248–249, 398, 415
Public Law 95–224, 142, 143–144, 145, 398, 415
Public Law 96–517, 245, 399
Public Law 97–35, 415

R

Radiation Oncology Study Center, 299
RAND Corporation, 299
Reasonable cost, defined, 165
Recombinant DNA: biohazards committee for, 266–267; compliance with regulations on, 122; information sources on, 268–269; institutional responsibilities for, 266–267,

283–284; legal and ethical requirements for, 264–269
Redecke, L. A., 131, 415
Rehabilitation Services Administration, 394
Reports for sponsors: activity, 220–221; analysis of, 219–235; financial, 222–223, 227–231; guidelines for, 235; of inventions, 223–224, 232–234; of project results, 221–222, 225–226
Request for Proposals, 394, 402
Request for Quotation, 394
Research: basic, defined, 5; purposes in, 5–6; sponsored projects for, 4–6
Research Administration Committee (RAC), 330
Research Career Development Awards, 394
Research coordinator, for developing capacity, 48
Research Corporation, and patents, 244
Research for Better Schools, 299
Research institutes. See Nonprofit research organizations
Research management, in nonacademic organizations, 30–31
Research Revitalization Act of 1981, 333
Research scholar awards, for developing capacity, 47–48
Research Triangle Institute, 299
Research universities, sponsored programs in, 25
Researchers, training of, 6
Resources for the Future, 294
Retina Foundation, 299
Retired Senior Volunteer Program, 394
Reward structure: as incentive, 40–41; and policy, 27
Riverside Research Institute, 299
Robert B. Brigham Hospital, 299
Rockefeller Foundation, 10, 408
Rodman, J. A., 59, 70, 415
Roosevelt, F. D., 8
Rosenberg, P., 246, 415
Ross, J. E., 70, 412
Roswell Park Memorial Institute, 299

Rural Development Service, 394
Rural Electification Administration, 394

S

Sabbaticals, for developing capacity, 47
Sacramento Peak Observatory, 297
St. Jude Children's Research Hospital, 299
Salk Institute for Biological Studies, 299
Sansone, K., 75, 412
Science and Technology Policy Office, 395
Science Information Services, 394
Science Manpower Improvement, 394
Scripps Clinic and Research Foundation, 299
Securities and Exchange Commission, 394
Service Corps of Retired Executives, 394
Shapp, M. J., 334
Skjei, E. W., x, 114, 415
Sladek, F. E., x, 100, 415
Sloan-Kettering Foundation, 317
Sloan-Kettering Institute, 294, 295, 299
Small Business Administration, 394
Smiriga, S. R., 193, 412
Smith, C. E., Jr., xiii
Smith, C. W., x, 114, 415
Smithsonian Science Information Exchange, 394
Social Science Research Council, 290, 394
Social Security Administration, 394
Society for College and University Planning (SCUP), 22
Society for Property Administrators (SPA), 22
Society of Research Administrators (SRA), 59, 394, 415; as professional organization, 15, 16, 20–21, 98, 114; publications of, x, 21
Society of University Patent Administrators (SUPA), 22, 246, 395
Soil Conservation Service, 394
Solar Energy Research Institute, 297

Southern Illinois University at Carbondale, 415–416; Office of Research Development and Administration at, 104, 106, 123–125; and recombinant DNA, 283–284; Special Research Program at, 346–351
Southern Methodist University, in consortium, 330
Southern Research Institute, 299
Southwest Foundation for Research and Education, 299
Southwest Research Institute, administration of, 294, 296, 299, 300, 301
Special Research Program, 346–351
Sperber, B., 249, 416
Sponsored programs: communication systems for, 96–110; decentralization and block grants related to, 338–340; facilities and equipment administration for, 187–218; goals of, 23–26; government-industry-university partnerships for, 331–336; history of, 7–11; indirect costs and cost sharing determination for, 127–140; legal and ethical requirements for, 236–284; management information systems for, 69–95; need for, future of, 341–342; policy considerations of, 26–29; proposal preparation and processing for, 111–126; purpose of, 2; and reports for sponsors, 219–235; and society, 2–4; support pattern changes for, 342–343. See also Administration of sponsored programs
Sponsored projects: administrative structures for, 29–36; attitude building for, 38–41; award negotiation and acceptance for, 141–162; capabilities for, 41–43; climate assessment for, 39–40; developing capacity for, 37–51; development of, in small organizations, 290–292; enhancement programs for, 44–51; financial management of, 163–186; incentives for, 40–41; industry-university cooperation in, 325–329; long-term planning for, 42–43; organizational units for, and capability,

Sponsored projects *(continued)*
42–43; priority establishment for, 43–44; and program development, 336–338; roles of, 4–7. *See also* Administration of sponsored projects; Administrators of sponsored projects

Sponsoring agencies: liaison with, 98–100; periodicals from, 102; reports to, 219–235; visits from, 47; visits to, 48, 98–99

SRI International, 294, 299

Staff: communication with, 109; educational attainment of, 59; in small organizations, 286–288; for sponsored projects office, 58–60

Stanford Linear Accelerator Center, 297

Stanford University: indirect costs at, 131; and industrial affiliations, 328; management information system at, 72, 73, 86

State colleges and universities, sponsored programs in, 24–25

State governments: history of support by, 10; industry and institutional partnerships with, 334–336

State University of New York (SUNY) Research Foundation: administration of, 294; management information system of, 72, 73, 303; newsletter of, 106; Sponsored Program Information Network (SPIN) of, 75–76, 91–92, 104

Statewide coordinating boards, and program development, 336–337

Stauffer, T. M., 28–29, 337–338, 416

Stein, E. L., x, 415

Steinberg, L., 53, 416

Stevenson-Wydler Technology Innovation Act of 1980, 332

Stores: automated inventory system for, 193–205; catalogue for, 201, 203–204; as facilities, 189–190; issue cards for, 193, 195; monthly issue-usage report for, 201, 205, 210–211; monthly update report for, 196, 199–200; order cards for, 196; transaction register for, 196, 197–198; voucher for, 201, 202

Strickland, S., x, 409, 416

Support: acceptance of, as policy, 26–27; changes in pattern of, 342–343; history of, 7–11; patterns of, 10–11

T

Tally, J. E., 315, 416

Tennessee, research partnership in, 335

Tennessee, University of: indirect costs at, 131; Institute for Public Service at, 335

Tennessee Valley Authority, 395

Texas A & M Research Foundation: administration of, 294, 303, 304–308; newsletter of, 106

Texas at Arlington, University of, in consortium, 330

Texas at Austin, University of, indirect costs at, 131

Texas at Dallas, University of, 417; awards at, 153–154, 160; in consortium, 104, 330; handbook of, 58; indirect costs at, 140; management information system of, 72, 73, 79–86, 93–95; newsletter of, 106; reference materials at, 104

Texas Christian University, in consortium, 330

Texas Tech University: faculty evaluation instrument of, 68, 352–354, 416; indirect costs at, 131

Treasury Circular, 395, 399

Truman, H. S., 8

U

Undergraduate Research Participation, 395

Union of Soviet Socialist Republics, specialized institutes in, 4

U.S. Air Force, 395

U.S. Army Medical Research and Development Command, 317

U.S. Coast Guard, 395

U.S. Code, 395

U.S. Department of Agriculture, 395; and laboratory animals, 238–239, 270, 416

U.S. Department of Defense, 9, 317, 342, 390; and contracts, 145; and cost sharing, 134; regulations by, 166

U.S. Department of Education, 290, 390

U.S. Department of Energy, 9; and contracts, 145; and partnerships, 331

U.S. Department of Health, Education and Welfare (DHEW), 389, 416; and cost sharing, 134, 137; and legal and ethical requirements, 239, 253

U.S. Department of Health and Human Services (DHHS), 389, 416; and cost sharing, 137; and indirect costs, 128, 129; invention statement for, 232; and legal and ethical requirements, 239–240, 253–255, 256, 257–258, 259–261, 262, 264, 271

U.S. Department of Housing and Urban Development, 391

U.S. Department of Transportation, 390

U.S. House of Representatives, 331–332, 417

U.S. Office of Education, 393

U.S. Training and Employment Service, 395

University City Science Center, 299

University-connected research foundations: administration of, 300, 302–310; benefits of, 302–303; concept of, 294, 302; models for, 303, 309–310; organization of, 304–308; and state regulations, 303–304

University Hospital, 299

University Patents, 244

Upward Bound, 6

Urban Institute, 299

Urban Mass Transportation Administration, 395

V

Veterans Administration, 237, 395

Veterans Employment Services, 395

Vocational Education Act, 395

Volunteers in Service to America, 395

Vossler, K., 335, 410

W

Washington, D.C., liaison with sponsors in, 99–100

Washington, University of, 131

Washington University, 131

Water Resources Council, 395

Waters, J. M., 170, 412

Western Interstate Commission for Higher Education, 395

White, V. P., 113

Wholesale Price Index, 395

Willner, W., 404

Wisconsin, University of, 131

Wistar Institute, 294, 299

Woodrow, R. J., x, 405, 417

Worcester Foundation for Experimental Biology, 299

Work Incentives Program, 395

Wright, R. A., 409

Y

Yale University, Institutional Biosafety Committee of, 267

Youth Opportunity Center, 395

Youthwork, 299